IN-DEPTH

CREATION BASICS & BEYOND

An In-Depth Look at Science, Origins, and Evolution

IN-DEPTH

CREATION BASICS & BEYOND

An In-Depth Look at Science, Origins, and Evolution

Henry Morris III, D.Min.
John D. Morris, Ph.D. • Jason Lisle, Ph.D.
James J. S. Johnson, J.D., Th.D.
Nathaniel Jeanson, Ph.D. • Randy Guliuzza, P.E., M.D.
Jeffrey Tomkins, Ph.D. • Jake Hebert, Ph.D.
Frank Sherwin, M.A. • Brian Thomas, M.S.

INSTITUTE FOR CREATION RESEARCH

Dallas, Texas
www.icr.org

CREATION BASICS & BEYOND
An In-Depth Look at Science, Origins, and Evolution

First printing: July 2013
Second printing: November 2013

Unless otherwise specified, all Scripture quotations are from the New King James Version.

ISBN: 978-1-935587-30-9
Library of Congress Catalog Number: 2013944862

Please visit our website for other books and resources: www.icr.org

Printed in the United States of America.

TABLE OF CONTENTS

INTRODUCTION

Creation or evolution? The debate on origins has a tendency to stir up passion for those on either side of the issue. If we have been created by God and made in His image, then this will have implications for the way we live our lives. Likewise, if we are the result of a long process of evolution, a product of the mindless forces of nature, then this too will naturally influence our thinking of how we should live. Our thoughts on morality, science, religion, politics—all of these will be strongly affected by our position on origins. The creation-evolution debate is therefore one of the most important issues of our time.

For the Christian, the motivation to study origins is even stronger. If the Genesis account of creation is untrue, then it casts doubt on the rest of the Bible. After all, the only way a Christian knows that Jesus, the Son of God, died on the cross to pay the penalty for sin and rose from the dead is from Scripture. But if the Bible cannot be trusted, then the Christian cannot truly know that he or she is saved. If the Bible is false on its very first page, then how can any rational person have confidence in what follows from it? Indeed, there have been many people who want nothing to do with Christianity because they believe the Bible to be untrustworthy. And this all begins by doubting Genesis.

For these reasons and many others, it is extremely important for all people to know the truth about origins. This doesn't mean that everyone needs to get a doctorate in science, but it is helpful to know a few of the basic lines of scientific evidence that surround the creation-evolution controversy. It is also very useful to understand the basic theology and moral implications of creation. It is for these reasons this book is so timely. In the following chapters, we provide the fundamental "big picture" facts regarding the origins debate in laymen's terms.

Although this book is written primarily *for* non-experts, it was written and reviewed *by* experts. This helps ensure that the book is as accurate and up to date as is humanly possible. Every contributing author is a researcher/speaker/ writer in full-time apologetics ministry at the Institute for Creation Research. The writers include five Ph.D. scientists (two in biology, one in physics, one in astrophysics, one in geology), a medical doctor/professional engineer, two science writers with master's degrees in science, and two writers with doctorates in theology.

Although the authors are capable of writing highly technical, detailed papers in their respective fields, they have taken great care to make this book introductory in nature. No extensive previous science or Bible knowledge is required on the part of the reader. The chapters have been kept intentionally short and readable. At the same time, the chapters do go into sufficient depth so that the reader can have confidence in the arguments presented. Some chapters present brand-new research. Others give an overview of previously established scientific facts.

The book is arranged into five major sections, each with a number of small chapters. The chapters are largely independent, so they may be read in any order, but they have been organized into a flow that will make sense to those readers who like to read books from the first page to the last.

The first section deals with biblical and worldview issues, tackling questions such as: Does the origins debate really matter? What about hybrid views that claim God created using evolution, or that He created progressively over millions of years? Can Genesis be taken as a parable without doing any harm to Christian doctrine? Does the Bible really teach a "young" earth? Are creation and evolution equally compatible with the methods of science? Is there a difference between operational science and forensic science? And does this topic really make a difference in our lives?

The second section deals with biology. Is it possible for the human body to have evolved in a gradual fashion? What about "bad designs" in nature? Does DNA support creation or evolution—and what about "junk" DNA? Are we really genetically similar to chimpanzees or other forms of life? Can life really come from non-life? Where did the different "races" of people come from?

Section three brings up issues in geology. Does it really take millions of years for rock layers to form? Was there a worldwide flood as described in Genesis, and, if there was, what would the evidence for it be? Are there geological indicators that support a "young" earth, or do they point to an "old" earth? What about radiometric dating? What about all those fossils—do they prove evolution? Was there an ice age? Is continental drift true?

The fourth section deals with questions about dinosaurs: Are they real? If so, when did they live? Does the Bible say anything about them? Did they really live and go extinct millions of years before human beings arrived? Is there scientific data or historical evidence that they lived more recently? Did they really turn into birds, as some evolutionists claim?

Section five delves into the origin of the universe. Is the Big Bang compatible with Genesis? Is the universe billions of years old? If not, then how can we see galaxies that are billions of light years away? Can a universe come from nothing? Is there more than one universe? What about UFOs?

In our ministry experience, these are the questions that people want answered. And for the most part, they are pretty easy to answer with a basic knowledge of the relevant facts. We are convinced that the Bible really is what it claims to be: the inspired Word of the living God. We are not ashamed to stand on biblical authority. Rather, we boldly proclaim that God's Word is true from the beginning.

We are convinced that the scientific evidence strongly confirms the biblical account of creation. Conversely, "particles-to-people" evolution happens only in the minds of its believers. It is a scientifically bankrupt conjecture. In that spirit, we present *Creation Basics & Beyond*. We hope that this will be edifying to believers as they see how the evidence confirms biblical creation. And we pray that it will challenge unbelievers as they see that evolution cannot stand up to careful scrutiny. We trust that God will be glorified in all.

Jason Lisle, Ph.D.
Director of Research

WORLDVIEW

GOD DETERMINES TRUTH
OR MAN DETERMINES TRUTH?

1

GENESIS AND THE CHARACTER OF GOD

Henry Morris III, D.Min.

The message of Genesis is not confusing. The repetitive information throughout the rest of Scripture is consistent. The universe was created by an omnipotent, omniscient, and transcendent Being. The words of Scripture insist that God's work was recent, complete, and "good." Our struggle with that message is that everything we observe is tainted by evil and death.

Secular history presupposes that the "normal" of today has been the dominant operational force behind everything that exists. Geological processes, fossil evidence, sociological development, all are interpreted with no God in the story. Some theologians attempt to explain the differences between the biblical message and secular naturalism by suggesting that dying processes were a normal part of God's creation. Some religions embrace the idea that "good" and "evil" are nothing more than two sides of the same reality—that our perception of such contrasts are merely a product of our experience and culture.

How can we resolve the conflicting message of a good creation with the evil that surrounds us? For those of us who believe that an omnipotent and omniscient God has existed from eternity past, we must correlate what *that* God has revealed to us and our growing understanding of science, with God's divine nature as the controlling factor. What does the revealed nature of God demand of the original creation? How does natural revelation (what we can observe in today's universe) shape the written words of Scripture?

Some have suggested that the processes of nature in that original creation could not have included a deathless universe since all natural processes function around deterioration and death. Living things would have worn out and died—even if the environment was much better than the environment we know today. Animals would have died normally, and Adam and Eve would have died eventually unless they ate of the Tree of Life that God planted in the garden "eastward in Eden."

But the Bible tells us that death is the result of Adam's sin, and as a result of God's judgment "death passed upon all men" (Romans 5:12, KJV). When God tells us death is the "last enemy" to be conquered by the Lord Jesus (1 Corinthians 15:26) and death will not exist in the new heavens and the new earth (Revelation 21:4), are we to expect the new bodies promised upon our resurrection to be still mortal in eternity?

Before we approach these issues, it is absolutely necessary to acknowledge what has been recorded about the origin of the universe.

God's Own Commentary

"Every thing…was very good." The repetition of God's comment is worth noting. Five of the six working days of the creation week are pronounced "good" by the Creator. It is the same Hebrew word each time and means just what would be expected: good, pleasant, agreeable, excellent, of benefit, etc. That word is used well over 500 times in Scripture. There is nothing very unusual about God's use of the word, except that it is repeated often and that it is God who uses the term.

Given that the Creator is using the term, we should consider the character of the Evaluator. We should gain some understanding of His attributes before we render an opinion of the meaning of the term "good"—especially as it applies to the original creation.

God Is Holy

Holiness is the preeminent attribute of God. Everything God does is subject to the unchangeable rock of God's holy nature. Even the love that drove Him to become man and die a substitutionary death for our sins is driven by the holiness that demands justice for the horrible rebellion against that very holiness.

> Who is like unto thee, O LORD, among the gods? who is like thee, glorious in holiness, fearful in praises, doing wonders? (Exodus 15:11, KJV)

> There is none holy as the LORD: for there is none beside thee: neither is there any rock like our God. (1 Samuel 2:2, KJV)

I will publish the name of the LORD…He is the Rock, his work is perfect: for all his ways are judgment: a God of truth and without iniquity, just and right is he. (Deuteronomy 32:3-4, KJV)

Because God is holy, He must reveal truth in the created things of the universe. He cannot lie (Titus 1:2). God's words and deeds are "true and righteous altogether" (Psalm 19:9, KJV).

God Is Omniscient

Everywhere we look—into the deepest recesses of space or the minutia of the microscope—the intricacy, precision, and complexity of all things stagger us with the enormity of details and vastness of information.

O LORD, how manifold are thy works! in wisdom hast thou made them all: the earth is full of thy riches. (Psalm 104:24, KJV)

I am God, and there is none else; I am God, and there is none like me, Declaring the end from the beginning, and from ancient times the things that are not yet done, saying, My counsel shall stand, and I will do all my pleasure. (Isaiah 46:9-10, KJV)

Known unto God are all his works from the beginning of the world. (Acts 15:18, KJV)

This is the consistent message of Scripture. God cannot be progressively aware. God's knowledge is immediate. God is free from imperfection. God knows all there is to know. God's purpose and order flow from His omniscience. His decisions are unchangeable and without confusion. God's specific will and pleasure are always implemented.

God's Flawless Good

Whatever God said was "good" would have to be in harmony with His divine nature. Since God is holy, He could not deceive us about the order of the creation week. Since God is omniscient, He could not guess or use trial and error methodology. God would not experiment. God would not produce inferior things. He can do only holy acts. He cannot create, make, or shape non-functional processes. All of this clear evidence requires that we who read Genesis 1 understand "good" to mean "flawless function."

- **God's "good" functions properly.**

God's own account of His work specifies His organization and purpose.

Because God is omniscient, everything in the universe works as designed. Because God is omnipotent, everything has all it needs to operate, live, reproduce, and populate under the orders of and in agreement with the Creator's design. Each component was designed to function without flaw. Every part works as ordered, and all living things function under the limits and in the places for their lives. Nothing was misplaced. Nothing was left to chance.

- **God's "good" could not include sin.**

For the holy, omniscient, omnipotent, loving Creator to conclude that everything that He had created was "very good," there could be nothing in that completed creation that did not function as designed. Nothing existed in conscious rebellion against the immutable nature of the Creator—there was no sin.

Sin became a part of human nature through Adam. Death was introduced into the creation because of the Creator's sentence upon Adam.

- **God's "good" could not include death.**

God is life. Everything that is revealed about God centers on His eternal Being. The most personal name that God reveals is "I AM"—the One who exists by the right and nature of who He is. Jesus insists that He is "the way, the truth, and the life" (John 14:6). The awesome *Apokalypse* of Jesus Christ opens with the loud voice "as of a trumpet, saying, I am Alpha and Omega, the first and the last" (Revelation 1:10-11, KJV).

There is absolutely no indication anywhere in the Scriptures that the living God—the God of life—created death. Nothing in the Bible suggests that death was a part of the good that God designed into His creation. Death in Scripture is separation from God. Death stops life. Death intrudes into and destroys everything. Death is *not* normal.

When God completed His work, *He* pronounced "it was very good" (Genesis 1:31). If words mean anything at all, "good" must include the flawless functioning of every molecule and all systems and all life. "Good" demands that nothing be out of order or in rebellion to His nature. No sin or death existed in all of creation—until the third chapter of Genesis.

Rebellion in the Garden

Most of us have wondered how much time elapsed between the end of Day Seven and the world-changing events that took place at the Tree of the

Knowledge of Good and Evil. No specific time period is stated, but it does not appear that it was very long. Eve did not conceive the first human child until after the pronouncement of the judgments and after they were cast out of the garden (Genesis 4:1). Given the basic command to "be fruitful and multiply," it is unlikely that either Adam or Eve delayed attempting to fulfill this mandate.

However one interprets the information, it could *not* have been "ages." More than likely it was less than a year—and probably only a few days after they both were created.

A Mixed Message

If physical death is part of the design of God in the original creation, that makes God the Author of death. Since the creation is part of the revelation of the nature of God (according to Romans 1:20), such a design would require that death is part of the holiness of God. How could this be? The Bible calls death the "last enemy" and insists that the Lord Jesus will destroy it. If God Himself created death, then why would He destroy it later? Did God deliberately confuse us?

If death is *not* the judgment for sin as the Bible insists, then the whole of the gospel message is foolishness. What would salvation rescue us from? If death is not the judgment for sin, then the death of the Lord Jesus on the cross at Calvary is nothing more than a foolish end to an idealist—a martyrdom for an illusionary cause.

The Bible demands that an innocent sacrifice be substituted for the awful sin of humanity. Christ's death is required for salvation. We are sanctified through the offering of the body of Jesus Christ on Calvary (Hebrews 10:10), done once, with, and for eternal consequences (Hebrews 10:12-14).

Twisting the words of Scripture so that Christ's physical death had no meaning is a terrible heresy. If eons of pain, suffering, and death existed before Adam's awful rebellion, then a whole sweep of biblical teaching is thrown into the black hole of allegory.

The Demands of God's Nature

God is omnipresent Spirit (John 4:24). God is not nature. God is not the universe. God is not a cosmic consciousness or a force of mystery. God is *not* man—He is greater than man (Job 33:12) and does not change His mind

(Numbers 23:19).

Since God is holy, God does *not* author confusion. He is Light (1 John 1:5). He is the truth (John 3:33; 14:6); therefore, God cannot deceive us.

Because of who God is, we can be assured of an original creation that functioned as it was designed—a creation that fits the Creator. The "groaning" of the creation now (Romans 8:22) is a constant reminder that rebellion against the holiness of the Creator required His judgment. God Himself reconciles His creation to Himself through the death of His sinless Son in substitution for our well-deserved guilt.

The "Good" News

The gospel message insists on the "birth from above" (John 3:3) that brings about a transfer from death to life (John 5:24). It involves a "new creation" (2 Corinthians 5:17) made possible by the death of the Creator Himself (Hebrews 2:9).

The earthy condition of flesh and blood cannot inherit the kingdom of God. Physical changes are required. Resurrection is the absolute opposite of physical death. Corruption must become incorruption. Dishonor must become glory. Weakness must become power. The natural must become spiritual (1 Corinthians 15:50-54). Physical death is an intrusion into the eternal order of things, and it takes a resurrection to correct it.

The "new man" must be created in God's righteousness and true holiness (Ephesians 4:24). We await the fulfillment of that promise when the Creator "shall change our vile body, that it may be fashioned like unto his glorious body, according to the working whereby he is able even to subdue all things unto himself" (Philippians 3:21, KJV).

2

GENESIS IS RELEVANT
TO CHRISTIAN DOCTRINES

Jason Lisle, Ph.D.

Christian Doctrines Are Based in the History of Genesis

Is the decline of Christianity in society really connected to the rejection of the history of Genesis? Christian doctrines are found throughout the Bible, so it is tempting to think that we could reject Genesis without affecting the rest of Scripture. But this would be a mistake.[1]

Every major Christian doctrine has its foundation (its "roots") in the book of Genesis. And while these doctrines are mentioned throughout Scripture, they cannot stand up to scrutiny apart from a literal Genesis any more than a tree can survive without its roots or a house can stand without its foundation.

Genesis Tells the Authoritative Truth about Origins

The Holy Bible tells us who God is—a triune Creator God who chose to make mankind in His image and who reveals Himself through Christ Jesus and His Word. Specifically, the book of Genesis tells us how God historically created everything. Accordingly, the Bible reveals to us what we could never know otherwise about origins, such as where we came from, how we got here, and why God made us. No other book does that.

Indeed, Genesis provides the biblical doctrine of origins, including yours and mine—and your origins matter![1,2,3]

Consider, just for starters, how only Genesis provides the biblical truth about these important origins—the universe (including the sun, moon, stars, and the earth), information, time, space, plants, animals, seed-based reproduction, humans, marriage and family, choice, food, morality, evil, persecution of believers by unbelievers, fallen angels, punishment, technology, prophecy, redemption (to be provided by Christ, and illustrated in the first use of clothing made from animal skins), God's earliest communications with humans, "kind"-based biodiversity, the world before, during, and after the worldwide Flood, languages, the beginning of capital punishment as a law of social responsibility, and humanistic religion (at Babel). The list could go on, but the point is clear: *Genesis' teaching on origins is comprehensive and specific.*

Let's look in detail at some of these important topics about human life.

1. Marriage. The Bible teaches that marriage is a holy union between one man and one woman for life. There are any number of passages in Scripture that address the topic of marriage. But where does the idea of marriage come from? God instituted marriage on the sixth day of creation. He made Eve from Adam's side to be a helper to her husband. The Bible specifically tells us in Genesis 2:24 that this historical event is the reason why we have marriage today. "Therefore a man shall leave his father and mother and be joined to his wife, and they shall become one flesh." There can be no doubt that this is the foundation of marriage because the Bible specifically tells us as much. We know marriage is between one man and one woman united by God for life because He clearly set it up that way at creation. God provided the prototype marriage, and we are supposed to follow His example. Jesus specifically affirmed this in Matthew 19:4-6.

Can the doctrine of marriage be defended apart from a literal Genesis? If Genesis were not true, could we still argue that marriage must be defined as a union between one man and one woman for life, as opposed to a homosexual pair? People have certainly tried. They have argued for traditional marriage simply because it is tradition. But a tradition is not a spiritual foundation, and having a tradition doesn't bind others to the same behavior; just because you may hide Easter eggs doesn't mean that others must do the same. Some people dress up in costumes on Halloween, but that doesn't mean you should. Likewise, just because marriage has traditionally been defined one way in our culture doesn't logically imply that it must continue to be that way. Cultures change, and so do traditions.

Some people have argued for traditional marriage because it seems right to them. But others might argue that a homosexual union seems right to them. Subjective feelings don't provide a logical foundation for anything significant. Some people might argue that marriage is one man and one woman for life because it is what the majority believes. But a majority opinion doesn't make something right. Again, if a majority of people dress up on Halloween, does that mean you must also follow suit? If a majority of people like pickles on their hamburgers, does that make it morally wrong for you to not like pickles on your hamburger? Clearly not. If evolution were true, then there really would be no fundamental basis for the doctrine of marriage. Marriage would simply be a cultural trend—one that is now evolving into something quite different than it was years ago.

2. Sanctity of Human Life. The Bible teaches that human beings are qualitatively different from the other organisms. We are made in the image of God and enjoy special rights that animals and plants do not. This is why it is fundamentally immoral to murder a human being; we dare not mar the image of God in such a way. And yet most people give little thought to the life that was extinguished in order for them to enjoy a good hamburger or fish sandwich. There are some people who have a problem with that, but even a staunch vegetarian seems to have no ethical problem destroying living cells as he or she bites into a carrot or watermelon. For that matter, every time we take a breath of air, multitudes of microorganism are absorbed into our body and destroyed by our immune system. Why is it no one cries "murder" when we consume a turnip? The reason is this: Everyone knows in his heart of hearts that plants and animals do not bear the image of God, but people do. Whether we admit it or not, we all recognize that human beings are not just another organism of the planet. Human life is sacred—we are set apart from animals and plants by the Creator Himself, having been made in His image.

And where do you suppose this biblical principle originates? Where is it we read that human beings are made in the image of God? Genesis 1:27-28 states:

> So God created man in His own image; in the image of God He created him; male and female He created them. Then God blessed them, and God said to them, "Be fruitful and multiply; fill the earth and subdue it; have dominion over the fish of the sea, over the birds of the air, and over every living thing that moves on the earth."

Genesis 1:29 indicates that plants were made for people to eat. That is why there is no moral problem "killing" a carrot and consuming it—God made it for eating. In Genesis 9:2-3, God extends our diet to include animals as well. But the murder of a human being is shown to be unacceptable in Genesis 4:8-

12. The sanctity of human life is an ethical truth with its foundation clearly set in the history of Genesis.

But if creation is just a myth, if people are just evolved animals, then how can they be distinct from animals? Indeed, animals have no real moral code at all. If a lion kills another lion, we don't view it as "wrong" and we don't throw the lion in jail. What one animal does to another is morally irrelevant. So how could the act of murder be considered wrong if humans are no qualitatively different than animals? Any distinction would be arbitrary and subjective.

Someone might say that humans are more intelligent than animals, which is why humans have more "rights" and should not be killed. But this standard is arbitrary and leads to the bizarre conclusion that smarter humans have more value and rights than less intelligent ones. Should a person with a very high I.Q. be allowed to kill people who have very low I.Q.? Clearly not, and yet that is the inevitable conclusion of such a line of thinking. From an evolutionary perspective, human beings are not fundamentally different from animals or plants, and consequently, any line of thinking that can justify killing animals or plants can also be applied to some group of people—whether it is a particular ethnic group, age group, or gender.

Indeed, why not abort inconvenient babies if they are just distant cousins of broccoli, as evolutionists insist? People have used such thinking to justify abortion, but such a perspective cannot, and will not, simply end with the unborn. What about killing an inconvenient child shortly after birth? What about a selfish two-year-old, or an ungrateful teenager, or the very sick or elderly? Life is continuous from conception until the point of death; any dividing line is necessarily arbitrary and subjective. Again, we don't mean to imply that all evolutionists employ such thinking. Some evolutionists are adamantly against abortion, or murder of any form. But the point is that they have no *basis* for such Christian morality according to their professed belief in evolution. Evolution is simply not logically consistent with the sanctity of human life.

3. Laws. We are all familiar with laws. There are civil laws, moral laws, and so forth. But they all have one thing in common—they put limitations on our behavior by threatening some sort of penalty if we do not comply. The Bible has a number of laws throughout which guide and constrain our actions. But where did the idea of laws originate? Why should we have laws anyway? We find the first laws were given to human beings by God in Genesis. He told Adam and Eve to go and multiply and rule over the creatures of the earth

(Genesis 1:28). God also told Adam not to eat from the tree of the knowledge of good and evil, and He attached a clear penalty for disobedience: death.

The reason we have laws is because our Creator God made us in His image. He therefore has the right to set rules for our behavior. And since God gave us freedom of choice—we are not mindless robots—He attached unpleasant penalties to laws when we break them and has promised blessings for obedience (e.g., Deuteronomy 28:1-14). We owe God our very existence, and so we have a moral obligation to obey any laws He has set forth. Additionally, we have a very good reason to obey God: He will hold us accountable for our actions. There will be a final judgment. Moreover, since we have a natural proclivity toward evil (inherited from our rebellious ancestor Adam), civil laws are also necessary to restrain evil in society. Laws make sense in light of the history given in Genesis.

But do laws make sense from an evolutionary perspective in which humans are just another animal? Animals do not have laws. They behave without any sense of fairness or justice. They have no government, no police, no crimes, and no penalties. Animals do what animals do; we don't throw a lion in jail if it kills another lion. So why do we put a human in jail if he kills another human?

The idea of evolution is supposed to be based on the concept of "survival of the fittest." The strong dominate the weak in the competition for resources, which eventually eliminates the weak, leading to a stronger, more adapted organism. In like manner, humans allegedly evolved from less-fit organisms. But if evolution were true, then how can we make sense of laws? Evolution is all about the strong overcoming the weak, so why have laws to protect the weak from the strong? That's what laws do—they prevent the stronger, more "fit" person from killing or abusing the weaker person. Laws are essentially opposite in principle to the notion of survival of the fittest. Most evolutionists do believe in laws, of course. But such beliefs would not make sense if evolution were true.

4. Seven-Day Week. The Fourth Commandment tells us to "remember the Sabbath day, to keep it holy" (Exodus 20:8). We are supposed to take one day a week to rest and honor God. Most Christians celebrate the Sabbath on Sunday, to honor the resurrection of Christ. But even non-Christians usually take one day in seven to rest. In fact, most cultures on Earth have a seven-day week. But where does this idea to rest precisely one day in seven come from?

Well, the Fourth Commandment is first listed in Exodus 20:8, but that is not where the idea of the seven-day week originated. It goes back to Genesis.

Genesis 1:1–2:2 tells us that God created in six days and then rested one day. Of course, the all-powerful God does not need to rest. Nor did He really require six days to make the universe. He had the power to do it all instantaneously if He had wanted to do so. God created in six days and then rested one day as a pattern for us. Exodus 20:11 specifically explains that the creation week is the basis for our work week.

It may interest you to know that there really is no secular basis for a seven-day week. All other units of time have a basis in astronomy. A day is the amount of time for Earth to rotate once with respect to the sun, a month is the amount of time for the moon to go through all its phases, and a year is the amount of time it takes the earth to orbit the sun. But there is no common astronomical phenomenon that corresponds to our seven-day week!

Some people have speculated that our ancient ancestors invented the week in honor of the five planets that are visible with the naked eye, plus the sun and moon. But there is no time function here; why seven *days*, and not years or hours or pounds or inches? The number of planets has nothing to do with time, so it doesn't make sense to use them as a basis for the week. It is far more reasonable to suppose that the days of the week were *later* named in association with the planets and the sun and moon, since they are both seven in number. As far as we know, the only basis for our seven-day week comes from the history in Genesis. And so the fact that almost all cultures on Earth have a seven-day week is evidence that they all knew about Genesis at one time.

5. The Gospel. We saved the best until last. Most Christians realize that the central-most important doctrine of Christianity is the gospel itself—the good news that Jesus died on the cross to pay for our sins. But where do ideas like "sin" come from? Where do we discover that death is the penalty for sin? Where do we learn that we need a Savior? All of the concepts necessary to understand the gospel have their foundation in Genesis.

Romans 6:23 tells us that "the wages of sin is death." But the connection between sin and death does not originate in the book of Romans; it originates in Genesis. It is Genesis where we learn that God is our Creator and we are made in His image (Genesis 1:26-27). As such, we owe Him our lives and our obedience. It is in Genesis we find that God holds people accountable for their actions; there is a penalty associated with disobedience to God (Genesis 2:17).

Therefore, we have a very good reason to obey Him.

In Genesis, we learn that the world was once absolutely perfect, the "very good" creation of an infinitely holy and most loving God. Adam was to rule over this world as a good steward, serving under the authority of his King, and having authority over God's creatures. If Adam obeyed God, he would live forever in perfect fellowship with His Creator, enjoying the perfection of the world in which he lived. But God is righteous and will not tolerate evil in His sight. In particular, God told Adam not to eat from the tree of the knowledge of good and evil (Genesis 2:17). And there would be a punishment if Adam disobeyed—he would immediately become mortal and would therefore eventually die (Genesis 2:17; 3:17-19).

It is not as if there was anything mystical about that one tree. It is simply what God chose as a test of Adam's allegiance. Would Adam submit to God as his Lord, learning from Him and interpreting experience in light of God's revealed knowledge? Or would Adam choose to be a "god" unto himself, rejecting the commandment of the Lord and choosing to interpret all experience in terms of his own subjective and arbitrary rules and limited thinking? Adam chose the latter, having been tempted by his wife, Eve, who had been tempted by the serpent. At that moment, Adam and Eve became mortal beings. Their perfect fellowship with God was broken by their treason; they would now age and eventually die as the just punishment for their insidious crime against their loving King.

The world itself was also marred by Adam's sin. Animals would now suffer pain and death (Romans 8:20-21), just like Adam. Why is this? Adam was in charge of the world, and so his sin affected everything under his authority—which is to say, the entire world. It is much like when the president of the United States makes a bad decision; it has a negative effect on all the people in the United States because those people are under the president's authority. It may seem unfair that animals must suffer and die because of what Adam did, but if the world remained perfect, then that would indicate that Adam did not really have authority over it. This would mean God was lying about Adam being in charge, and God does not lie (Hebrews 6:18). The integrity of God demands that both Adam and the world would suffer a curse as the right penalty for Adam's sin.

People today are descended from Adam and Eve and have inherited a sin-nature from them. This is to say that we are all conceived in a state that is

25

alienated from God's perfect glory—a state that seeks rebellion against God. But God was incredibly merciful to humanity. Rather than leaving Adam and Eve to their rebellion, God promised that He would provide a Savior, someone to pay the penalty of death for Adam and Eve so they could eventually be restored to perfect fellowship with God. God indicated that it was the "seed of the woman"—a descendant of Eve—who would accomplish this. As a symbol of that coming salvation, God killed an animal or animals (perhaps a lamb) to provide skins of clothing for Adam and Eve. This covered the shame of their treason and showed them the nature of their salvation. One day, a perfect "Lamb"— a descendant of Eve and yet also God Himself—would die so that Adam and Eve could live again, forever in perfection with their Creator. The gospel message is rooted in Genesis!

Apart from Genesis, the gospel message makes no sense. Death has always existed in the evolutionary worldview—long before people. So how could death be the penalty for sin? And if death is not the penalty for sin, then why did Jesus die on a cross? Is the concept of "sin" even meaningful in an evolutionary universe? If the world has always been full of death and suffering, then why would anyone think that he needs to be reconciled with God?

The Bible teaches that we may only be redeemed (freed from the slavery of sin) by a blood relative (Leviticus 25:47-49). There are a number of reasons for this, which we won't address at this time. The point is that only a human being—a relative of ours—can be our savior. This is one reason why God became a man—to save us as our "kinsman-redeemer." Jesus is not only God, but also our blood relative. Thus, His shed blood counts as ours. The Bible makes it very clear that the blood of animals cannot pay for sin (Hebrews 10:4). The reason is that we are not related to animals. But if evolution were true, then animals could also be our savior, since we would be related to them. There would have been no need for Jesus to die on the cross.

Now, we certainly do *not* mean that a person who believes in evolution cannot be a Christian. Clearly, someone can be a genuine Christian, having professed Christ as Lord and serving Him faithfully in many ways, and yet still believe in a theistic form of evolution. But those two beliefs (Christianity and evolution) are inconsistent with each other. Like water and oil, evolution and Christianity simply do not mix. Fortunately, logical consistency in our beliefs is not a requirement for salvation, or we would all be in real trouble! God shows mercy on us, even when our thinking is muddled. But that doesn't mean it is okay to have muddled thinking. Out of gratitude for our salvation, we need to learn to reason in a consistent way that honors God's Word as our supreme and ultimate standard. And that means realizing all Christian doctrines only make sense in light of the history of Genesis.

6. Morality without History? In response to all of the above, some Christians might say, "Yes, Christian doctrines do go back to the stories in Genesis. But that doesn't mean it has to be real history. The Bible is a morality book, not a history book. It's a bit like the tale of the tortoise and the hare. You get the point of the story, even though no one believes that it really happened."

But there is a false analogy here. Genesis is clearly written as narrative history. It gives the historical basis for why we should hold to Christian doctrines. That's quite different from a fable like the tortoise and the hare. A fable does not provide a *foundation* for morality; it merely illustrates a truth (perhaps a moral truth) that most people already know. If someone doesn't understand a moral truth, a fable may clarify how to apply it. But if someone does not believe in a moral claim, a fictional story about its application would be irrelevant! A fable can illustrate a truth, but it cannot provide the *foundation* for a truth since it is not itself true. *Truth cannot be based on fiction!* The moral principles founded in Genesis can only be true if the history in Genesis is literally true.

In fact, not trusting God's truthfulness is at the core of mankind's original sin. It was Adam who accepted the serpent's denigration of God's Word (see Genesis 3), and that was the beginning of everything that has gone wrong in human history since. In other words, trusting God's Word is really at the heart of mankind's most important choices in life—good versus bad, right versus wrong, true versus false, life versus death, redemption versus doom, God versus Satan.

Words can't fully express how authoritatively relevant Genesis is. You better believe it!

Notes

1. Lisle, J. 2012. *Why Genesis Matters*. Dallas, TX: Institute for Creation Research.
2. At the personal level, it is God's role as Creator that matters first, because if you aren't created to start with, nothing else really matters! See Johnson, J. J. S. 2012. Of Grackles and Gratitude. *Acts & Facts*. 41 (7): 8-10.
3. Because our origins matter, it makes sense that researching our origins is worthwhile. See Lisle, J. 2012. The Importance of Creation Research. *Acts & Facts*. 41 (8): 6.

3

DAY-AGE THEORY: A DAY LATE AND A SCHOLAR SHORT

Jason Lisle, Ph.D., and James J. S. Johnson, J.D., Th.D.

The Hebrew word *yôm* is translated as "day" in Genesis 1, but some say it should instead be translated as "age." These "day-age" advocates insist that God didn't create in six ordinary, literal days, but rather over six long ages or eons of time—each representing millions or billions of years. They contend that the word *yôm* might mean a period of time longer than a real day, citing phrases like "in the days of Saul" (1 Chronicles 5:10) or "the day of the LORD" (e.g., Joel 2:1).

This dodge, however, is a "straw man" distraction, because how *yôm* may or may not be used in Hebrew poetry or in Hebrew apocalyptic prophecy (which Genesis 1 is not) is irrelevant to how it is used in narrative history (which Genesis 1 is). Even more important, the real analytical issue is how *yôm* is used within the Genesis creation account.

Day-age advocates often argue that their view is supported by the apostle Peter's statement "that with the Lord one day is as a thousand years" (2 Peter 3:8). They claim this verse means that time is very different to God, and so the days of Genesis 1 don't mean ordinary days as we understand time. But is this really what it means? Is it about the creation week, telling us that the days are actually thousands of years each? No. The context of 2 Peter 3:8 focuses on the apparent "delay" in Christ's promise to return; it is not referring to creation week days.

Ironically, even if Peter was saying that the creation week days were a thousand years each, this still would not support the day-age theory, because that would only add 7,000 years to the 6,000 to 7,000 years that has elapsed since Adam and Eve lived on Earth. The day-age theory needs the Bible to "allow" the secular timescale of *billions* of years—12,000 to 14,000 years won't work!

It is also noteworthy that day-age advocates usually only quote the first part of the verse. They leave out the last part. It's not just that a day is as a thousand years with God, but also "a thousand years as one day." So why not argue that the 2,000 years between Adam and Abraham were really only two 24-hour days, since "one day is as a thousand years"? Wouldn't that be absurd? And yet people don't seem to see the absurdity of applying this same line of thinking to the first part of the verse.

2 Peter 3:8 is simply indicating that God is beyond time, and so it doesn't bother God to wait a thousand years any more than to wait one day. Some people might still try to use the verse to alter the timescale in Genesis by saying, "Since God is beyond time, when He talks about 'days' it could mean any period of time." But this isn't logical. God Himself is both beyond time and also immanently participates in time, which He invented!

God not only invented time, He invented language—and He chose to use language to report how the creation week happened. So when God talks about time, He does so perspicuously (i.e., using meaningful and accurate words so that we can understand the information He wants us to know).

The Word "Day" in Context

When critiquing the day-age theory, the most critical inquiry is what *yôm* ("day") means in Genesis 1.[1,2] Obviously, it is only rightly understood when we study it within the context of a specific biblical text. It is the Hebrew word *yôm* that ultimately matters, not how we use the English word "day." The Bible itself provides the authoritative context for discerning the divine Author's meaning.[2,3]

For example, when *yôm* is used with a number as part of an ordered list—the first day, the second day, the third day, etc.—it is *always* translated as "day" (there are no exceptions in the Bible!) and clearly means an ordinary day. Thus, when Jonah was in the great fish for "three days," there can be no doubt that these are ordinary days, not millennia or eons of "geologic time"!

Also, when "day" is mentioned in the context of "morning," it clearly means an ordinary day, as in "morning seemed to come early that day." Likewise, when mentioned in the context of "evening," it is obviously referring to an ordinary day. Such expressions occur 23 times each in the Old Testament (not including Genesis 1), and there is really no disagreement that they are referring to ordinary days. When "evening" and "morning" are combined, this obviously refers to an ordinary day even if the word "day" is not used, since evening and morning mark the boundaries of the day.

Likewise, when "day" is contrasted with "night," it is clearly an ordinary day. This contrast occurs over 50 times outside of Genesis 1, and no one doubts that these refer to ordinary days.

When we examine the creation week days in Genesis 1, what do we learn from the surrounding context? Consider Genesis 1:5: "And God called the light Day, and the darkness He called Night. So the evening and the morning were the first day." There are number of factors that constrain the meaning of *yôm* to that of an ordinary day.

1. In the first sentence, the word "day" is contrasted with "night."

2. In the second sentence, "day" is associated with a number: "the first day" (or some translations read "one day").

3. The word "day" is associated with "morning" and "evening."

4. The occurrence of "evening" and "morning" together constitutes a normal, 24-hour day.

There is no logical room for doubt: Context demonstrates that Day One was an ordinary day—not some immeasurable timeframe!

What about the other days of creation? Each of these is marked by the phrase "so the evening and the morning were the [second...sixth] day." Each of the six days of creation contains at least *four* contextual markers, any one of which constrains the meaning of "day" to that of an ordinary day! It is apparent that God did not want there to be any possible misunderstanding of the length of the days, so He qualified each day of creation at least four different ways! There can be no doubt that the creation week consisted of six days in the ordinary sense of the word "day."

What about the seventh day? The biblical text does not bracket the seventh day with the words "evening" and "morning." Some opine that this allows for an insertion of billions of years into Day Seven. But such thinking errs. First, Genesis 2:2-3 refers to the "seventh day" as the day when God rested. Since it has a number linked to it (as explained above), this constrains *yôm* to mean an ordinary day.

But even if we (hypothetically) assumed that the seventh day was a long time (which it wasn't!), this would not affect the measurable age of the earth at all! Remember, Adam was made on Day Six, not Day Seven (Genesis 1:26-31). Genesis provides chronological data that show that the time span from Adam to Abraham was less than 2,000 years. So, in terms of computing the age of the universe (using the data in Genesis), the length of Day Seven is actually irrelevant! Six days before Adam, plus ~2,000 years between Adam and Abraham, plus slightly more than 4,000 years between Abraham and now, yields less than 7,000 years.[4]

In fact, the claim that Day Seven was not an ordinary day because Genesis does not list an "evening" and "morning" with it tacitly admits that the first six days were ordinary days, since Genesis *does* specify evenings and mornings for them. (This shows how biblical creation critics ignore what the Bible says.) Day Seven is a day of rest, not a day of creation, so Day Seven is listed in a slightly different way. But it still has a number with it, so it still must be an ordinary day.

Another day-age objection is that the sun wasn't made until the fourth day, so how could the days be ordinary? This objection betrays an ignorance of astronomy. It is not the sun that primarily determines the length of the day. It is *the rotation of the earth* that defines a "day." The sun simply provides a relatively permanent source of light; then as the earth rotates on its axis, we experience morning and evening. As long as we have a rotating planet and a source of light, there will be ordinary days.

Was there light before the sun? Yes! Genesis 1:3 states, "Then God said, 'Let there be light'; and there was light." God provided a temporary source of light for the first three days, and then made the sun on the fourth day as a permanent light-bearer. The earth was already rotating for the first three days, because there was "evening" and "morning." All the days of the creation week lasted the amount of time we call a day.

As a last-ditch effort, some try this argument: "Since God's 'ways' are not our ways (Isaiah 55:8), perhaps His 'days' are not our days. So when God speaks of days, it doesn't mean the same thing as when man speaks of days." But, because the Bible is perspicuous (i.e., written to be understandable), this argument is absurd. If words meant different things to different people, then communication would be impossible and language would be pointless![2,3]

Think about it...when I say "hello," if it means something different than when you say "hello," we could never understand each other. After all, your "hello" might be something totally different, such as "eat more spinach." If words don't have a common meaning between speaker and listener (or between writer and reader), no ideas could ever be communicated.[2] In such a case, reading the Bible would be pointless, because when God says, "Turn [repent] and live" (Ezekiel 18:32), for all we know He might really mean "put lutefisk in your ears."

Sequencing the Creation Week Events

Those who believe they can reconcile (or "harmonize") Genesis with secular cosmogony concepts by redefining the creation days are ignoring another inconsistency—the sequence of events in the creation week. Note that the Genesis account of the creation reports a specific order of events, but this sequential series clashes with the secular scenario imagined by atheistic (and many theistic) evolutionists.

According to Genesis, the earth was made on Day One and the stars were made on Day Four. But the secular view has this reversed; secularists (and generally old earth creationists) believe that stars existed billions of years before Earth! Also, Genesis teaches that fruit trees were made on Day Three and fish on Day Five. But the evolutionary timeline says fish evolved eons before fruit trees (fish are found in deeper layers of rock strata than fruit trees)! Also, Genesis teaches that birds were created on Day Five and all land animals were made on Day Six (this would include dinosaurs). However, the evolutionist myth has dinosaurs evolving long (i.e., eons) before birds arrive!

The bottom line is that redefining the creation week days into evolutionary ages is a theistic evolutionist's compromise. Such bait-and-switch tactics cannot reach the day-age theorist's goal of harmonizing Genesis with evolutionary dogma.

Notes

1. See Lisle, J. 2006. *Taking Back Astronomy.* Green Forest, AR: Master Books, 51-53.

2. See Johnson, J. J. S. 2009. What a Difference a Day Makes. *Acts & Facts.* 38 (3): 13.

3. For clarification, review Johnson, J. J. S. 2010. Every Nation Under Heaven: Using Scripture to Understand Scripture. *Acts & Facts.* 39 (11): 8-9.

4. For range-qualified biblical proof of the Adam to Abraham timeframe, see Johnson, J. J. S. 2008. How Young Is the Earth? Applying Simple Math to Data Provided in Genesis. *Acts & Facts.* 37 (10): 4-5.

4

GAP THEORY: A FORMLESS AND VOID ERROR

Jason Lisle, Ph.D., and James J. S. Johnson, J.D., Th.D.

Like a high-speed, head-on collision, the Bible's creation account directly smashes into the modern majority opinion on origins, especially on the topic of how old the earth is.

Because of this conflict, many have tried to produce a third option—a lopsided compromise that attempts to "harmonize" the evolution myth's old-universe concept with the "six days during the creation week" narrative content of Genesis. Perhaps the cleverest example of this kind of compromise is the gap theory, the most popular version of which is called the "ruin and reconstruction theory."

What Is the Gap Theory?

There isn't any legitimate exegetical reason to believe that the "days" reported in Genesis 1 were anything but ordinary, 24-hour days, yet some Christians insist that we must somehow accommodate the idea that the universe is billions of years old. They may think that this age has been established by science, but nothing could be further from the truth. (See the chapters in this book on the age of the earth and the universe.)

Whatever the reason, since it is clear within the scriptural context that the days of creation were ordinary days, some people have suggested that there was an enormous span of time between Genesis 1:1 and 1:2. They redefine the creation week as more of a "re-creation" (i.e., restoration) week. Some in this camp believe that God originally made the world billions of years ago and then it was ruined, perhaps by Satan, so that the creation week of Genesis 1 recounts how God (re)made the world in six ordinary days.

This view is called the gap theory because its advocates aver that an enormous "gap" of time (billions of years) lies between the first two verses of Genesis.

Imagine "Gap," Insert Evolutionary "Time"

Some Christians mistakenly believe that the billions of years (originally it was just "millions") featured in the gap theory are an accommodation of Charles Darwin's "natural selection" theory. Not so! The gap theory was championed by Thomas Chalmers in 1814, 45 years before Darwin's *Origin of Species*![1] So those who think the eons-of-time "gap" was inserted in response to Darwin have misdiagnosed the real explanation for why Christians decided to "implant" eons of time into the space between the Bible's first two verses.

Unfortunately, Thomas Chalmers invented the time gap in order to accommodate deists (like Charles Lyell and James Hutton) who taught old earth theories that disagreed with Moses' writings. Perhaps Chalmers thought that he was helping to make the Bible more "credible" to the educated people of his generation. This so-called solution to what would in time be called the creation-vs.-evolution problem demonstrates a failure, during the early 1800s, of due diligence to recognize who is *right* and who is *wrong*.

Called a "synthesis" (or "hybrid") solution, this syncretistic theory attempts to hybridize Bible history with secular mythology.

> *The widest rift between science, so-called, and traditional Christianity is the controversy over the age of the earth.* Is it not possible that the Christians have been as badly mistaken as the scientists?... [The world] may have been revolving quite a while before Adam ever caught sight of it. *There is room for all the geologic ages between the first two verses of the Bible.*[2] (emphasis added)

Why has the idea of a gap of "deep time" between Genesis 1:1 and 1:2 been so carelessly and quickly endorsed by so many Christians? Why the big rush to endorse billions of years that are not actually mentioned in the Bible?

Many people try oh-so-hard to please both sides of the fence, but all such amalgamations are logically inconsistent. Biblical creation and Bible-rejecting evolution[3] are, in reality, mutually exclusive explanations for Earth's origins, so there cannot be any true mixture of the two (see Amos 3:3; Luke 16:13). The yoking of Genesis 1 with imagined eons of time presents a challenge in trying to force-fit these disparate epistemologies: How can someone believe in the six literal days of the creation week, followed by a Sabbath day of rest, while *simultaneously* allowing the so-called geologic ages of millions or billions of evolutionary years?

The proposed "harmonization" is this: The creation week is recognized as a true week of six 24-hour days of God's work, followed by one literal day of God's rest—*yet eons of time elapsed before any of the creation week days.*

In short, the gap theory teaches that Day One was not really Day One.

But how can this idea measure up to the text of Scripture? The gap theory uses these assumptions:

1. It is okay to have a literal creation week *after* the action described in Genesis 1:1;

2. So, the creation week does not include Genesis 1:1; and

3. Therefore, God's actions described in Genesis 1:1 may be read as taking countless *eons* of (pre-creation week) time.

But this question logically follows: What Scriptures, including Genesis 1, do gap theory proponents argue from as they advocate their gap of "deep time" lodged between Genesis 1:1 and 1:2?

First, they contend that the Hebrew verb *hayah* is evidence that Earth qualitatively changed between the Bible's first and second verses. Carey Daniel illustrates how the gap theory argues that the original "orderly" creation changed catastrophically, somehow, into a formless "waste":

> But if the word "created" [in Genesis 1:1] refers more correctly to an instantaneous action, and if it means that our world, together with all others, was called suddenly into being (Heb. 11:3), the question remains as to why Moses said it was a formless waste and Isaiah pronounced it an orderly creation [in Isaiah 45:18]. In this case the only answer is that there must have been a lapse of time between the first and second verses of the first chapter of Genesis, during which there took place some great upheaval that overthrew the primitive creation. That such a catastrophe did occur as the result of God's judgment on the early inhabitants seems to have [occurred]....Just who these inhabitants were we dare not venture to say [*ironically, the author promptly ventures a guess anyway!*]. They could scarcely have been human beings, for of such Eve is

called the "mother of all living" (Gen. 3:20). Some hold that they were the angels who like Lucifer, lost their first estate (Jude 6; II Pet. 2:4; Isa. 14:9-14). This supposition is probably as credible as any other.[2]

Note the conjecture, imagining a pre-Adamite world.[4] But what does the Scripture say (and not say) about pre-Adamite "ruin" and "reconstruction"? Likewise, is there any legitimate basis for a gap of time between Genesis 1:1 and 1:2?

Genesis 1

Gap theorists believe that the phrase "in the beginning" used in Genesis 1:1 refers to the "original" creation, which occurred sometime in the very distant past, billions of years ago. The next verse becomes the key to their theory:

And the earth was without form, and void. (Genesis 1:2)

Gap theorists would prefer to translate this as "And the earth *became* without form and void," and suggest that a "formless" creation means some kind of ruin, some change from "very good" to "wasted."[5]

But should 1:2 say "became" (which denotes a *change* of condition) instead of "was" (which denotes a condition that continues *the same* as before)? In fact, there is no philological need to replace the English translation verb "was" with "became." The Hebrew word *hayah* used here is the normal Hebrew verb that means "to be." This same verb is the etymological root of God's special name *YHWH* (Yahweh = "He is" or "He who is," emphasizing God's *unchanging* being), as is confirmed by Exodus 3:14 ("I AM WHO I AM" twice uses the verb *hayah*). God never changed; God can't change. So why would He pick a form of *hayah* to be His own name if *hayah* must mean "change"?!

The Hebrew verb *hayah* likewise appears in Genesis 2:18, when God stated that it was "not good that man [Adam] *should be* alone." The English phrase "should be" translates the verb (specifically, a simple active infinitive construct form of *hayah*), yet Genesis reports nothing to suggest that Adam's singleness at the time was a "changed" condition, as if he was *then* alone *after* a previous marriage!

In some cases, a sentence using *hayah* can make sense whether it is translated as a form of "to be" or a form of "to become," but it also appears that a form of "to be" makes better theological or historical sense in those contexts (e.g., Genesis 13:8; Judges 18:19; 2 Samuel 7:24).

Does Isaiah Support a Billions-of-Years-Old Earth?

As noted above, gap theory advocates claim that the description of Earth in Isaiah 45:18 clashes with the creation history reported in Genesis 1:2:

> In Isaiah 45:18 we are told that God created the world to *not be formless* (*lô' tohû*), yet in Genesis 1:2 we are told that the world *was formless* (*tohû*). Likewise, we read in Genesis 1:2 that earth was "void" (*bohû* = "empty," i.e., empty of inhabitants), yet in Isaiah 45:18 it says God created the earth "to be inhabited" (a form of *yashab* = "to inhabit"). How can both verses be true, unless they are describing different times in earth history?"[6]

Yes, the Hebrew word *tohû* does appear in both Genesis 1:2 and Isaiah 45:18. Isaiah 45:18 says that God, the Creator, "established" (an intensive perfect form of the verb *kûn*) the earth so it would not be a formless mass. And it's not! Before Day One, God had a plan in mind. At the beginning of the creation week, God already knew what His goal was for planet Earth—a world that was orderly, completely formed, and populated with inhabitants. And by the end of Day Six, sure enough, that goal was accomplished and the result was "very good."

But notice that God's complete goal for forming the earth and populating it was *not yet* accomplished on Day One, so Genesis 1:2 correctly reports that *on Day One* the world was "formless," waiting for God to further develop it geologically and geographically.

Likewise, it was always God's planned intention to "establish" Earth as a home for both human and animal inhabitants. That plan of God is noted in Isaiah 45:18, using an infinitive construct form of the common Hebrew verb *yashab* ("to dwell"), emphasizing that God's action was pointed toward that teleological target. As of Day One, that divine plan was not fully implemented, because none of the animals would appear until Day Five. And it would be Day Six before Earth's first human inhabitants arrived, along with land-dwelling animals.

Genesis is a chronological narrative reporting *how* and *when* God created the universe and its inhabitants, and what He did, sequentially, to implement His intended purposes for creation. Isaiah, however, emphasizes *why* God created stuff and later developed it because He wanted an inhabited, orderly world.

A careful analysis of Genesis 1:1-2 and Isaiah 45:18 does not justify inventing a "gap" of evolutionary "geologic time." There is no need for pre-Adamite races, either! The Bible makes perfect sense as it is.

Notes

1. See Johnson, J. J. S. 2011. Just Say No to Trojan Horses: Worldview Corruption Is Lying in Wait. *Acts & Facts*. 40 (2): 17-18. See generally Whitcomb, J. C. and H. M. Morris. 1961. *The Genesis Flood*. Phillipsburg, NJ: Presbyterian & Reformed Publishing Company, 91-99. Regarding the fact that the phrase "in the beginning" in Genesis 1:1 really means "in *the* beginning" (not "in *a* beginning"), see Johnson, J. J. S. 2013. Does *Bereshith* Mean "in a beginning"? *Creation Matters* 18 (3): 6-7.

2. Daniel, C. L. 1941. *The Bible's Seeming Contradictions: 101 Paradoxes Harmonized*. Grand Rapids, MI: Zondervan, 83-84.

3. In the phrase "Bible-rejecting evolution," we are using the broader meaning of the word "evolution"; i.e., the common notion that all of creation was generated from a materialistic Big Bang that somehow, over eons of time and accidents, converted itself into stars, planets, Golgi bodies and bacteria, gecko lizards and bugs, girls and boys. The more narrow use of the word "evolution" would pertain only to the imagined processes beginning with abiogenesis (i.e., life spontaneously generating from non-life), followed by all life forms somehow morphing into other kinds of life.

4. The notion of pre-Adamite creatures populating the earth, with death on Earth before Adam sinned (notwithstanding Romans 5:12 and Romans 8:20-22), has spread. For example, note that theistic evolutionist William Dembski promotes old earth, pre-Adamite subhuman primates, death before sin, and a miraculous amnesia supposedly provided by God that caused Adam and Eve to forget "their former animal life." See Johnson, J. J. S. 2011. Culpable Passivity: The Failure of Going with the Flow. *Acts & Facts*. 40 (7): 8-10, quoting William Dembski's "Christian Theodicy in Light of Genesis and Modern Science" paper (n.d.), as quoted in Ham, K. and G. Hall. 2011. *Already Compromised*. Green Forest, AR: Master Books, 174 and 202, especially endnotes 3 and 7.

5. Gap theorists say Genesis 1:2 reports events that occurred billions of years *after* "the beginning" mentioned in Genesis 1:1; i.e., after an unrecorded history dominated by pre-Adamite death and suffering.

6. This hypothetical quote paraphrases correspondence received by ICR personnel from gap theory advocates.

5

GENESIS IS NARRATIVE HISTORY, NOT HEBREW POETRY

James J. S. Johnson, J.D., Th.D.

"Why are you guys so literalistic about Genesis? Don't you know that it's just Hebrew poetry? There's no need to treat it like real history!" This was the smug comment of a young English literature teacher at a Christian educators' conference that featured Institute for Creation Research speakers. What followed was an energetic discussion that exposed hidden assumptions and misinformation about what Hebrew poetry is *and is not*.

The bottom line is that Genesis is not Hebrew poetry. Genesis is Hebrew *narrative prose*. In other words, Genesis is a record of accurate, true history. Not mysticism or mystery or myth. There is no need for anyone to guess about what Genesis is. Anyone who can read an English Bible can prove that Genesis is not Hebrew poetry.

Why is this important? Because the New Testament's theology of our salvation in Christ Jesus hangs upon the historicity of the Genesis record (Romans 5:12-21).

What Hebrew Poetry Is and Is Not

To see why the young English teacher was wrong, we must first recognize that English poetry and Hebrew poetry are different—hugely different. The difference is not like comparing apples and oranges; the difference is more like contrasting apples and aardvarks.

English poetry is defined by its verbal "hardware," with its pronounced *sounds* qualifying the text as poetry. Hebrew poetry, however, is defined by its "software," its verbal information and *meaning*, presented with parallelism of thought (not sound).

41

In short, Hebrew poetry is defined by parallelism in meaning, whereas English poetry is defined by the format of verse and sound (rhyme, alliteration, assonance, and/or meter). This is easier to illustrate than to explain. Consider the examples below of both kinds of poetry.

Example of English Poetry, Using a Limerick Rhyme and Meter Format

Some Get a "Bang" Out of Fables

The Bible, to read, some are able,
Yet prefer to read a false fable;
   Though God's Word says "six days,"
   A "Big Bang" gets their praise,
Their doctrine, therefore, is unstable.[1]

Verses of English poetry routinely rely on *rhyme*. In limerick poems, the rhyme pattern is AA, BB, A (because *able*, *fable*, and *unstable* all rhyme, as do *days* and *praise*). Other poems use other patterns, but almost without exception some kind of rhyme is used to identify English verse-based literature as poetry.

English poetry, being dominated by sound, also relies on *meter*, the poem's rhythmic "beat." The number of stressed syllables in all A lines should match, as should those in the B lines. One English tradition uses iambic pentameter, employed by poets John Donne, William Shakespeare, and John Milton.[2] Note that rhyme and rhythm neither provide nor depend upon a poem's meaning.

Unlike the sound-dominated rhyme and rhythm of English poetry, Hebrew poetry is defined by informational parallelism—i.e., parallelism of *meaning*.[3] The paralleled thoughts may emphasize good and bad, wise and unwise, reverent and blasphemous. They may or may not recount historical events, although time and place, if mentioned at all, are less emphasized than in narrative prose. This informational parallelism—using comparative lines and phrases—portrays similarities (synonymous parallelism) and/or contrasts (antithetical parallelism), or comparisons of whole and part, or some other kind of logical associations of meaning.

Knowing this linguistic trait helps us to correctly read biblical Hebrew poetry. Since such poetry requires complementation of meaning (not sound), both halves of a verbal parallelism must be reviewed together as a complementary unit in order to understand fully what either half means, as well as to understand how they complement each other in meaning.

In Hebrew poetry, almost always the paralleled lines come in pairs,[4] but sometimes a triplet is used.[5]

Major examples of Hebrew poetry in the Old Testament are Psalms, Proverbs, Lamentations, and Song of Solomon—but not Genesis.

Example of Hebrew Poetry, Illustrating Parallelisms of Similarity and Contrast

Psalm 104:29
> You hide Your face, they are troubled:
> You take away their breath, they die and return to their dust.

Psalm 104:30
> You send forth Your Spirit, they are created:
> And You renew the face of the earth.

Note how both lines in verse 29 show parallel similarity of meaning, as do both lines in verse 30. Yet verse 29 informationally contrasts with verse 30; verse 29 tells how God controls the *death* of certain creatures (like leviathan, mentioned in verse 26), but verse 30 tells how God controls the *life* of His creatures. In order to get the full meaning of either verse 29 or verse 30, the total parallelism must be appreciated. This is the hallmark of Hebrew poetry.

For another example, read any chapter in Proverbs. They are dominated by parallelism of meaning, verse after verse. Sometimes the parallelism spreads over consecutive verses, as in Proverbs 28:15-16 ("wicked ruler" in verse 15; "a ruler" who is a "great oppressor" in verse 16). Sometimes the parallelism is condensed within one verse, as in Proverbs 28:28 ("when the wicked arise, men hide themselves: but when they perish, the righteous increase").

Parallelism dominates the informational structure of Hebrew poetry. Careful reading cannot miss it.

Example of Genesis History, Exhibiting the Format of Narrative Prose

> Now Cain talked with Abel his brother; and it came to pass, when
> they were in the field, that Cain rose up against Abel his brother
> and killed him. And the LORD said to Cain, "Where is Abel your
> brother?" He said, "I do not know. Am I my brother's keeper?"

43

And He said, "What have you done? The voice of your brother's blood cries out to Me from the ground. So now you are cursed from the earth, which has opened its mouth to receive your brother's blood from your hand." (Genesis 4:8-11)

There is no informational parallelism in this passage. What we read is history. Genesis 4:8-11 provides the reader with a narrative account of the first hate crime—an unbeliever tragically persecuting a believer, a terrible precedent that preceded millions of later copycat martyrdom murders. It's a terribly sad report of real history (except that for Abel it was not sad for long, because as a redeemed believer he went to heaven).

There is no poetic parallelism anywhere in Genesis 4, with the only apparent exception being the wicked "song" of Lamech the polygamist recorded in Genesis 4:23-24.

And Lamech said unto his wives,

> Adah and Zillah, hear my voice;
>> Wives of Lamech, listen to my speech!
> For I have killed a man for wounding me,
>> Even a young man for hurting me.
> If Cain shall be avenged sevenfold,
>> Then Lamech seventy and sevenfold.

Note the synonymous parallelism format of meaning in the first two-thirds of the poetic boasting of Lamech.

> Adah and Zillah = wives of Lamech
> Hear my voice = listen to my speech
> A man (I killed) for wounding me = a young man for hurting me

The last part of Lamech's boasting exhibits comparative parallelism, where Cain is compared in a somewhat contrasting way with Lamech. Cain was to be avenged sevenfold if he was killed (Genesis 4:15), yet Cain's murder of Abel was unprovoked. Lamech, however, felt himself morally superior to Cain, because Lamech was provoked by a man who "wounded" him (i.e., the young man who hurt him), so surely—Lamech self-righteously rationalized—Lamech would be avenged much moreso than Cain, perhaps eleven times more.

The fact that the book of Genesis records Lamech's "song" does not mean that Lamech was theologically correct. However, its inclusion—in its Hebrew poetry parallelism format—proves that Hebrew poetry as a literary genre was known to the divinely inspired author of Genesis (i.e., Moses[6]), but it was not used to report any of the historical events of Genesis other than in Lamech's song.

Except for this song, Genesis 4 is not unusual in its narrative prose presentation of early Earth history. There is no poetic parallelism in Genesis 1, 2, 3, or any other chapter in Genesis. (Note that the restrictive features of Hebrew poetry, as Lamech's song illustrates, contrast with Genesis 1, 2, and 3, which narratively chronicle the sequential events of Earth's first week and Adam's first sin.)

Why? Because Genesis is narrative history; it introduces God the Creator, and then introduces the family history of Adam's race. Virtually all of Genesis illustrates what we expect from historical narrative—careful attention to sequenced events (this occurred, then this occurred, then this occurred, etc.), as well as inclusion of time-and-space context information (when such is relevant to the narrative) and a noticeable absence of Hebrew parallelism.[7]

Conclusion: No Meaning-Based Parallelism Structures the Sentences in Genesis

The sentences in Genesis read like narrative history (i.e., prose), *not* informational parallelism (poetry). But the "elephant in the room" question is: Why would anyone even pretend that Genesis 1–11, or any part of Genesis, is Hebrew poetry?

For those who know better, it is intellectual dishonesty to avoid the obvious truth that Genesis is real *history*. Their most likely motive is a desire to accommodate evolutionary mythology by discounting the real history of our origins, stealing credit from Christ so that a fable called "natural selection" can be credited with "selecting" (and creating) Earth's creatures.

Some think Genesis is Hebrew poetry because they have been misled by an "expert." Hopefully, this quick summary can clear up any such confusion. But an even simpler test is this: How did Jesus treat Genesis? As *real history*, just like Paul.[8]

Genesis 1–11 is easy-to-understand narrative prose. Don't naïvely fall for the misinformation of a so-called scholar who, because he wants to rationalize his own evolutionary mythology, tries to dissuade you from believing that Genesis is an inerrantly inspired *historical* narrative—because that's exactly what it is.

Notes

1. Quoting Johnson, J. J. S. The Religion-and-Science Connection Between *Pseudônumos* and *Pseudomarturia*: How Special Revelation Describes the Limitations of General Revelation, technical paper presented at the Southwest regional meeting of the Evangelical Theological Society at The Criswell College, Dallas, Texas, March 27, 2009.

2. Another traditional poetic meter is trochaic tetrameter, used in the German translation of the Finnish national epic *Kalevala* and later mimicked by American poet Henry Wadsworth Longfellow in his fictional epic *Hiawatha*. Both *Kalevala* and *Hiawatha* also use parallelism, though parallelism is not "required" to be recognized as poetry in German or English. Johnson, J. J. S. Finnish Literature, Language, and Lore. *Baltic Heritage Review*. April 2006: 5-7, citing Lönnrot, E. 1963. *The Kalevala, or Poems of the Kaleva District,* F. P. Magoun, Jr., transl. Cambridge: Harvard University Press, 162-163.

3. Robert Lowth is often recognized as clarifying this trait of Hebrew poetry in his *Lectures on the Sacred Poetry of the Hebrews,* published in 1753. See also Lisle, J. 2012. *Why Genesis Matters.* Dallas, TX: Institute for Creation Research, 22-23.

4. For example, Psalm 2:1 compares the raging of "the heathen" with "the people" imagining a vain thing. Likewise, Psalm 2:2 compares the "kings of the earth" setting themselves against the Lord with the "rulers" taking counsel together against the Lord.

5. For example, Psalm 1 compares a triplet of "walking" in the counsel of the ungodly with "standing" in the way of sinners and "sitting" in the seat of the scornful.

6. John 5:39-47. See also Morris, H. 2005. *The Long War Against God.* Green Forest, AR: Master Books, 132-133. For a thorough confirmation of Genesis' Mosaic authorship, see Cooper, B. 2011. *The Authenticity of Genesis.* Portsmouth, UK: Creation Science Movement.

7. Genesis 1–11, as well as 12–50, also routinely uses the *vayyaqtil* forms (i.e., conjunction-modified verbs that older Hebrew grammars call *waw* consecutives or *waw* conversives), an awkward Hebrew language feature that pervades Hebrew narrative prose but *not* Hebrew poetry. See, e.g., Practico, G. D. and M. V. Van Pelt. 2001. *Basics of Biblical Hebrew Workbook.* Grand Rapids, MI: Zondervan, 192-205. See also the discussion of consecutive preterite verb forms in Hackett, J. A. 2010. *A Basis Introduction to Biblical Hebrew.* Peabody, MA: Hendrickson, 89-94.

8. Compare Mark 10:6 with Matthew 15:1-9, John 5:44-47, and Romans 5:12-21.

6

GENESIS DATA ADD UP
TO A YOUNG EARTH

James J. S. Johnson, J.D., Th.D.

Time matters. Likewise, measuring time matters—especially where origins are concerned. Every Christian should recognize that the age of the earth is theologically important, for two reasons: First, because God records important time data in the Bible (so that its chronological information must be authoritatively true and relevant); and second, the Bible teaches a history of Earth time that wholly rejects the "deep time" of millions or billions of years imagined and advocated by evolutionists (so evolution's deep time notions must be false).

As we shall see, the Bible presents a relatively young Earth—between 6.1 and 6.2 thousand years old—and that range of time is certain because the Bible teaches that timeframe through a combination of verses. Consequently, for anyone who trusts the Bible as divinely inspired, understandable, and accurate, the deep time required by evolutionary theories is out of the question.

Likewise, the young age of the earth is highly relevant for showing that a Christian cannot logically rationalize being a theistic evolutionist—i.e., someone who believes God used evolution to make His creation. Because the historical information recorded in Genesis is authoritatively relevant to understanding Earth history, theistic evolutionary thinking should be recognized as the Trojan horse[1] that it really is.

Also, proof that the earth is young is a major problem for anyone who tries to persuade Christians that evolution is compatible with the Bible. In short, evolutionists cannot bluff anyone with their theory *apart from eons of deep time*, so the importance of disproving the possibility of such deep time—using biblical data alone—should be obvious to anyone who regards the Holy Bible as divinely inspired and therefore inerrant, infallible, and authoritative about Earth history.

Some Argue That Genesis "Gaps" Permit Old-Earth Creation Interpretations

Some Christians promote a form of theistic evolution that features an old earth that somehow originated from a primordial Big Bang, even though those notions are foreign to the text of Genesis.

Question: If old-earth Christians claim to believe the Holy Bible is inerrant, infallible, and authoritative—and some say as much—how do they reconcile the chronological data in Genesis with their old-earth theories?

Answer: By a "straw man" analysis of what Genesis says about time. Some Big Bang proponents argue against the Genesis record's young-earth data by dodging behind the assumption that the Genesis genealogies contain gaps.

> A common argument against young-earth creationism is that gaps exist in the genealogies listed in the fifth and tenth chapters of Genesis. The old-earth proponent assumes that if gaps exist, then one cannot claim to know an approximate age of the earth based on biblical data. As a result, they say we must rely on extra-biblical sources to discover the age of the earth.[2]

This argument proposes that the chronological data in Genesis are open to interpretation because we cannot be certain whether the genealogical lists in Genesis 1–11 are complete ("closed") or whether they skip generations and have gaps (and are thus "open"). In effect, the "open genealogy" theory claims that the genealogies contain gaps that are stretchable into huge numbers of years, enough to accommodate human evolution and "geologic time" theory timescales.

An example of this kind of Big Bang-promoting old-earth cosmogony is illustrated by evangelical philosopher Norman Geisler, who confidently dismisses the chronological data in Genesis by endorsing the open genealogy theory and then immediately assuming that if the Genesis genealogies are open, there are no biblical data that provide proof of the actual timeframe from Adam to Abraham.

> Bishop James Ussher (1581–1656), whose chronology was used in the old Scofield Bible, argued that Adam was created 4004

B.C. However, his calculations are based on the assumption that there are no gaps in the genealogical tables of Genesis 5 and 11. But we know this is false.[3]

Geisler quotes no Scripture to support his confidence that "we know this is false." And as Dr. Jonathan Sarfati has shown, there is no good reason to impute any gaps to the Genesis genealogies.[4] However, the open-versus-closed controversy is itself a red herring distraction, because it employs a straw man counterfeit in lieu of the Genesis record's actual data—as the Institute for Creation Research has demonstrated previously.[5]

Even If Genesis Had Genealogy Gaps, They Would Be Irrelevant to Earth's Age

When Abraham was born, how old (or young) was the earth? Can we know the answer with confidence? Yes, because God has given us the information we need in Genesis. But to recognize it requires reading, writing, and 'rithmetic—and one more critical ingredient: avoiding the irrelevant issue of whether Genesis genealogies are open or closed. *Read that last sentence again; it is the key to avoiding confusion.*

As indicated above, some people assume that the historical events related in the early chapters of Genesis cannot be precisely dated because we cannot be certain whether the genealogical lists are complete ("closed") or whether they skip generations and have gaps (and are thus "open"). The issue is irrelevant, however, because the timeframes given in Genesis are measured by the number of years between one event and another event, regardless of how many generations occurred between those "bookend" events.

For example, Genesis 5:3 states that Adam was 130 years old when Seth was "begotten" (which likely refers to Seth's conception). How old was Adam when he begot Seth? Adam was 130. Does it matter whether Seth was Adam's son, grandson, great-grandson, or an even later descendant? No, the answer is the same: 130. Seth's exact filial relationship to Adam is irrelevant to the chronology, because the timeframe reported in Genesis 5:3 is measured by the number of years that separated one historical event (God creating Adam) from a later historical event (Seth being begotten)—regardless of how many generations may have occurred between Adam's creation and Seth's begetting.

One obvious "wrinkle" in measuring the above timeframe involves the probable presence of a partial year, since Seth was not likely begotten on Adam's birthday. For a precise range to use in our calculations, we must consider that Adam was at least 130, but not yet 131. To allow for this extra time, we need to include a partial number in our calculation of not more than one year. That is why this study counts time with precision ranges...yet the ranges themselves are absolute!

The begetting of Seth begins the next timeframe "link" in the unbroken chain of events from Adam to Abraham. At this point, another range adjustment is needed to include the normal duration of a human gestation (i.e., "womb time") to take Seth from conception to birth. No gestation will take longer than one year, so an extra year of precisional tolerance is added to each timeframe that is bordered by a "begetting."

A couple of our timeframes are not linked by a begetting, but by a geological event. In Genesis 7:6, Noah's age at the time of the Flood is given as 600 years. Since the preceding bookend event was the begetting of Noah, the length of the timeframe connected to Genesis 7:6 will need to include a "womb time" of not more than one year (since Noah's birth started the count to 600 years), and will also need to include a partial amount of not more than one year, since it is unknown how much past 600 years old Noah was when the Flood arrived.

One more range adjustment is needed for the begetting of Arphaxad, Noah's grandson. Genesis 11:10 states that Shem beget Arphaxad two years after the Flood. It is logical to assume that this refers to two years after the Flood first began, rather than when it ended, since the start of that cataclysmic event is when the earth changed forever. When the Flood hit Earth, the "clock" of humanity was dichotomized as "pre-Flood" and "post-Flood." (A weightier event, the first advent of Christ, would later divide Earth time as B.C. and A.D.) So the timeframe defined as the time between the Flood's outbreak and the begetting of Arphaxad includes two years, plus another partial amount of not more than one year, since Scripture does not indicate how many days past the two-year mark Arphaxad was begotten.[6]

Otherwise, it is straight *event-to-event* math, with the number of generations that are included between the bookend events being irrelevant. The 19 sequential links in this unbroken chain are given in the chart below.

The timeframe in years from Adam's creation to Abraham's birth, based on event-to-event timeframe links as recorded in Genesis					
Timeframe Links	Bookend Events	Womb Time	Stated Years	Partial Year	Total Years
1. Genesis 5:3	Adam is created / Adam begets Seth	n/a	130	≤ 1	≤ 131
2. Genesis 5:6	Seth is begotten / Seth begets Enosh	≤ 1	105	≤ 1	≤ 107
3. Genesis 5:9	Enosh is begotten / Enosh begets Cainan	≤ 1	90	≤ 1	≤ 92
4. Genesis 5:12	Cainan is begotten / C. begets Mahalalel	≤ 1	70	≤ 1	≤ 72
5. Genesis 5:15	Mahalalel is begotten / M. begets Jared	≤ 1	65	≤ 1	≤ 67
6. Genesis 5:18	Jared is begotten / Jared begts Enoch	≤ 1	162	≤ 1	≤ 164
7. Genesis 5:21	Enoch is begotten / E. begets Methuselah	≤ 1	65	≤ 1	≤ 67
8. Genesis 5:25	Methuselah is begotten M. begets Lamech	≤ 1	187	≤ 1	≤ 189
9. Genesis 5:28-29	Lamech is begotten / Lamech begets Noah	≤ 1	182	≤ 1	≤ 184
10. Genesis 7:6	Noah is begotten / Flood hits	≤ 1	600	≤ 1	≤ 602
11. Genesis 11:10	Flood hits / Arphaxad is begotten	n/a	2	≤ 1	≤ 3
12. Genesis 11:12	Arphaxad is begotten / A. begets Salah	≤ 1	35	≤ 1	≤ 37
13. Genesis 11:14	Salah is begotten / Salah begets Eber	≤ 1	30	≤ 1	≤ 32
14. Genesis 11:16	Eber is begotten / Eber begets Peleg	≤ 1	34	≤ 1	≤ 36
15. Genesis 11:18	Peleg is begotten / Peleg begets Reu	≤ 1	30	≤ 1	≤ 32
16. Genesis 11:20	Reu is begotten / Reu begets Serug	≤ 1	32	≤ 1	≤ 34
17. Genesis 11:22	Serug is begotten / Serug begets Nahor	≤ 1	30	≤ 1	≤ 32
18. Genesis 11:24	Nahor is begotten / Nahor begets Terah	≤ 1	29	≤ 1	≤ 31
19. Genesis 11:26	Terah is begotten / Abraham is born	≤1=≤1	70	≤ 1	≤ 73
			Total: ≥1,948		Total: ≤1,985

The chart above assumes that Abraham was born during the 22nd century B.C., which is not a controversial assumption among serious biblical history students, whether they be liberals or conservatives.[7]

Accordingly, using generous qualifications for gestation periods and for birthday-qualified partial years, the qualified timeframe links become:

Least time: 130 + 105 + 90 + 70 + 65 + 162 + 65 + 187 + 182 + 600 + 2 + 35 + 30 + 34 + 30 + 32 + 30 + 29 + 70 = not *less* than 1,948 years

Most time: 131 + 107 + 92 + 72 + 67 + 164 + 67 + 189 + 184 + 602 + 3 + 37 + 32 + 36 + 32 + 34 + 32 + 31 + 73 = not *more* than 1,985 years (*roughly 1/3 of all time!*)[8]

The bottom line is that the Genesis record from Adam to Abraham pro-vides *event-to-event* timeframes, each measured in *literal years,* and those time-frames connect sequentially together like adjoining links in a gapless chain. God provided inerrant biblical chronological information in Genesis, one of the Mosaic books that Christ Himself regarded as perfect,[9] so whether the ge-nealogies are open or closed is *irrelevant* to the question of the age of the earth (as applied to the Adam-to-Abraham years).

Accordingly, the "open"-or-"closed" genealogy question is a needless dis-traction. There is no good excuse for doubting this biblical chronological data, especially since these event-to-event timeframe links all connect in sequence, so open-versus-closed genealogy arguments are beside the point.[10]

Therefore, the total Earth-time in years from God's creation of Adam to the birth of Abraham *cannot be more than 1,985 years*, although it is likely somewhat less than that,[11] yet it *cannot be less than 1,948 years.*

Add five days[12] and you have the age of the earth when Abraham arrived here. The same Genesis time data detailed above, assuming Abraham was born in the 22nd century B.C., prove that the earth must be between 6.1 and 6.2 thousand years old.[13]

Yes, it was a young earth into which Abraham was born—*absolutely!*

Notes

1. Johnson, J. J. S. 2011. Just Say No to Trojan Horses: Worldview Corruption Is Lying in Wait. *Acts & Facts.* 40 (2): 17-18, especially endnotes 4 and 5.

2. Chaffey, T. and J. Lisle. 2008. *Old-Earth Creationism on Trial: The Verdict Is In.* Green Forest, AR: Master Books, 179.

3. Geisler, N. L. 1999. *Baker Encyclopedia of Christian Apologetics*. Grand Rapids, MI: Baker Books, 272, quoted in Chaffey and Lisle, 180. Not only does Geisler provide no scriptural or other evidence to support these purported genealogical gaps, his non-literalist approach to Genesis history also leads him to bypass Genesis' Flood data (especially the catastrophically violent character of that divine judgment) for the so-called "tranquil flood" theory, thus placing human-based, fallible "science" (with its ever-changing explanations of Earth history) over the authority of Scripture. See Johnson, J. J. S. 2011. Biblical Devastation in the Wake of a "Tranquil Flood." *Acts & Facts*. 40 (9): 8-10, quoting from Morris, J. D. 2009. *The Young Earth: The Real History of the Earth—Past, Present, and Future*. Green Forest, AR: Master Books, 128-129.

4. Sarfati, J. 2009. *Refuting Compromise*. Green Forest, AR: Master Books, 296, cited in Chaffey and Lisle, 181.

5. Johnson, J. J. S. 2008. How Young Is the Earth? Applying Simple Math to Data in Genesis. *Acts & Facts*. 37 (10): 4-5. See also Johnson, J. J. S. 2012. Staying on Track Despite Deceptive Distractions. *Acts & Facts*. 41 (5): 9-11.

6. It should be noted that since timeframes 10 and 11 are linked to the "bookend" event of the Flood, the consideration of Noah's age at Shem's begetting and Shem's age at the begetting of Arphaxad is irrelevant.

7. See, e.g., page 478 of *The Genesis Flood* by John C. Whitcomb and Henry M. Morris (Philadelphia: Presbyterian and Reformed Publishing Co., 1961), which suggests 2167 B.C. as Abraham's probable birth year. The authenticity of Genesis history is well-established in the New Testament, and is corroborated in many extra-biblical sources. See Cooper, W. R. 2011. *The Authenticity of the Book of Genesis*. Portsmouth, UK: Creation Science Movement, 1–423.

8. Gestation time is included for both Terah and Abraham, since the timeframe being measured is from Adam's creation to Abraham's birth. In particular, see timeframe 19 in the chart above.

9. Compare Mark 10:6 with Matthew 15:1-9 and John 5:44-47. See also Romans 5:12-21.

10. This analysis is an adaptation of a more detailed analysis by Thomas D. Ice and James J. S. Johnson (with preparation help from Dr. Bill Cooper) titled "Using Scriptural Data to Calculate a Range-Qualified Chronology from Adam to Abraham, with Comments on Why the 'Open'-or-'Closed' Genealogy Question Is Irrelevant," originally presented to the Evangelical Theological Society, Southwest Regional Meeting, March 1, 2002. A copy of this paper is available on www.icr.org.

11. The range-qualified high is extra high, since adding a "buffer" of one extra year for every period of human gestation is overly generous—no mother would want a 12-month pregnancy!

12. Adam and Eve were created on Day Six (Genesis 1:23-31).

13. The Earth time calculation, which assumes that Abraham was born in 2167 B.C. and which recognizes that there is no year "0," provides these minimum and maximum timeframes, as of 2013—At least: 1,948 + 2,167 + 2,013 − 1 = 6,127 years (minimum); At most: 1,985 + 2,167 + 2,013 − 1 = 6,164 years (maximum). To the extent that Abraham was *not* born in 2167 B.C., these numbers would need to be shifted accordingly, but the result would still be very close to the same. (Thus, Archbishop Ussher hit very close to the bull's-eye!) Therefore, assuming Abraham was born in a year close to 2167 B.C., the absolute age of the earth must be between 6.1 and 6.2 thousand years old—no millions or billions! *This is an absolute age range for planet Earth.*

7

NO DEATH BEFORE ADAM SINNED

James J. S. Johnson, J.D., Th.D.

Death was alien to God's "very good" creation, until Adam sinned.

The trustworthiness of the Holy Bible hangs upon the accuracy of this fact: *There was no death before Adam sinned.* To err about when and why death came to Earth is to err about the theological and historical foundation of the gospel. The death of Christ, and therefore the gospel of Christ, won't make sense if death came to Earth any other way than by Adam's sin in Eden. If death came first, the New Testament would be worse than unreliable—it would be irreparably wrong about salvation.

Although more could (and should) be said about how and why Adam's sin triggered death,[1] two major points will be reviewed here: (1) The gospel of Christ depends on the truth of Adam's sin triggering death on Earth; and (2) the reliability of the Bible depends upon the truth of Adam's sin triggering death on Earth.

Put bluntly, if death somehow came to earth *apart from Adam's sin,* we cannot be confident that hell is escapable. Those reasons guarantee that this topic is anything but trivial. The stakes are as high as can be.

"Very Good" Creations Don't "Groan"

The original condition of God's creation at the end of Day Six was "very good" (Genesis 1:31), displaying the perfection of providence. However, the earth is now fallen—the current condition of God's creation is good (Acts 14:17) yet "groaning" (Romans 8:20-22).

That groaning now includes the reign of sin and death over humans and animals, a terrible situation that will one day be overcome (1 Corinthians 15:26, 54-56; Revelation 21:4; 22:3).

What caused this change? God did not leave us to guess the answer: Genesis 3 provides the *history* of that change; the New Testament (especially in Romans 5 and 8) provides the *theology* of that change.[2]

If we ignore God's authoritative explanation in Genesis and Romans by relying on theistic evolutionist mythologies—in which death was supposedly a necessary part of God's "creative" activities—we err.[3, 4, 5] Why? Because only the Bible's teaching of the history and theology of human sin reveals the true etiology of death (Romans 5:12).

The Bible's First Mention of Death

Death had a beginning; death is not eternal. In order to have the possibility of death, there must first be mortal life. Accordingly, death could never occur unless and until God created living creatures that were capable of dying. Genesis 1 and 2 describe and report how God created such creatures.

To understand how "life" can be lost to "death," it is important to note that God worked in different ways during the creation week. Some of God's deeds were acts of *absolute creation* (i.e., God making something *from nothing*), while other deeds God did were acts of *creative development* (i.e., God modifying *something that already exists* into something else).

Various Hebrew verbs help us to distinguish when God was "creating" versus when God was "developing" His creation into the diverse products that He wanted to exist. As we shall see, the creation week involved three kinds of "creating": (1) God creating physical stuff on Day One; (2) God creating animal life on Day Five; and (3) God creating human life on Day Six.

The Hebrew word that means "to make something from nothing" is *bara'*—in English, this verb is almost always translated as some form of the verb "to create."[6] However, various other construction/development-related verbs appear in the Genesis creation report, such as "made," "divided," "gathered together," "brought forth," etc.[7]

Genesis 1:1 is the *first* verse to use the Hebrew verb *bara'* ("created"). This verse reports that God created (i.e., made from nothing) something new: physical stuff. There was no physical stuff before Day One. Period. It was decreed into existence, by God, on Day One.

Physical stuff is not "alive," so it cannot "die." Nothing made on Day One was mortal (i.e., capable of dying) because there was no created life yet. Between Genesis 1:1 and 1:21, through Day Four, God worked with the physical stuff He made on Day One. God continued this work on Day Five, yet added something new.

Genesis 1:21 is the *second* verse to use *bara'*. This verse reports that God created the first kinds of animal life—"every living thing that moves"—life with a *nephesh* (often translated as "soul"). These marine and flying creatures—such as birds, bats, barnacles, bass, butterflies, barracudas, and brittle stars—had something qualitatively new that had never been created before: *life!*[8]

Animals are much more than reprogrammed heaven-and-earth physical "stuff." Something that has never had life cannot die. Life "that moves" on Earth, however, can die.

The first blessing in the creation week was pronounced when God blessed the animals of the air and waters in Genesis 1:22 as He commanded these living creatures to "be fruitful and multiply, and fill" the earth's aquatic and terrestrial habitats. Animals are blessed!

Genesis 1:27 is the *third* and last verse in Genesis 1 to use *bara'*. This verse reports that God "created" mankind (i.e., male and female) in God's own image, a unique kind of life that is infinitely different in quality from that of animal life. (In time, God would eventually provide redemption for human life, proving that God prizes human life moreso than any other kind of life that He created.) The creation of mankind was so important that the verb *bara'* is used thrice in this one verse.

Like Day Five, God's blessing was tied to His decree to "be fruitful and multiply, and fill" the earth (1:22; 1:28), with an extra responsibility to mankind: subdue and dominate.

This extra "dominion" responsibility that God imposed upon Adam would make a difference in the destiny of all life forms on Earth, because Adam's jurisdictional authority over the world (including all of its animals) would eventually mean that Adam's subsequent Fall would include all that belonged to him (as Romans 8 explains).

At the end of Day Six, all was "very good" (Genesis 1:31)—which means that there could not be any death on Earth at that time because death is not good (Romans 8:20-22; 1 Corinthians 15). The Bible reports no animals dying before Adam sinned. (Note that no animals were to be eaten by man until after the Flood, according to Genesis 1:29-30 and 9:1-4.) Likewise, theistic evolutionists' imaginations notwithstanding, the Bible reports no pre-Adamite subhuman primates of any kind, much less any dying before Adam sinned. Furthermore, the Bible reports no humans dying before Adam sinned.[3]

Rather, the Bible clearly reports that it was Adam's sin that triggered the curse of death, in fulfillment of God's warning:

> Therefore, just as through one man [i.e., *Adam*] sin entered into the world, and death through sin, and thus death spread to all men, because all sinned—(For until the law sin was in the world, but sin is not imputed when there is no law. Nevertheless death reigned from *Adam* to Moses, even over those who had not sinned according to the likeness of the *transgression of Adam*, who is a type of Him who was to come....For if by the one man's offense death reigned through the one, much more those who receive abundance of grace and of the gift of righteousness will reign in life through the One, *Jesus Christ*.) Therefore, as through one man's offense judgment came to all men, resulting in condemnation, even so through one Man's righteous act the free gift came to all men, resulting in justification of life. For as by one man's disobedience many were made sinners, so by one Man's obedience many will be made righteous. Moreover the law entered that the offense might abound. But where sin abounded, grace abounded much more, so that as sin hath reigned in death, even so grace might reign through righteousness to eternal life through Jesus Christ our Lord. (Romans 5:12-14, 17-21, emphasis added)

Death was unknown to Adam and Eve before Adam sinned. Adam had never seen death before. Just as people on Earth today do not personally see "heaven" and "hell," God teaches us via Scripture vital truths about the conditions of eternity. When we are taught what we should believe about such things, our own faith in God's Word is tested: Either we believe what God reveals to us about the unseen (e.g., heaven and hell), or we don't. God is pleased to test our faith about such unseen things, just as God was pleased (6,000+ years ago) to use information about unseen realities to test Adam's faith and loyalty. That kind of testing is the essence of faith (Hebrews 11:1-3).

Note that, like Adam's testing by God, God's testing of our faith and our loyalty to Him (as our Creator) is always coupled with *consequences*—good consequences for good choices, bad consequences for bad choices.

Then the LORD God took the man and put him in the garden of Eden to tend and keep it. And the LORD God commanded the man, saying, "Of every tree of the garden you may freely eat; but of the tree of the knowledge of good and evil you shall not eat, for in the day that you eat of it you shall surely die." (Genesis 2:15-17)

Adam, the first human to sin, quickly learned a lot about consequences—the consequences of his sin included a new thing, death (Romans 5:12; 6:23).

The Bible Teaches That the Wages of Sin Is Death

Consider how God chose to test Adam's faith and loyalty. The test was simple: Don't eat from one specific tree in the Garden of Eden. God designed Adam's test to have built-in consequences. Adam could make the choice, but Adam could not control the consequences that would flow from that choice. Why not? Because the consequences were built in to the alternative choice options: The good choice would produce a good result (life eternal); the bad choice would produce a bad result (death).

In effect, God designed the gun, including the trigger—but it was Adam who aimed the gun and pulled the trigger, thus starting the dying process ("you shall surely die" could be rendered "dying, you will die") that leads ultimately to death itself.

The test was all part of God's glorious plan for human history, and God foreknew what would happen.[2] However, Adam's choice was nonetheless a true test of Adam's faith and loyalty, because Adam did not *experientially* know the outcome in advance.

Adam could have believed God to avoid the "death" that God warned of, but he chose otherwise. Only then did Adam *experience* the "dying" condition that God had warned him about. Dying began, as did thorns, pain in childbirth, and, in time, death itself.

But the dying was not limited to Adam!

Because God had placed all of the life forms of the world under Adam's authority (Genesis 1:26-31; Psalm 8), the world fell with Adam and was "cursed" with death (Genesis 3:17-19).

For the creation was subjected to futility, not willingly, but because of Him who subjected it in hope; because the creation itself also will be delivered from the bondage of corruption into the glorious liberty of the children of God. For we know that the whole creation groans and labors with birth pangs together until now. (Romans 8:20-22).

Consequently, all of the world's living creatures—both humans and animals—have been "groaning" under the curse of sin and death ever since, although eventually the time will come when Christ's redemption will be applied to the earth itself to overcome the Edenic curse of death (Revelation 20:11; 21:1-5; 22:3).

Faith and Unbelief Are Tested in Time and Space

The Bible never says that Adam was punished *before* he sinned. Any such advance punishment (based on God's foreknowledge) would not truly *test* Adam's faith and loyalty. God never punishes a human sinner *before* he or she sins, because to do so would be *unjust*. Also, to punish a bad choice *in advance* would negate the decision as a true *test of faith and loyalty.*

Accordingly, even though God foreknows all human choices,[2] He does not disqualify the testing of our spiritual character by showing us (in the sense of visible experience, since a decision's real test is whether we will "walk by faith," not by sight) the future in advance, so there cannot be retroactive consequences for a human sinning against God.

Consider how people are tested by choices in real time. If you see the consequences of a choice in advance, how much of a real test is it?

Joseph tested his brothers in space and time (Genesis 42–44), not revealing himself to them *until after* they made character-revealing choices.

Daniel's three friends Shadrach, Meshach, and Abednego were tested in time and space (Daniel 3). They *did not know in advance* whether their godly choices would be rewarded with a miraculous deliverance or by an agonizing (and very painful) martyrdom.

What kind of testing of faith in and loyalty to God would there be if the consequences were provided before the choices were made?

Consider the amazing testing of Job's faith in and loyalty to God. Satan accused Job of worshiping God only if, as, and when God blessed Job—as if God was not worthy of being worshiped just because He is who He is. Satan was wrong, of course; Job praised God throughout his undeserved suffering

(James 5:11; 1 Peter 4:19). But what if Job had been allowed to read the last chapter of the Bible book that bears his name—what kind of faith/loyalty test would all of that suffering have been?

Adam was tested in time and space. Eden was a real test in real time, and Adam failed the test. The test had real consequences, *dying* (i.e., the cursed process of mortality that inexorably leads to death) being the most immediate consequence for Adam's immoral and tragic choice.

Thankfully, God had a redemptive provision tied to the Curse's punitive outcome—a redemptive solution God did not reveal until the Messianic promise of Genesis 3:15 (which foreshadowed the truth of Romans 6:23).

In fact, God foreknew the need for human redemption; He planned for it before He created space, time, matter-energy, and bio-information (Revelation 13:8 and 17:8).

But, because God wanted to truly test Adam's character (as He later would test Job), God did *not* reveal the consequence of Adam's sin, *visibly*, until Adam actually made his historic choice. Only then did this horrible cursed reality called death arrive on Earth, in real time.

What's Wrong with "Backdating" Adam's Punishment for His Sin?

In order for theistic evolutionary theories to work, death had to have existed before Adam arrived and rebelled against God. Some have argued that backdating the punishment of his sin (i.e., applying the penalty of death "retroactively") by imposing death on creation *before* Adam sinned is juristically acceptable (i.e., acceptable as a matter of justice), because the sins of modern Christians were punished retroactively at Christ's crucifixion.

But this lopsided analogy is illogical and misfitted. It is not a mere comparison of apples and oranges, it is more like the contrast between *apples* and *aardvarks*!

Christ's advance choice to *voluntarily* accept *undeserved* punishment as the innocent substitute for Adam's race is not at all like Adam's *involuntary* experience of receiving *deserved* punishment for his sin in Eden.

Christ foreknowingly agreed to His Messianic role—including His redemptive death and resurrection—*before* the vicarious punishment was imposed upon (and accepted by) Him at Calvary. As a matter of God's holy justice, this voluntary consent on Christ's part made all the difference in how

God's justice fit the situation.

In other words, before Christ ever created the heavens and the earth, He consented to the Trinity's plan for His incarnation so that He would, as the Lord Jesus Christ, be sacrificed (in future Earth time) as the Lamb of God, fulfilling the Messianic Kinsman-Redeemer role necessary to provide a just redemption for Adam's race. God foreknew prior to the creation week that the human race would fail and thus would need a rescue (see Revelation 13:8).

The punishment of Christ as the innocent substitute for human sinners would occur chronologically *after* some people sinned (those who lived during Old Testament times), as well as *before* others sinned (those who lived during New Testament times and afterwards). Yet all of that sin was foreknown to Christ *before* He committed to accepting punishment for it, as the Just suffering for the unjust in order to justify many. There was no punishment imposed, historically, *prior* to Christ's consent.

There is therefore no "retroactive injustice" problem, because Christ's voluntary decision to pay for all of the foreknown human sin before any of it occurred was a fate that Christ willingly volunteered for *before* He created the heavens and the earth (John 1:3, 10-13). It was *not unjust* for Christ to accept that role in advance of performing it.

In other words, Christ was not being "cheated," as a matter of justice, by being punished before He failed a test of moral accountability, because He never failed at anything! Rather, Christ's punishment was volunteered for, and that punishment occurred *after* He voluntarily accepted the role of the Lamb of God who would take away the sin of the world.

Even in our profane human experience, we do not regard it as unjust when someone pays in advance for anticipated debts of an intended beneficiary. For example, although it is not a common practice in this selfish world, there is nothing shocking about the idea of one unselfish man depositing a sum of money to pay for the expected expenses of someone else. The good Samaritan provided an advance payment for the foreseeable expenses of the robbery victim he had rescued (Luke 10:35).

As a matter of justice, the Samaritan was not "cheated," because his money was not involuntarily taken from him *before* a debt was incurred. Rather, he anticipated a foreseeable debt that would soon be owed, and he chose voluntarily to provide for its payment, *as a matter of grace*, before it was incurred.

(Of course, in the case of Christ's substitutionary sacrifice for our sins, there will *never* be a supplemental payment, because the death of Christ is a once-for-all and more-than-sufficient payment for all of the sins of the human race, no matter how many sins that may ultimately add up to.[9])

However, in Adam's case, the punishment, which included the Curse of sin and death chronicled in Genesis 3 and explained in Romans 5, was *involuntarily* imposed on Adam. Because Adam did *not* volunteer for his punishment, it would be unjust to impose that punishment on him (even though God foreknew that Adam would sin) *unless and until he actually sinned*, in space and time. When Adam actually sinned, it was then a just time for him to receive the "wages of sin"—death.

In other words, Adam was not "cheated," as a matter of justice, by being punished before he sinned (as theistic evolution would require), because (1) God warned Adam of the consequence of sinning *before* he sinned, and (2) God did *not* impose the Curse of sin and death until *after* Adam actually sinned.

There was no miscarriage of justice in Eden! Rather, God's justice was manifested in Adam's lifetime (as it is reported to us in Genesis), for those who have the eyes to see it. Also, there was no *ex post facto* punishment (i.e., defining an action as wrong only after it was committed). Adam had advance notice of what God prohibited, but knowingly committed the sin anyway; only then was the just penalty to Adam imposed by God.

There was no "backdated" involuntary punishment in Eden (or anywhere else). Adam never received a penalty from God *until* the time when he deserved it.

God is just. Because He is just, any theological compromise of the Genesis 3 narrative, or its New Testament commentaries (e.g., in Romans 5 and in 1 Corinthians 15), is an insult to God's perfect justice.

Appreciating the Bible's Authoritative Relevance

All of this is plainly taught in the history of Genesis 1–5, and is clarified theologically in Romans 5 and 8. So why do some people, especially theistic evolutionists, have a problem understanding that there was no death until Adam sinned? The simple answer is that theistic evolutionists are ignoring the *authoritative* truth in Genesis and Romans—due to negligent or willful ignorance of those biblical texts.

In sum, theistic evolutionists prefer to *accommodate* secular evolutionary teachings, so they ignore or distort the plain teaching of Genesis and Romans.[3, 4, 5]

But such unbiblical accommodation is not Christ-like. The Lord Jesus Christ did *not* "accommodate" unbiblical teachings when He physically walked this earth—rather, He healed the blind on the Sabbath (e.g., see John 9) just to prove that the Pharisees were false teachers espousing bad theology.

Why Does It Matter?

The New Testament directly links the gospel of salvation to the sin of Adam (Romans 5; 1 Corinthians 15). Note that Paul's definition of the gospel of Christ in 1 Corinthians 15:3-4 twice contextualizes the gospel as being "according to the [Old Testament] Scriptures"—the gospel is dependent upon the Old Testament being true!

Indeed, the Old Testament is authoritatively relevant and true and perfect—every "jot and tittle" of it—from Genesis forward. So much so that Christ Himself said that Moses would judge people according to whether they believed the words of Moses (John 5:45-47).

In other words, if the Bible's five books of Moses (which include Genesis) were authoritatively good enough for the Lord Jesus (Matthew 24:35; John 17:17), they are authoritatively good enough for us.

What we really believe about death being the consequence of Adam's sin in Eden is *a test of our own faith in and loyalty to God*.[10] And that test is an open Book exam.

Notes

1. Chaffey, T. and J. Lisle. 2008. *Old-Earth Creationism on Trial: The Verdict Is In*. Green Forest, AR: Master Books, 23-30, especially 27-29. God's moral character is another hugely important truth, tied directly to Genesis 3 and Romans 8. This theological issue is addressed elsewhere in this book by Dr. Henry M. Morris III. Theologically speaking, this chapter also relies upon the analytical critiques of the gap theory and day-age theory, as well as interpreting Genesis exegetically (as the Lord Jesus Himself role-modeled, e.g., in Matthew 19:4 and Mark 10:6), as well as the clarification that the book of Genesis is *not* Hebrew poetry (see the earlier chapters on these topics).

2. Regarding the balance of God's sovereignty, and human choice, accountability, and suffering, see Johnson, J. J. S. 2011. Human Suffering: Why This Isn't the "Best of All Possible Worlds." *Acts & Facts*. 40 (11): 8-10.

3. Theistic evolutionists (whether they endorse gap theory, day-age, or Intelligent Design Movement cosmogonies) routinely posit millions or billions of years of cosmic time before Adam, as well as eons of animal death

before Adam, and pre-Adamite races of subhuman primates—all of which imaginary concepts accommodate secularists' evolutionary dogmas. See, e.g., Dembski, W. 2009. *The End of Christianity: Finding a Good God in an Evil World.* Nashville, TN: Broadman and Holman Academic, 77, 154-155; and William Dembski's "Christian Theodicy in Light of Genesis and Modern Science" paper (n.d.). Both are quoted and cited in Ham, K. and G. Hall. 2011. *Already Compromised.* Green Forest, AR: Master Books, 173-174, and endnotes 3, 4, and 6 on page 202.

4. Johnson, J. J. S. 2011. Just Say No to Trojan Horses. *Acts & Facts.* 40 (2): 17-18, citing Whitcomb, J.C., and H. M. Morris. 1961. *The Genesis Flood: The Biblical Record and Its Scientific Implications.* Phillipsburg, NJ: Presbyterian & Reformed Publishing, 91-99. See also Morris, J. D. 2007. *The Young Earth: The Real History of the Earth—Past, Present, and Future.* Green Forest, AR: Master Books, 128-129, cited in Johnson, J. J. S. 2011. Biblical Devastation in the Wake of a "Tranquil Flood." *Acts & Facts.* 40 (9): 8-10.

5. Johnson, J. J. S. 2011. Culpable Passivity: The Failure of Going with the Flow. *Acts & Facts.* 40 (7): 8-10.

6. Wigram, G. V. 2001. *The Englishman's Concordance of the Old Testament.* Peabody, MA: Hendrickson, 270 (reprint of 3rd edition of 1874).

7. Hebrew verbs used to describe God's creative work in Genesis 1 besides *bara'* ("created") include *hayah* ("let there be," vv. 3, 6, 14, 15); *badal* ("divided," vv. 4, 6, 7, 18); `*asah* ("made," "yielding," vv. 7, 11, 12, 16, 25, 26); *qavah* ("be gathered together," v. 9); *ra'ah* ("appear," v. 9); *rasha'* ("bring forth," v. 11); *zara`* ("yielding seed," i.e., "seeding," vv. 11, 12); yatsa' ("bring forth," vv. 12, 24); *nathan* ("set," vv. 17, 18); *sharats* ("bring forth," vv. 20, 21).

8. Wigram, 829-833. Plants were created on Day Three, but, biblically speaking, they don't have what the Bible calls "life," so "life" did not exist until Day Five. Life was something completely new to God's creation, so the Hebrew verb *bara'* ("created") is used in Genesis 1:21 to described it being commanded into being. Regarding the animated life of animals ("that moves"), in contrast to plants, see Morris III, H. M. 2012. It's Alive! *Acts & Facts.* 41 (8): 4-5.

9. Regardless of how much sin is ultimately committed by humans, the aggregate (although huge beyond human comprehension) is still a finite amount of sins, committed by a finite number of fallen humans. By contrast, the worth of the human life of Christ, however, is infinite, because Christ is both God and man simultaneously. Christ's perfection and infinite value, as the incarnate Creator God, immeasurably outweighs all of the possible wrongs that could ever be committed by any possible number of fallen humans. Accordingly, the vicarious death of Christ when He shed His blood at Calvary more than pays for all of the possible sins of humans, for all time. See Romans 5, especially verses 9, 10, 15, 17, and 20.

10. This controversy is best understood when it is recognized that it is one major battlefront in a larger war over Genesis's perfect authenticity, accuracy, authority, understandability, and authoritative relevance. See especially pages 22-27 of Cooper, W. R. 2011. *The Authenticity of the Book of Genesis,* Portsmouth, UK: Creation Science Movement, as well as pages 7-21, 33-99, 109-130, 162-359, and 369-405. See also Johnson, J. J. S. 2012. Tonsils, Forensic Science, and the Recent Fabrication Rule. *Acts & Facts.* 41 (6): 8-9; and Morris, H. M. 1976. *The Genesis Record.* San Diego, CA: Creation-Life Publishers, 17-25.

8

EVOLUTION IS LOGICALLY IMPOSSIBLE

Jason Lisle, Ph.D.

Many of the chapters in this book show how evidence from diverse fields of science confirms biblical creation and challenges evolution. It might seem to some that if only evolutionists were aware of this evidence, they would then cease to be evolutionists and would embrace creation. But surprisingly, many evolutionists are already aware of this body of evidence and yet still persist in their beliefs. Why is this? And how do they get around the obvious evidence of biblical creation?

Worldviews

One of the most important overlooked points when considering debates on origins is the fact that every person has a worldview—a way of thinking about life and everything one experiences. In a sense, it's a filter through which we perceive reality. This worldview consists of our most basic beliefs and assumptions, which we are not quick to abandon: "I exist. My mind is rational. There is a universe. My memory and senses are basically reliable. There are laws of logic." And so on. This worldview largely determines how we understand our experiences. It constrains what conclusions we draw from the evidence we examine. Evolutionists and creationists have different, competing worldviews. As a result, creationists and evolutionists can look at the same evidence (fossils, DNA, rocks, etc.) and draw very different conclusions about what the evidence means.

Imagine a magician who seems to make a person float in the air. A young child might think the magician actually has the power to make people levitate. The child has a rather immature and naive worldview; he has too much confidence in his sensory experience, and not enough confidence in the orderliness of nature. But an adult knows better. An adult knows that there is some sort of gimmick at work. Perhaps the magician is using wires, or mirrors. But regardless, the adult spectator knows that what his eyes see is not the complete picture of what is actually happening. Both the child and the adult have exactly the same evidence. But they draw very different conclusions because they have different worldviews.

The origins debate is very much like this. It's a matter of worldviews—not evidence, as such. Creationists and evolutionists have different rules for how each believes the evidence should be interpreted. Evolutionists often believe in naturalism—the claim that nature is "the whole show." This view excludes the possibility of supernatural creation by God. There is no evidence whatsoever that a naturalist would accept as proof of biblical creation, because biblical creation is not even allowed as a possibility within that worldview—supernatural miracles are against their rules. Likewise, a biblical creationist accepts biblical history as accurate. The creationist consistently interprets evidence in light of biblical history, despite the evolutionist's insistence that such evidence really supports evolution. It is not possible to resolve such a debate by simply adding more evidence. Each side will interpret it according to his or her respective worldview.

How Then Do We Settle a Worldview Debate?

The only way to resolve a worldview debate is with an internal critique. That is, we accept (merely for the sake of argument) the worldview of our opponent for the purpose of showing that it leads to an absurd or impossible result. For example, both evolutionists and creationists agree that science is an extremely useful tool for learning about the universe. But which worldview makes science itself possible? We will find that biblical creation makes sense of science, while evolution does not. That is, if evolution were actually true, then there would be no reason to trust in the methods and procedures of science. Yet evolutionists do trust in such methods and procedures. They claim that evolution is supported by science, though evolution would essentially make science impossible. It is a self-refuting worldview and therefore must be false. Let's examine why this is so and see why biblical creation does not have this difficulty.

In order for science to be possible, certain things about our universe must already be true. For example, the universe would have to be somewhat organized. It would have to obey laws that are consistent over time and space. At least some of these laws would have to be simple enough to be discovered and understood by the human mind. Also, the human mind must be able to be rational, to examine the options and choose the best one. Human senses (sight, hearing, touch, etc.) would have to be basically reliable. (There would be little point in studying a universe that is merely an illusion generated by the mind.) These facts are called "preconditions of intelligibility" because they must be true in advance and assumed at the outset in order for us to make sense of the universe.

But which worldview can make sense of these preconditions? The Christian worldview certainly does. There is organization to the universe because it was designed and created by God, and it is consistently upheld by the expression of His power (Hebrews 1:3). Naturally the universe obeys laws that reflect the consistent and rational mind of God. It's not surprising that these laws are consistent over time and space, since God is beyond time (2 Peter 3:8) and sovereign over the entire universe (Deuteronomy 10:14). Of course our senses would be basically reliable; they were specifically designed by God to be so (Proverbs 20:12). And our mind is a finite, limited reflection of God's nature (Genesis 1:27). So we expect that we have an ability to be rational—to think in ways that are consistent with God's character. The Christian worldview with its foundation in Genesis certainly gives us justification for science.

But what about an evolutionary worldview? Many evolutionists teach that the universe was not created by God, but was simply an explosion from "nothing"—an inexplicable Big Bang. They tell us that nature is all there is, and there is no mind of God upholding or controlling the universe. If that were so, is there any reason to expect any kind of organization in the universe? Would there be any reason to think that the universe obeys laws if there is no lawgiver? Even if we grant the existence of laws, would there be any reason to expect the laws to be understandable by the human mind, or for them to be highly rational or mathematical in nature?

And here is an extremely important consideration: Even if we grant mathematical, rational laws of nature, understandable by the mind (which is being quite generous to the evolutionists), would there be any reason to expect that these laws would be exactly the same everywhere and at all times? So many things within the universe change—stars explode, gas expands, and species go extinct. Why would laws of nature be different? Why are they somehow exempt from change? And why would they be the same everywhere when the universe itself is so very different in various regions? Such uniformity is impossible to justify in a chance universe.

We all expect that gravity will work tomorrow as it does today. When a person wakes up in the morning, he doesn't brace himself just in case gravity might suddenly reverse direction and throw him toward the ceiling. He expects it to work as it did in the past. But if the universe were really nothing more than chance, then there would be no reason to expect such uniformity. Yet we all do. How is it that we all "know" that laws of nature will work the same tomorrow as they do today?

Some people will say, "Well, it's always been that way." But unless they follow that statement with "and therefore it always will," they haven't proven anything at all. But if they do follow up and conclude that because it has in the past, it will in the future, they have begged the question. They have merely assumed the very thing they are supposed to be proving. Any time we use past experience as a basis for what is likely to happen in the future, we are assuming uniformity (that laws of nature will act in the future as they have in the past). So we cannot use this assumption as the sole reason for why we know it is true. That's simply assuming the very thing we are attempting to prove. We need another independent reason. The Bible gives us one. Evolution does not.

Likewise, scientific analysis requires the use of logical reasoning. Scientists use the laws of logic to draw conclusions from various premises. Which worldview can make sense of logical reasoning? Certainly not evolution. If the human brain is simply the result of chance mutations that were preserved because they conveyed some kind of survival value in the past, then there is no reason at all to think that it would necessarily be rational. After all, your big toe has some survival value, but would you trust it to make rational decisions about what is true? Chemical reactions are not "true" or "false," they simply are. If our brain were just chemistry, then there would be no reason to expect it to be rational.

For that matter, there would be no reason to believe in the existence or properties of laws of logic in a chance universe. Why would there be laws at all? Laws of logic are rules for correct reasoning. But who decides what "correct" reasoning is in a chance universe? And why do laws of logic work everywhere? Why do they not change with time? A chance/evolutionary universe does not make sense of this.

The biblical creationist has an answer. He has a standard for correct reasoning—God Himself. The creationist expects that the laws of logic will not change with time, since they are a reflection of the mind of God who is beyond time. Since God is sovereign over all creation, then of course laws of logic apply everywhere. And since people are made in the image of God, they are far more than just happenstance chemistry. So we expect that the human mind can be rational, as it reflects its Creator.

The Critic of Air

The origins debate can be thought of like a debate on the existence of air. Can you imagine a person making an argument that air does not exist? He makes a long-winded speech about how air does not exist, while simultaneously breathing air and expecting his audience to hear his voice as the sound travels through the very air he denies. Ironically, the critic of air must use air to argue against the existence of air! The very fact he can make an argument at all demonstrates that he is wrong.

Likewise, the critic of biblical creation must use biblical creation principles such as uniformity in order to make a scientific case against creation. The very fact that he can make such an argument demonstrates that he is wrong. If biblical creation were not true, then there would be no logical reason to believe in uniformity in nature, and therefore the reliability of science. In this respect, evolution is inherently irrational. It is allegedly derived from a scientific procedure that cannot exist if evolution were actually true! It is a self-refuting conjecture. If it were true, it would be false. Therefore, it is false.

9

HOW SHOULD WE THEN INTERPRET GENESIS?

Jason Lisle, Ph.D., and James J. S. Johnson, J.D., Th.D.

Observation, carefully reading the Bible's text, is the first requirement for understanding the Bible (Acts 17:11)—what does Scripture *say*? But, carefully reading the actual words of the biblical text must be followed by recognizing the text's intent—what does a particular text of Scripture *mean*? Addressing that second question is what biblical "interpretation" is all about.

Accordingly, understanding any part of Genesis requires first observing what its text (i.e., its words, in the exact arrangement that God put them in) says, and then recognizing what that text means.

Anyone Can "Interpret" Scripture; Most Do So Incorrectly

Since our culture is so saturated with evolutionary teaching, it can be a strong temptation for Christians to accept evolutionism and try to interpret the Scriptures to match. After all, Christians sometimes disagree on how certain difficult verses should be interpreted.

Can Genesis really be "interpreted" in such a way as to be consistent with evolution? If so, *should* it be interpreted that way?

Obviously, a normal reading (i.e., reading the text using ordinary rules of reading) of Genesis certainly doesn't sound like it is referring to random mutations and "natural selection" acting over millions or billions of years. A normal reading of the text provides a history that reports the Creator God supernaturally speaking into existence everything in the universe—including discrete kinds of plants and animals and two humans—all within one calendar week.

But should Genesis be read and understood in such a straightforward way?

Perhaps you have heard people say, "Well, that's your interpretation." It is worth pointing out that you *can* indeed interpret the Bible (or any book) any way that you like. In most countries, the police will not break through the door and arrest you for doing so. Maybe you choose to interpret the Bible as poetic ideas expressed in a dramatic "framework," or as a forgery of pretended history, or as a historical narrative that is literally true. Maybe you would treat a modern science textbook the same way—interpret it as symbolic poetry, an allegory of historical events, a moral-teaching fable, or something else.

So when people say that there are multiple interpretations of Scripture, they are technically correct. There are an infinite number of "interpretations" of the Bible (or any other book, for that matter), some good, some bad, and some ugly.

However, not all interpretations are *true to the author's intended communication*, and that authorial intent is what distinguishes a correct interpretation from a wrong one.

The co-authors of the Bible (or any other book) had a particular meaning in mind when they penned the biblical text. Remember, the *correct* interpretation is that which corresponds to the author's intention.

And, in the case of the Bible, there are co-authors involved; God, the primary Author, miraculously guided human co-authors to write the very words God wanted written, yet God did this in a way that did not obliterate the personalities and individual writing styles of the human co-authors (2 Peter 1:20-21). So the Holy Bible, in that respect, is absolutely unique when it comes to interpretation, because discerning the authorial intent of its text requires understanding not only the human author's expressed intent, but also the expressed intent of God Himself.

Here is another way to put it: Although Genesis has an infinite number of *interpretations*, it has only one *meaning*. A person could (hypothetically) interpret Genesis as a cookbook on how to make a banana cream pie. But that certainly was not Moses' intention, or God's, when they co-authored it. So only one interpretation of Genesis gets its meaning right—the one that matches authorial intent.

When studying Scripture, the terms *exegesis* and *eisegesis* are used to contrast readers who, respectively, succeed or fail to recognize the meaning of a particular biblical text. Exegesis is the act of accurately recognizing (extracting) the author's intended communication—i.e., "pulling out" of a text the meaning that the author placed into it. Eisegesis, however, is the opposite. Eisegesis is the act of improperly "reading into" a text what the author did *not* intend to communicate.

For a picturesque simile, consider a dental surgery scenario. Exegesis can be compared to *extracting* a tooth—a dentist pulls out what was already there. Eisegesis can be compared to an *implant*—a dentist installs something that was not there to start with. Exegesis is what the Berean Christians did (Acts 17:11); eisegesis is what the Pharisees did—nullifying the true meaning of Scripture by substituting an improper "meaning" that they preferred (Mark 7:9-13).

So, while there are an infinite number of possible interpretations of Genesis, only one can be exegetical. In other words, we need to learn what the Lord (through Moses) intended when He wrote Genesis. This will be the correct interpretation—the one that corresponds to the intended authorial meaning.

Biblical Instruction on Interpretation

Not only can we learn from grammar and context, but the Bible itself contains instructions on how it should be interpreted. It does this in a number of ways, one of which is that it gives both positive examples (people interpreting the Scripture properly—exegesis), and negative examples (people who twist the meaning of the Scriptures and are rebuked for it—eisegesis).

Let us consider some of the positive examples. The best interpreter of Scripture who ever walked on Earth is Jesus Christ. He is God, and as such, He understands perfectly how to interpret the book that He Himself inspired (2 Timothy 3:16; John 8:58). Therefore, we can trust that all of Christ's interpretations are exactly right.

So how did Jesus interpret Genesis?

If you have ever read any one of the gospels, you are undoubtedly familiar with the fact that Jesus often quoted the Old Testament Scriptures. He would often respond to His critics with "it is written" and "have you not read," followed by a relevant scriptural quotation (e.g., Matthew 4:4; 12:3). But it sometimes surprises people to learn how much Jesus quoted from the book of Genesis.

In fact, Jesus quoted from Genesis about as much as all the other books of the Old Testament *combined*. Roughly half of Christ's references to Scripture were quotations from Genesis. He obviously understood the importance of origins to Christian doctrines.

Moreover, Jesus did not take Genesis as a metaphor, as poetry, as a parable, or as a myth. He took it as literal history. When Jesus spoke of Moses, He referred to him as a real, historical person (John 5:46-47). There is no hint that Jesus took any of the narrative of Genesis as anything less than literal history. In fact, Christ understood that the moral truths of Christianity have their foundation in the literal history of Genesis. This is demonstrated with the doctrine of marriage.

In Matthew 19:3-12, Jewish critics of Christ asked Him about divorce.[1] Specifically, they wanted to know if a man could divorce his wife for any reason. Christ answered that divorce is only permitted for cases of infidelity. He went on to explain that divorce legislation was made necessary because of the sinful hardheartedness of man. That is, if human beings were righteous in all their attitudes and actions, divorce laws would be totally unnecessary because there would be no such thing as infidelity. Had human beings not fallen into sin, divorce would be unnecessary. God intended marriage to be one man and one woman united for life. And what Scripture does Jesus quote to support this doctrine? He quotes Genesis 1 and 2. Christ understood that the basis for the doctrine of marriage (as well as the unfortunate need for divorce legislation) is the history of Genesis.

It is also worth noting that some people have erroneously claimed that Genesis 1 and 2 are two different and contradictory creation accounts. However, Jesus (who was fluent in Hebrew and perfectly knowledgeable in the Scriptures) quotes both chapters in the same breath. Christ Himself recognized no such "contradiction," because there isn't one. Genesis 2 is just a more detailed description of the events of the sixth day of creation.

Some claim that Jesus "went along" with His culture's popular view of Genesis in order to "accommodate" what other people thought was true—supposedly even though Jesus disbelieved their view of Genesis. Besides being blasphemy, this outrageous imputation of deceptiveness fails the historical reality test: Jesus went out of His way to clash with popular religious opinions that were wrong, such as when He healed on the Sabbath (e.g., John 9) or when He took time out to bless little children (e.g., Mark 10).[2]

It is surprising (and disappointing) to find that some professing Christians seem to have little regard for what Christ actually believed and taught in His earthly ministry. When it comes to interpreting Genesis, *do people really think they are smarter than the Lord Jesus Christ?* Incredibly, many Christians are tempted to try to blend a belief in evolution with their faith in Christ. But Christ clearly accepted a literal Genesis.

Does it really make sense to be a Christian—a follower of Christ—without accepting what He accepted? Does it really make sense to say, "Yes, I am a Christian and trust Jesus Christ completely—except that I don't trust His view of creation"? If Christ was wrong about how to interpret Genesis, He would not really be God, for God cannot be wrong about anything. If we cannot trust that Jesus is right about Genesis, why trust that He is right about John 3:16 (salvation)?

Besides Jesus, the New Testament apostles and prophets also taught Genesis as true history.

- The apostle Paul referred to Adam and Eve as historical people (see Romans 5:12-14; 1 Corinthians 15:21-22; 2 Corinthians 11:3). Paul based Christian doctrines on this fact (e.g., 1 Timothy 1:12-15). Indeed, the entire theological system espoused by Paul would come crashing down if Genesis were not literal history.

- For example, Paul contrasts Adam with Christ in 1 Corinthians 15:21-22. He refers to Christ as the "last Adam" who takes Adam's (and our) place on the cross (1 Corinthians 15:45-47). If Adam were just a fictional character, then Paul's comparison would make no sense.

- The apostle Peter also took Genesis as literal history. He writes about Noah and the Flood as real history (1 Peter 3:20; 2 Peter 2:5).

- The apostle John clearly believed Genesis is real history, since he wrote about Cain and Abel (1 John 3:12).

- Jude, as well, refers to events and people in Genesis—the destruction of Sodom and Gomorrah (Jude 1:7) and Cain (Jude 1:11).

- James refers to Abraham as a real person (James 2:21).

- The author of Hebrews refers to people in Genesis as real, historical figures, including Cain and Abel (Hebrews 11:4), Enoch (v. 5), Noah (v. 7), and Abraham (v. 8). Hebrews 11 is nonsensical if these were fictional characters.

Nowhere does the Bible ever suggest that Genesis should be taken as anything other than real, literal history. Like the rest of the Bible, Genesis teaches us true history and how to be made right in the eyes of the Creator God who rules all and who redeems "whoever" believes in Christ Jesus (John 3:16).

If Genesis was good enough (i.e., perfectly reliable and authoritatively relevant) for the Lord Jesus—and it was—it is certainly good enough for us.

Notes

1. The apostle Paul gave supplementary teaching in 1 Corinthians 7.

2. By prioritizing His time with small children, Christ clashed with the Pharisaic teaching of Rabbi Dosa ben Harchimas. See Johnson, J. J. S. 1987. When Jesus Took Time Out to Bless the Children. *Biblical History*. October: 50-55.

3. Lisle, J. 2011. *Taking Back Astronomy*. Green Forest, AR: Master Books, 112-113.

10

FOSSIL FORENSICS DISPROVE DARWIN

James J. S. Johnson, J.D., Th.D.

Evaluating evidence is a key component in the search for truth, not only in science but in other areas of life. There are times, however, when *nothing* (i.e., the complete absence of something that should be there, but isn't) counts just as strongly as "positive" evidence.

Rules of Evidence

Over the past centuries, the search for truth in empirical (i.e., observation-based) science has been formalized into the process known as the scientific method, whereby scientific theories are developed and tested according to generally accepted standards. The ability to identify supporting facts and data is vital for proving or disproving a hypothesis about how things operate in the observable world of the present.

In the arena of forensic science (which, unlike empirical science, investigates facts and events of the unobservable past), the legal and judicial professions operate by the Rules of Evidence.[1]

Developed over hundreds of years and brought to America via English Common Law, these forensic evidence rules are relied upon to decide disputes over financial transactions, inheritances, land use and ownership, parental custody of minor children, and criminal matters, such as whether a convicted killer should be executed. Circumstantial evidence, analyzed by principles of forensic science, may involve a broken knife at the scene of a burglary, or pistol discharge evidence on the clothes of a killer.[2]

For generations now, we Americans (and other countries that have adopted the British norms of forensic evidence analysis) have trusted these Evidence Rules with our lives, our liberties, and our properties. Accordingly, in legal controversies, the Rules of Evidence serve as a vital vehicle for seriously searching out and reliably reaching (it is hoped) the truth. Real truth stands up to being tested. And even the absence of evidence can operate as a "silent witness," testifying to a circumstance where there is nothing, when there should be something.

But what would happen if we applied the same principles of the Evidence Rules to analyzing other types of disputes, such as scientific controversies about origins? Before answering that question, let us consider how the evidence of "nothing, when there should be something" was used to sentence a medical doctor to jail time for asserting false claims.

Circumstantial Evidence of "Nothing"

This Medicare fraud case involved years of federal court proceedings, with one of the appeals being decided in 2007.[3] Part of the convicting evidence was *nothing*—literally nothing, when there should have been something. In the related cases of *Okoro* and *Akpan*, Victor Okoro, M.D., in concert with others, was accused of fraudulent Medicare billing practices, which conflicted with his "medical missionary" trips and a bogus charity called the Sisters of Grace.

The appellate court said this about Dr. Okoro's Medicare fraud:

> Although some of the patients [in Texas] received physical therapy treatments and some were examined by Okoro, each patient signed blank sign-in sheets and blank patient forms. In addition, Okoro signed most of the forms himself, yet many of the patients testified that he had never examined them....Okoro signed patient documents that stated that he had treated those patients on specific dates and at specific times on which Okoro could not possibly have rendered services. For example, many of the dates on which Okoro alleged that he provided services were dates when he was in Nigeria.[4]

Of course, the federal prosecutor had no difficulty proving that Okoro was absent from Texas, due to his using airports to exit the United States. Likewise, federal records provided the dates when Dr. Okoro re-entered America, so the official federal government records were relevant (and admissible) for showing the dates of Okoro's travels in and out of the country.

Yet just as important, from a circumstantial evidence standpoint, was the government's proof of "nothing" on other legally important dates. The federal government's trial proof included official government records with *absences* of entries on the dates in question, showing that Dr. Okoro was not recorded as having re-entered the United States in time for him to have performed the medical services for which he billed Medicare.

This illustrates the power of an argument from silence—the forensic force of such a silent witness can buttress a sentence of felony jail time. So, technically speaking, how can "nothing" become admissible circumstantial evidence at trial? Federal Evidence Rule 803(10) provides one such forensic possibility:

> **Absence of Public Record or Entry.** *To prove the absence* of a record, report, statement, or data compilation, in any form, or *the nonoccurrence or nonexistence of a matter* of which a record, report, statement, or data compilation, in any form, was regularly made and preserved by a public office or agency, evidence in the form of a certification in accordance with rule 902, if necessary, or testimony, that *diligent search failed to disclose* the record, report, statement, or data compilation, or entry. (emphasis added)

Evidence Rule 803(7) is similar, but it applies to admitting as trial evidence the fact that regularly recorded "business records" have a relevant "absence" of an entry, as well as where and when a documentary "nothing" is forensically important.[5]

Origins, Biodiversity, Fossils, and the Evidence of Nothing

So how does the evidence of nothing demonstrated by this particular Medicare fraud scheme relate to the question of origins?

The comparison can be illustrated by applying the Evidence Rules that govern "nothing, when there should be something" to the evolutionists' paleontological problem of "missing links." This evidentiary insight may be analytically unusual, but it is certainly not new.[6]

Consider how "the evidence of nothing" pertains to Earth's biodiversity.[7] What explains the voluminous variety of animals on Earth today? Does it show a phylogenetic common ancestry shared by animals and humans?

The biodiversity we see today does *not* match evolutionary predictions. Evolutionary assumptions imagine a globally integrated scenario where all life forms gradually branch off from common ancestors and somehow end up as one seamless biotic community—one big family reunion—with *everything and everyone* (from maggots to mankind) genealogically interlinked "cousins."

But reality is different; sharp biodiversity boundary lines between created kinds exist. And the "missing links" between discrete kinds are still *missing*. If Darwin-presumed missing links ever really existed, why are they still missing?

Canines (dogs, coyotes, wolves, dingoes, and foxes) are genetically compatible—they can all interbreed. Likewise, bears (black bears, grizzlies, and even polar bears) can interbreed. Similarly, equids (horses, donkeys, and zebras) can interbreed. But canines and bears cannot interbreed—there's no common ancestor "link" here! Likewise, equids can't mate with canines, and bears can't mate with horses.

There is a God-installed fixity of kinds in the animal kingdom, providing a permanent barrier to the kind of procreative progeny animals can have. Variety within limits is what God intended, and that is what we see, all over the world. This reality not only corroborates the Bible, it also disproves Darwin's imagined "common ancestry" natural selection theory of animal origins.

If Darwin's theory of evolution were really true, as even modern-day (neo-Darwinian) evolutionists imagine, the earth should be inundated with common-ancestry "transitional forms," evidenced by both fossils and living life forms *with no sharp biodiversity boundaries between the interbreedable kinds.*

Accordingly, when examining the quixotic quest for Darwin's missing links, the real-world evidence is like *déjà vu* all over again—literally nothing, when there should have been something!

To use Evidence Rule 803(10)'s logic, a diligent search for these so-called transitional form fossils, over a period of 150 years, has failed to disclose them. What kind of empirical data (and, when analyzed, what kind of forensic evidence) is that, applied to the origin of Earth's life forms?

Generations of diligent searching of the fossil record still indicates a glaring *absence* of molecules-to-man evolutionary phylogeny. In other words, the empirical data of Earth's fossils, if analyzed forensically, show that evolutionary phylogenetic notions are just *empty imaginings* refuted by the evidence of nothing.

Dr. John Morris has summarized what the global fossil record contains, and (more importantly) what it does *not* contain.

> Evolutionists often speak of missing links. They say that the bridge between man and the apes is the "missing link," the hypothetical

ape-like ancestor of both. But there are supposed missing links all over the evolutionary tree. For instance, dogs and bears are thought to be evolutionary cousins, related to each other through a missing link. The same could be said for every other stop on the tree. All of the animal types are thought to have arisen by the transformation of some other animal type, and at each branching node is a missing link, and between the node and the modern form are many more. If you still don't know what a missing link is, don't worry. No one knows what a missing link is, because they are missing! We've never seen one.[8]

This argument from silence is a *complete absence* of evolutionary "transitional forms" in the evidentiary record—a "nothing, where there should be something" if evolutionary theory were true. In other words, forensically speaking, when it comes to evolutionary claims about the fossil record, there is a lot of "science falsely so-called" (1 Timothy 6:20, KJV).

Some may say that the above forensic analysis is "much ado about nothing." However, now this "silent witness" is buttressed by dinosaur soft tissue evidence—collagen protein, nucleated blood vessels, osteocyte tendrils, and even DNA fragments—which is even more powerful proof that the fanciful fairytale of evolution is just a scam.[9]

Conclusion

Forensically speaking, when it comes to the importance of missing links in the fossil record, "nothing" (where there should be something) is itself a powerful proof, confirming that the Bible is right and that Darwinian evolution is wrong.

Notes

1. The Federal Rules of Evidence have been cloned, with only small modifications, by the 50 U.S. states. According to Rule 102, the Federal Rules of Evidence are supposed to be applied "to the end that the truth may be ascertained and proceedings justly determined." This article focuses mainly on Evidence Rules 803(7) and 803(10), which respectively govern the admissibility as evidence of an absence of information that could have been (but was not) entered into a regular business record or an official government record. Regarding Evidence Rule 801(d)(1)(B), applied to origins controversies, see Johnson, J. J. S. 2012. Tonsils, Forensic Science, and the Recent Fabrication Rule. *Acts & Facts.* 41 (6): 8-9.

2. See page 41 of *The Testimony of the Evangelists: The Gospels Examined by the Rules of Evidence* by Simon Greenleaf, originally published in 1874, reprinted in 1995 (Grand Rapids, MI: Kregel).

3. Trial in federal district court began in 2002. One appellate ruling was published as *United States v. Akpan*, 407 F.3d 360 (5th Cir. 2005). A later appellate decision appears at *United States v. Okoro*, 213 Fed. Appx. 348, 2007 WL 98804 (5th Cir. 2007) (non-precedent).

4. Quoting from *United States v. Akpan*, 407 F.3d at 364-365.

5. The same forensic evidence principle can be applied to critiquing historical data. See, e.g., page 146 in Dr. Bill Cooper's *After the Flood* (Chichester, UK: New Wine Press, 1995).

6. Greenleaf, *The Testimony of the Evangelists*, 41.

7. Biodiversity is the scientific word used to summarize the variety of life forms on Earth. Noah's Ark, which God used to caringly preserve the genetic potential for post-Flood biodiversity, is proof that God loves biodiversity.

8. Morris, J. 2006. What's a Missing Link? *Acts & Facts*. 35 (4).

9. Morris, J. D. and Frank J. Sherwin. 2010. *The Fossil Record: Unearthing Nature's History of Life.* Dallas, TX: Institute for Creation Research, 7–186. Snelling, A. A. 2009. *Earth's Catastrophic Past: Geology, Creation, and the Flood.* Dallas, TX: Institute for Creation Research. Regarding how dinosaur soft tissue discoveries are embarrassing evolutionists, see Tomkins, J. 2009. Dinosaur Protein Sequences and the Dino-to-Bird Model. *Acts & Facts*. 38 (10): 12-14; Johnson, J. J. S., J. Tomkins, and B. Thomas. 2009. Dinosaur DNA Research: Is the Tale Wagging the Evidence? *Acts & Facts*. 38 (10): 4-6; Thomas, B. 2009. Dinosaur Soft Tissue Is Here to Stay. *Acts & Facts*. 38 (9): 18.

11

EVOLUTIONISTS FLUNK BASIC FORENSIC SCIENCE

James J. S. Johnson, J.D., Th.D.

Those who criticize the factual history recorded in Genesis are like the foolish Pharisees whom the Lord Jesus condemned as inconsistent hypocrites. Christ gave them credit for filtering out "gnats"—yet He condemned them, simultaneously, for irrationally swallowing down whole "camels."

> Woe to you, scribes and Pharisees, hypocrites! For you pay tithe of mint and anise and cumin, and have neglected the weightier matters of the law: justice and mercy and faith. These you ought to have done, without leaving the others undone. *Blind guides, who strain out a gnat and swallow a camel*! (Matthew 23:23-24, emphasis added)[1]

This word-picture actually fits evolutionists of today.

In essence, Genesis critics flunk the basics of forensic science. In fact, although they try to act like "experts" when discussing and teaching forensic science principles, most evolutionists are completely clueless about what such science even is. To appreciate how this occurs, we first must differentiate between *empirical* science and *forensic* science, because they are not the same thing.

Note that the Pharisees were correct in their careful attention to tithing mint, anise, and cumin. However, they completely missed the boat when they "neglected the weightier matters" (the obligations of justice, compassion, and personal belief in God's Word). Likewise, evolutionists today (both atheistic and theistic evolutionists) get some "lightweight" science right, but not the "heavier matters"—as we shall see below.

Straining Out Bugs from Beverages

To appreciate this metaphor, which applies to modern-day evolutionists, consider the following account by Alaskan explorers.

> How in the world could there be this many bugs?…We tried once to have hot chocolate and coffee, but heating water without making mosquito tea first was impossible. The mosquitos are attracted to heat, and one could always count on a dozen or so [mosquitos] ending up in the drink before it was boiling.[2]

In biblical times, before serving or drinking a beverage, it was not unusual to use filters to strain out bugs and other impurities.[3] The hygienic practice of straining out gnats would have been quite common and understandable to the Lord's immediate audience. But the idea of swallowing whole an *entire camel* while drinking would have been a jarring thought to imagine! Christ criticized the cleanliness-obsessed Pharisees for practicing outrageous irrationality that resulted in truly unclean results.[4]

This picturesque metaphor describes the nonsensical illogic of the Pharisees, who filtered out small impurities from their daily living while ignoring gargantuan intrusions. That same failure of logic infects the uniformitarian approach routinely used by evolutionists to (supposedly) learn about our beginnings.

Beginnings Are the Key to the Present, Not Vice Versa

If humans really want to understand themselves, their world, their destinies, and their Maker, they need to understand their *origins*. Origins are the key to understanding cause and effect relationships. Present effects are often not representative of what their temporal causes physically looked like. It is the past that provides the key to understanding the present, not vice versa—because *past causes* produced *present effects*.[5]

For an extreme example, look at a city devastated by an earthquake or by an atomic bomb. Just by looking at the physical results, how would one guess at the physical causes?

For a less extreme (yet miraculously more complex) example, consider the amazing processes and details that accompany the conception, gestation, and birth of a human baby. The way a baby "breathes" inside the womb has virtually no resemblance to how it acquires oxygen after it is born. Placentas serve

86

as super-organs during gestation, yet after birth they are superfluous. Baby lungs don't breathe inside the womb, yet afterward they begin to breathe. Life inside the womb is starkly different from life after birth.[6]

Consider also the amazing processes and details that accompany the formation of an acorn—its fall to the ground, its burial and germination, and its early sprouting above its burial site. The beginning of an oak tree's botanical life as an acorn is not much like its growth and development after it sprouts above the soil level.

This is not surprising because *beginnings* are qualitatively different from what follows a beginning. This is seemingly so basic that any well-educated scientist could not miss it; yet missing the distinctiveness of earth's beginning is exactly what uniformitarian evolutionists routinely do. This does not negate the fact that evolutionary scientists sometimes do good *empirical* science work, but it does mean that the *forensic* aspect of origins science is frequently botched by their uniformitarian thinking habits.

Straining Out Cosmological Bugs, Swallowing Cosmogonical Camels

A gigantic stumble in scientific thinking occurs when *cosmology* is confused with *cosmogony*.[7] Cosmology is the empirical (i.e., present observations-based) study of the cosmos as it exists today.

> Cosmology: The science of the world or universe; or a treatise relating to the structure and parts of the system of creation, the elements of bodies, the modifications of material things, the laws of motion, and the order and course of nature.[8]

Cosmogony, however, is the non-empirical study of how that cosmos began in the unobservable past.

> Cosmogony: The generation, origin or creation of the world or universe. In physics, the science of the origin or formation of the universe.[9]

Cosmology involves using observation tools (such as radio telescopes and spectrophotometry equipment) to learn about presently existing matter in the universe. Cosmogony, however, is an origins science, a type of forensic science that focuses on learning the past, not examining the present.

Some methods that work well for understanding present processes do not work equally well for understanding past events. For example, at what temperature does water boil at sea level today? To learn the answer, use a repeatable experiment: Boil water at sea level and read the thermometer. This is empirical science, analyzing a present process.

But what if the question concerns the causality of a past event? For example, what physical cause produced a patient's fever last Saturday night? A thermometer reading today tells nothing about the cause of a previous thermometer reading.

Or, for another example, what physical cause produced a patient's drop in blood pressure yesterday? Measuring blood pressure today tells us nothing, directly, about why a patient's blood pressure was low then.[10]

The prior two questions seek specific information about the *historical past*, not how natural processes generally operate in the *observable present*. Accordingly, doing a repeatable experiment is not a scientific methodology that works well, *directly*, for answering questions about *historically past* cause and effect questions.

Perhaps the best-known examples of this kind of inquiry are legal investigations, such as forensic autopsies used to understand murder crimes,[11] or courtroom cross-examinations of eyewitnesses that test witness reliability while trying to determine who proximately caused an accident by committing negligence in a traffic intersection.[12]

Such investigations of the past involve the specialized history analysis that we often call forensic science, because discovery and analysis of the past is vital to the forensic contexts of criminal and civil evidentiary proceedings. Forensic science methods—which include testing the probative value of eyewitness testimony and trial exhibits with process-of-elimination logic—are used to learn about past events that are historically and geographically unique. They can never occur again—they are singular events in history.

The beginnings of our cosmos, the heavens and the earth, and the beginnings of the human race, starting with Adam and Eve, are all unrepeatable and unique historical events. The methods of empirical science are *evidentiarily inadequate* to determine meaningful or accurate truth about what actually happened during those beginnings. Only God was there to witness it.

That is why Charles Lyell's uniformitarian assumption—that "the present is the key to the past"[5,13]—will never be adequate for learning about those eternally important beginnings.

In other words, when evolutionists preach that "the present" (cosmology) is the key to "the past" (cosmogony), they are blindly swallowing a camel of illogic.

Past Events or Present Observations?

The *forensic* character of origins science, as opposed to the observational nature of *empirical* science, is routinely bungled and botched by uniformitarian evolutionists. They strain out "gnats" of empirical science data and analysis, yet they drink down whole "camels" of forensic science illogic, illustrating a kind of hypocritical foolishness—an intellectual blindness—that the Lord Jesus spoke of during His earthly ministry.

But God wanted us to know about our origins—the beginnings of the heavens and the earth, the beginnings of the human race (man and woman), the beginnings of sin and death, the beginnings of God's promised redemption in Christ, and much more.[14]

God wanted us to know these important beginnings, so He took action to reveal this otherwise unknowable information in an error-free text of understandable words—the Holy Bible.

The book of Genesis tells us, *infallibly,* what empirical science cannot—the factual details of our real-history origins.

Notes

1. "Swallowing" refers to *drinking* rather than to *eating*. The word translated "swallow" in Matthew 23:24 is a form of the Greek verb *katapinô*, the same verb that appears in Hebrews 11:29 (referring to the Red Sea swallowing up the Egyptian army) and in Revelation 12:16 (referring to a flood being swallowed up). This verb is an accentuated form of a simpler Greek verb, *pinô*, which is translated 75 times as "drink."

2. Davis, B., M. Liston, and J. Whitmore. 1998. *The Great Alaskan Dinosaur Adventure: A Real-Life Journey Through the Frozen Past.* Green Forest, AR: Master Books, 23, 30.

3. According to an ancient Hittite inscription, a water carrier named Zuliyas was executed for his carelessness in allowing a hair to be found in the king's water pitcher. See Pritchard, J. B., ed. 1992. Instructions for Palace Personnel to Insure the King's Purity. *Ancient Near Eastern Texts Relating to the Old Testament,* 3rd ed. A. Goetze, transl. Princeton: Princeton University Press, 207.

4. Both gnats and camels were "unclean" (see Leviticus 11:4, 20-23), i.e., not *kôsher* for Hebrew cuisine purposes.

5. Morris, H. M. 2008. *The Biblical Basis for Modern Science*, rev. ed. Green Forest, AR: Master Books, 65-66, 282-286.

6. Guliuzza, R. J. 2009. *Made in His Image: Examining the complexities of the human body.* Dallas, TX: Institute for Creation Research, 32-33.

7. See the entries for "cosmology" and "cosmogony" in *New American Heritage Dictionary of the En-*

glish Language. 1976. Boston: Houghton Mifflin, 301. Unsurprisingly, this secular dictionary presupposes an evolutionary origin for the cosmos.

8. *Noah Webster's First Edition of an American Dictionary of the English Language.* San Francisco, CA: Foundation for American Christian Education (2006 reprint of 1828 edition), page COS-COS, 3rd column.

9. *Noah Webster's First Edition of an American Dictionary of the English Language.* San Francisco, CA: Foundation for American Christian Education (2006 reprint of 1828 edition), COS-COS, 2nd column.

10. Physicians and surgeons are especially qualified to understand empirical and forensic sciences, because they must use proper scientific methods to understand a patient's medical history (*past condition*) and his current symptoms (*present condition*) to promote health. Dr. Randy J. Guliuzza, P.E., M.D., who has often practiced medical science (and engineering science) in the real world, used just such a forensic science-oriented analysis to expose and refute the unscientific fallacies of so-called "natural selection" theory in his Darwin's Sacred Imposter series of *Acts & Facts* articles.

11. The slang for a crime mystery novel—"whodunit"—illustrates that the investigation and discovery of truth about the no-longer-observable past is a matter of forensic science, not a matter of repeated observations and experiments by a scientist with laboratory equipment.

12. Johnson, J. J. S. 2012. Tonsils, Forensic Science, and the Recent Fabrication Rule. *Acts & Facts.* 41 (6): 8-9.

13. The "willful ignorance" that 2 Peter 3:4-6 describes is perfectly illustrated in evolutionary uniformitarian thinking. Because God has revealed our beginnings to us in Genesis, there is no logical reason for the scientific community to endorse the forensically illogical Big Bang theory of Belgium's Monsignor Georges Lemaître, or to endorse the forensically illogical natural selection theory of England's Charles Darwin.

14. Lisle, J. 2012. *Why Genesis Matters*, Dallas, TX: Institute for Creation Research.

12

EVOLUTIONIST VOCABULARY ON CELLULAR COMMUNICATION DISPLAYS FAULTY LOGIC

James J. S. Johnson, J.D., Th.D.

Secret codes and ciphers are serious business—just ask Paul Revere.

Listen, my children, and you shall hear
Of the midnight ride of Paul Revere,
On the eighteenth of April, in Seventy-Five;
Hardly a man is now alive
Who remembers that famous day and year.

He said to his friend, "If the British march
By land or sea from the town to-night,
Hang a lantern aloft in the belfry arch
Of the North Church tower, as a signal light—

"One if by land, and two if by sea;
And I on the opposite shore will be,
Ready to ride and spread the alarm
Through every Middlesex village and farm,
For the country-folk to be up and to arm."[1]

Obviously, espionage relies on very precise and carefully crafted communication. Many spies and secret agents *die* when their messages are intercepted. Communications to and from spies, therefore, are often accomplished by using very clever codes to intelligently transmit valuable information. No one who honestly studies the use of coded information in clandestine espionage activities would attribute such carefully coded (and decoded) communications to mere chance or accident.

91

Coding and Decoding at the Biomolecular Level

Illogically, however, many look at the more cleverly coded communications that are sent and received inside living cells and explain what they see as products of blind chance and "evolutionary accident." Yet genetic code-based communication is informationally more complex and detailed than any system humans could create, and it displays engineering complexity beyond our wildest imagination. And these biomolecular communications are being sent and received all the time, every millisecond! How can this be?

Evolutionists describe this remarkable communication system's supposedly "accidental" parts and processes using vocabulary that sounds like the cryptographic vocabulary of spies and secret agents, thus demonstrating the *inexcusable* illogic[2] of crediting the system to "natural selection." In other words, evolutionists use words that prove they are observing providentially programmed biomolecular communication at work. How is this?

When accurately describing the organized activities that routinely occur inside a eukaryotic cell's nucleus or mitochondria, evolutionary geneticists routinely describe what they see using terms like code (e.g., genetic code, protein coding, coding regions, encode, decode, codon, anti-codon), transcription, translation, blueprint, program, information, instruction, edit, decipher, messenger, reading, proofreading, signal, alphabet, letter, language, gene expression, surveillance (for detecting nonsense), etc. It is important to recognize that these genetic message-oriented terms were not imposed on the evolutionists by the creationists!

The details of *how* immeasurably ingenious all of this biochemical information machinery is—and it is!—have been documented, at least to some degree, by many who have honored God, *intentionally* or *unintentionally*, by their respective research in the related fields of microbiology, molecular biology, biochemistry, and genetics.[3]

The main point of the lengthy vocabulary list above is to illustrate how scientists have chosen to describe the micro-world of DNA, RNA, ribosomes, mitochondria, endoplasmic reticula, protein synthesis, etc., in vocabulary that befits intelligent and purposeful communication.

Specifically, genetic science reveals God's purposeful *encoding* of genetic messages, with mind-bogglingly complex *instructions* on how to build living things from the biomolecular level upward, with those same encoded messages being efficiently *decoded* and recognized with sufficient accuracy to produce responsive compliance with those biomolecular instructions![4]

Unintelligible Messages Are No Good

In the world of spies and counterspies, intelligent agents use codes with language that is designed to be recognizable by the intended recipient. Codes have been employed from time immemorial to prevent messages from being intelligible to unintended recipients.

However, a coded message is no good at all if the intended recipient cannot understand its encoded meaning. Accordingly, every code-based message must be informationally devised (i.e., created), encoded, and sent to the intended readers. The readers must then decode the message, recognize the information it contains, and act on that information in a way that corresponds to the original purpose of the message's creator. It is vital that the intended recipient understand the sender's meaning, because the message itself is unrecognizable unless both sender and receiver share a common understanding of what the words (or other symbols) mean.

Consider the following message: "One if by land, two if by sea." What does that sequence of words signify? Because that message used a language shared by the sender (Robert Newman, with the help of John Pulling) and receivers (those awaiting word on the movement of British troops), it provided a recognizable warning that "the Regulars [British soldiers] are coming" by water, not by land. Two lanterns lit in the Old North Church on the night of April 18, 1775, provided a signal—but it was recognizable as such only to those who knew the "language" shared by Paul Revere and his allies.

This principle of coded information transfer is illustrated at the subcellular level. If a protein-coding "message" borne by a portion of DNA cannot be transferred by RNA and translated on ribosomes providentially fitted for the task, the DNA's instructions cannot be complied with, and that would mean no protein synthesis—which can be a fatal failure for whatever life form is involved, whether girl or gecko, boy or bacterium.

Metaphors Describe Genetic Information Transmittal

In short, genetic realities must be expressed using human communication metaphors, because only such metaphors accurately portray the underlying realties of biochemical information processing.

93

It is quite proper to use metaphors to talk about natural science topics if they accurately assist in communicating truth. DNA and RNA are heavily involved in encoding and decoding information, and the biochemical "language" used truly exhibits transcription, translation, editing, and the like.

Some Metaphors Are Misleading, Even Deceptive

The genetic code metaphors listed above are helpful because they help communicate *real truth* about how biomolecular information is sent and received at the subcellular level.

However, not all metaphors employed by scientists are helpful for conveying truth. The term "natural selection" is a metaphor that has often been used by evolutionists to promote their model of biodiversity origins. Creationists have long admired how living creatures are superbly designed for their various environmental niches, so creationists rhetorically ask, "How could this possibly be without a Designer?" It is all too common for the evolutionists to respond, "Natural selection is the answer. Nature 'selected' those organisms with such traits, catalyzing organisms to adapt to their environment."

But such an answer is horribly misleading. It falsely attributes a real power to an abstraction ("nature"). This is a reification fallacy, to say the least. Nature cannot literally "select" because nature has no mind. Even some evolutionists recognize this and are embarrassed:

> The answers that have been suggested so far have not been convincing. In particular, though there is no end of it in popular accounts of adaptationism, it is a Very Bad Idea to try and save the bacon by indulging in metaphorical anthropomorphisms. It couldn't, for example, be literally true that the traits selected for are the ones Mother Nature has in mind when she does the selecting; nor can it be literally true that they are the traits one's selfish genes have in mind when they undertake to reproduce themselves. There is, after all, no Mother Nature, and genes don't have, or lack, personality defects. Metaphors are fine things; science probably couldn't be done without them. But they are supposed to be the sort of things that can, in a pinch, be cashed. Lacking a serious and literal construal of "selection for," adaptationism founders on this methodological truism.[5]

It is a good thing that Paul Revere did not wait on nature to "select" a code-message about the British, because there is no intelligent, decision-making "Mother Nature" who can select anything or anyone.

There is, however, a Creator who used infinite intelligence and engineering skill to provide the providential programming that is observed in the interactive coded and encoded communication that occurs, non-stop, in nuclear and mitochondrial DNA, RNA, and ribosomes.[6] That Creator is the God of the Bible. He has revealed Himself in and through the Lord Jesus Christ, and He is the one we should gratefully *revere*.

Notes

1. Longfellow, H. W. 1863. Paul Revere's Ride (a.k.a. The Landlord's Tale). In *Tales of a Wayside Inn*. Boston: Ticknor and Fields. Paul Revere historically said "river" (alluding to the Charles River) and not sea, but Longfellow apparently wanted a noun to rhyme with the word "be." The poet also took a few liberties with the actual details of that night's events.

2. Romans 1:18-25, especially verse 20 (literally "without apologetic").

3. See, generally, Gitt, W. 2007. *In the Beginning Was Information*. Green Forest, AR: Master Books, 15-254; Wilder-Smith, A. E. 2003. *The Natural Sciences Know Nothing of Evolution*. Costa Mesa, CA: The Word for Today, 5-100, 137-163; Sanford, J. C. 2005. *Genetic Entropy and the Mystery of the Genome*, 2nd ed. Lima, NY: Elim Publishing, 1-151, 185-188. See also unintended admissions from a famous evolutionist geneticist in Sykes, B. 2002. *The Seven Daughters of Eve*. London: W. W. Norton, 22-62.

4. A recent example of highly detailed research on DNA coding as it relates to human hearing is Ahmed, Z. M. et al. 2011. Functional Null Mutation of MSRB3 Encoding Methionine Sulfoxide Reductase Are Associated with Human Deafness DFNB74. *American Journal of Human Genetics*. 88 (1): 19-29. The article analyzes protein-coding exons, transcription, translation stop codons, translation initiation codons, the encoding of a mitochondrial localization signal, and other examples using communication terminology, showing that information transfer terminology is needed to aptly describe the content and function of DNA sequences that code for construction of proteins needed for human hearing.

5. Fodor, J. 2007. Why Pigs Don't Have Wings. *London Review of Books*. 29 (20):19-22.

6. For more information on the remarkable processes of living cells, see Tomkins, J. 2012. *The Design and Complexity of the Cell*. Dallas, TX: Institute for Creation Research.

13

ONLY BIBLICAL CREATION PROVES GOD LOVES YOU PERSONALLY

James J. S. Johnson, J.D., Th.D.

When was the last time you saw a bird—perhaps a common grackle or a pigeon—and shuddered with the scary realization: *That could have been me!* Maybe you have never thought about a grackle that way.

Yet it is true—God did not need to make us just as we are. He had many other options. God could have created each of us as a bird, a butterfly, or a basalt rock. God could have made you (or me) a uranium-bearing rock, a nudibranch, an ice worm, a quince fruit, an ultraviolet ray, or an egret.[1] Yet, He deliberately chose otherwise. He chose to make us one-of-a-kind humans. What a fearful and wonderful reality!

Thinking about how God uniquely planned for us and how we are precious to Him is biblically logical. But it cannot logically fit the impersonal randomness of evolutionary thinking.

At a biblical apologetics conference hosted by a local church, a Genesis skeptic approached me and quickly displayed that he was "angry at the world." Likewise, he demonstrated hostility and disdain for God and His Word, attacking biblical truth and God's character. He accused "the Christian God" of being impersonal—of not "personally loving individuals."

Perceiving this skeptic as one with no stable assurance regarding his own personal worth as a valuable human individual created in God's image, I reminded him that God commended His love to all of us—even the skeptic—by having Christ voluntarily die for the sins of each of us, to pay the just price for personal forgiveness, reconciliation with God, and an abundant life here and later. That conclusively proves God's love for us individually, because Christ died for each of us.

When confronted with this truth, the skeptic coldly retorted, "But that is not really *personal*—the Bible teaches that Jesus died for all of humanity simultaneously, so it's not like He did it *just for me*; there is nothing personal about that. If I didn't exist, it would still be the same, so there is nothing personal about that kind of love."

How would you reply to this skeptic's accusation that God is "not personal" in His love?

This was my answer: "The proof that God cares about you, in an absolutely personal way, is in the obvious fact that He providentially, thoughtfully, and caringly made you. In fact, your very existence is proof of how personally God loves you. It doesn't get any more personal than God making you as the unique person that you are! If God had neglected to make you as you are or had made you something else, such as a lizard or a loon, you wouldn't even have the ability to falsely accuse Him of being impersonal! God had lots of options—He did not have to make you who you are."

At this point, the skeptic digressed into some excuses—what the Bible calls "science falsely so called" (1 Timothy 6:20, KJV)—that he had for disbelieving the truths of Genesis. None of the excuses were scientifically or logically sound (Romans 1:20), and all of them were logical fallacies flawed with arbitrariness, inconsistencies, and intelligibility precondition failures—pitiably posing as "poster child" examples of the logical fallacies Dr. Jason Lisle analyzes in his logic textbook, *The Ultimate Proof of Creation*.[2]

The skeptic had brushed aside the obvious truth that God made him as the unique person that he was, even though God could have made him as a gull or a gooney bird. The skeptic also rejected the example of Christ's recognition of the Scriptures as God's authoritative truth—the text of absolute truth (John 17:17). Though this skeptic professed to honor "the historical Jesus" (whom he "knew" could not be the Jesus described in the New Testament), he had no logical explanation for Christ's exemplary recognition of Genesis as the authoritative and trustworthy text God co-authored with Moses.[3]

The practical apologetics lesson should be obvious: If we deny the authoritative truth of Genesis, then we have no sure foundation for creation truth. And we, likewise, have no sure foundation for the unique worth of any one human being—you, me, or anyone else.

If Genesis is wrong about creation (which is impossible), I cannot prove that I am truly worth anything, much less precious to God, *as the unique person that I am.*

Five of our Creator's actions prove that He is worthy of our thanksgiving for making us exactly as we are: (1) God chose to make us; (2) God controlled how we were made; (3) God condemns ingratitude; (4) God cares for our needs; and (5) God cherishes our uniqueness, unlike most of the world around us.

God chose to make each one of us a unique creation.

God made many careful and complicated decisions, literally thousands of years ago, in order to providentially and procreatively make each of us, personally, as who He wanted each of us to be.

Science fiction writers sometimes imagine "alternative" universes, qualifying their fanciful fantasies with the phrase "what if?" God, however, really can imagine other options, including *all* of the "what if" contingencies, all the possible domino-chain causality scenarios. God can truly tell us what consequences would have followed events that never really happened.

Christ, as omniscient deity, knows all of the past, present, and future. He even knows what would have and could have occurred if this or that detail of real-world history *had been different.* For example, Christ did not exaggerate when He described how Sodom and Gomorrah would have reacted to the miracles He powerfully performed in the region of Galilee (Matthew 11:23). Likewise, foreknowing literally all of the possible options and outcomes, our Creator purposefully chose to make you and me exactly as we are. Considering the "what if" scenarios is intellectually "fearful," yet appreciating God's actual choices is "wonderful."[4]

God controlled how we each were made.

How did God mastermind our procreative origins? Consider Psalm 139—how we are "fearfully and wonderfully made," biologically and biochemically, inside the specific mother whom God selected, to make each of us who we are. That "fearful and wonderful" development did not stop at birth. God's biochemically programmed instructions equip and adjust our physical bodies throughout our lives.[5]

But God's control of our existence began thousands of years before we were physically procreated inside our respective mothers. Human life began on Day Six. Parental procreation began in Genesis 4. All of us descend—through literally hundreds of ancestral lines—from eight Ark passengers who sailed the one-of-a-kind high seas about 4,500 years ago. The social details of our genealogical ancestries thereafter—even ignoring the biogenetics—are astounding beyond any fiction novel, more detail-laden than any supercomputer's database.

The family history facts unique to each of us are so detailed that we cannot learn them all during this earthly lifetime. The best that we can hope for, realistically, is to discover some informative family history records and to learn from them many examples of how God worked in human history to make us who we are.

How did God providentially orchestrate the circumstances of our parents' meeting each other, or their parents, or our great-great-great-great grandparents? What close calls with death did your ancestors encounter before they contributed to your personal genealogy? What if God had let someone die a few years earlier? Maybe you (or I) would have never existed![6]

When we fail to thank God for His creation, God condemns our ingratitude.

When God condemns something, whether an action or inaction, that proves its importance. What about the ingratitude that we, as unique creations, demonstrate when we fail to thank Him as our Creator?

> Because, although they knew God, they did not glorify Him as God, nor were thankful, but became futile in their thoughts, and their foolish hearts were darkened. (Romans 1:21)

Obviously, we should thank God for making us, because failure to thank Him is wrong—so wrong that the integrity of our minds and hearts are at risk of becoming "reprobate" (Romans 1:28, KJV).

God demonstrates how much He values us through caring for our needs.

Most Christians are well aware that the Lord is "our shepherd" (Psalm 23; John 10). He cares for our personal needs, like a good shepherd cares for every single sheep (Luke 15:4-7), not just 99 percent of them!

God's care for us displays our worth to Him—so much more than sparrows (Matthew 10:29-31; Luke 12:6-7) or field lilies (Matthew 6:28; Luke 12:27).

God cares for our physical and spiritual needs better than any human parent (Luke 11:11-13). God regulates climate dynamics that provide rain for both the just and the unjust (Matthew 5:45). Seasonal cycles and nourishing food are both continuing proofs of God's providential care for human creatures.[7]

God cherishes our uniqueness.

Even more amazing than God's care for us—His human "sheep"—is how He cherishes our uniqueness. No one is exactly like you, and God designed you that way. God prizes variety. Even in something as supposedly "simple" as a snowflake (just a frozen water crystal!), God proves that He appreciates and values uniqueness. No two snow crystals are the same.

> Ice crystals are composed of simple, repeated internal patterns that produce beautiful, external shapes. And built into the laws that govern ice crystal growth patterns are temperature dependencies that add filigrees to the basic hexagonal form. Columnar shapes, needle shapes, plate shapes, stellar shapes, and dendritic shapes are just some of the additional patterns in which snow crystals grow. In fact, because of the myriad of possible combinations of the millions of individual molecules that make up a single ice crystal, it can truly be said that *no two snow crystals are exactly alike!*[8]

Who sees and appreciates the countless snowflakes that fall on Earth? Only God. Yet He treasures them (Job 38:22); each one is singularly fashioned by His artistic genius. Most of these fragile and ephemeral snowflakes are never seen by humans. The rare few that are observed by human eyes (and even fewer photographed by microscopists) are quickly forgotten, no matter how beautifully and carefully they were made by God.

And, sadly, so it is with human lives—most people will never know that you (or I) exist, and most of the few who see us, for a while, will not care much. Many will quickly forget us.

But, thankfully, not so with God!

While God appreciates the "simple," yet unique, snowflakes that are ignored by busy humans, God treasures our personal lives (created in His image) infinitely more, as if we were His precious jewels (Malachi 3:17). In fact, He providentially planned our lives to be exactly what they are, and if we belong to Him, He artistically "works together for good" the component details of our lives (Romans 8:28).

Surely we should thank Christ for being our very *personal* Creator.

So the next time you see a grackle, think thankfully for a moment, "That could have been me!" And be grateful to your Creator, who made you a unique, one-of-a-kind creation.

Notes

1. These six options produce the acrostic UNIQUE.

2. Lisle, Jason. 2009. *The Ultimate Proof of Creation.* Green Forest, AR: Master Books, 36-43, 56-66, 84-96.

3. John 5:39-47, especially 5:46-47. For documentation on Genesis' Mosaic authorship, see Cooper, W. R. 2011. *The Authenticity of the Book of Genesis.* Portsmouth, UK: Creation Science Movement.

4. See Psalm 139:14 and Matthew 11:23, especially in light of Colossians 1:12-17 and John 15:16.

5. Guliuzza, R. 2009. *Made in His Image: Examining the complexities of the human body.* Dallas, TX: Institute for Creation Research, 32-33.

6. For example, see Johnson, J. J. S. 2011. Czech into Texas, at Last! From Bohemian Roots, to a Moravian Log Cabin, to the Lone Star State. *České Stopy* [Czech Footprints]. 13 (1): 15-22.

7. Isaiah 55:10-11; Matthew 5:45; Acts 14:17.

8. Vardiman, L. 2007. Microscopic Masterpieces: Discovering Design in Snow Crystals. *Acts & Facts.* 36 (12): 10. See also Libbrecht, K. 2003. *The Snowflake: Winter's Secret Beauty.* Stillwater, MN: Voyageur Press, 1-109.

BIOLOGY

CREATED KINDS
OR COMMON ANCESTRY?

14

ALL-OR-NOTHING UNITY
IN THE HUMAN BODY

Randy J. Guliuzza, P.E., M.D.

The familiar question "which came first, the chicken or the egg?" illustrates a powerful but underutilized strength to design-based thinking—evidence for design is found not only in how things work, but also in how they must be put together. Chicken/egg-like situations almost immediately let people see that there are a minimum number of parts—*all* necessary—to make things work...or *nothing* works. That phenomenon is called *all-or-nothing unity* (or by a more technical name, *irreducible complexity*, promoted in a tremendously popular book by Michael Behe[1]).

At first, a chicken/egg-like impasse looks like only a timing dilemma. That problem is real, but so is the quandary elicited if there were not the *information* in an egg for making a chicken that could then make an egg. And if there is a failure in the controlling *conditions* for the parts—these being (1) available quantity, (2) localized together, (3) capable of functioning together, (4) for a purpose, and, of course, (5) at the right time—it doesn't matter if the goal is the chicken or the egg; the absence of the information, conditions, or any vital part is a definite showstopper.

Regarding function, design engineers need to know if all, some, or none of it is maintained without the full set of parts. They know that some aspects of their project can be built by increments, but at certain phases, *all* of those parts must be collected together and built together or *none* of that specific function can be obtained. In the living world, these are called *vital* parts. The chicken/egg scenario is really about the absolute *unity* of certain vital parts to vital functions.

When all-or-nothing unity exists, the known source is always real design.

So, when it is found in the living world, it is reasonable to conclude that it is evidence of a real Designer's work.

How to Explain the Vital Unity of Parts and Function

It is not difficult to present the case for all-or-nothing unity. A powerful, yet easily understood, statement is this: "In organisms, some parts are so important to the function of life that if they are missing, life stops." The difficulty is deciding on a great example.

Genesis 1:11 records God's formation of plants, each kind with its own "seed." It is notable that the first and foremost unified biological process—reproduction—is absolutely contrary to classic evolutionary origins of these vital systems. How do organisms "arise" by an iterative process until they can reproduce? For evolution to proceed, it is not enough just to attain some physiological function; what is needed is *reproductive* life. Fortunately, reproduction is a science topic of which almost everyone has some knowledge.

When you discuss reproduction from a design-based perspective, most listeners will hear for the first time something that totally defies evolutionary dogma. They will be astounded to learn that the minimum number of parts necessary for an organism to reproduce *is the organism itself*. The whole organism is vital. This is scientific fact. It doesn't mean that every part is vital, but it does mean that only the organismal unit encompasses all of the critical *parts*, *information*, and *conditions* necessary to reproduce itself according to the constraints of its life cycle. In order to produce a human baby, a man and a woman, and all of their vital interdependent parts, are the essentials—science has shown that it cannot be broken down to any smaller level.[2]

This fact is so indicting that evolutionists will push back with all kinds of arguments, but these explanations will all cheat. Every example given will always start and end by using some vital things from the organism itself, so be looking for this. For example—yes, there is in vitro fertilization, but that starts with donor egg and sperm, and the embryo is returned to the normal realm of development.

Reproduction: A Perfect Example of All-or-Nothing Unity in Humans

A new life is started the moment a human sperm cell unites with a human egg. It may sound simple, but it isn't. In fertilization, a sperm is needed to fertilize an egg, but only a single sperm. How is that accomplished?

All-or-nothing unity is seen in human reproduction. The interrelated matching parts from father, mother, and baby must all be in place or the reproductive process will yield nothing in regard to offspring.

A sperm's head must be coated in proteins exactly matching a receptor on an egg—just like lock and key—since only human sperm can fertilize a human egg. In less than a second after sperm contact, many channels in the egg's membrane open, allowing an inrush of positively charged sodium ions. This creates an electrical charge across the outer surface of the egg, detaching any remaining sperm on the outside. Also, all remaining receptors on the egg are inactivated. Concurrently, substances inside the egg's cell membrane are released that bind water molecules. This causes the membrane to swell up to permanently block other sperm from fertilizing. These blocks prevent entrance of multiple copies of genetic material from any other sperm into the egg, which would be fatal to baby and maybe to mother as well.

Once united, tube-like structures in the egg rapidly build and then project from the egg and pull the nucleus of the sperm into the egg—the first cell of a new person.

From this point on, the real star of the show is the developing baby. This takes all-or-nothing unity to a level way past just male-female compatibility. Until recent times, the baby was viewed as simply a passive object being built by mother's body. Nothing is further from the truth. In terms of guiding its own implantation into the uterus all the way to instigating labor and delivery, it is the baby-placenta unit orchestrating its own destiny. Mom's body, in great measure, is now under the control of a new person.

The baby has unique genetic material that expresses foreign markers on its cells that are not recognized as "self" by mother. Mother's immune system could (and should) easily destroy the first cells of the new baby within just a few cell divisions. But substances secreted by those first cells suppress the maternal immune response. Later, the placenta will continue to modulate immune responses, though only at the uterine implantation site. Mother's body, therefore, accepts it. Without this immunological acceptance, no baby would ever survive.

A hormone produced by the earliest cells after fertilization travels in mom's bloodstream back to her ovary. Ovarian cells detect that hormone and respond by producing *progesterone*—the very important hormone that will calm uterine contractions for nine months and maintain the pregnancy. Later, the placenta will produce progesterone at even higher concentrations.

Other adaptations in mom's body that are absolutely necessary for its own survival begin after her body senses even more hormones produced by baby. These changes include a sizable expansion of mom's blood volume, an increase in cardiac output, agents to modulate blood pressure, increases in blood flow to the kidneys, and cranking up mom's metabolism. The placenta will also extract nutrients from maternal circulation so efficiently that baby's needs will always be met first—then mother's.

In the last weeks of pregnancy, estrogen produced by baby reaches a high concentration in mom's blood. This has two important consequences: Once detected, muscle cells of the uterus begin to express abundant receptors for the hormone *oxytocin*, and it slowly opposes progesterone's quieting influence. At term, certain cells of the baby begin to produce oxytocin, which is a powerful uterine muscle stimulant (man-made oxytocin is called Pitocin).

Since the uterus is now highly sensitive to oxytocin, labor begins. As baby descends, a pressure sensor in the birth canal sends a signal to mom's brain and triggers her body to produce even more oxytocin—which causes stronger uterine contractions. Fortunately, for weeks before delivery, another hormone called *relaxin* has increased concentration. Augmented by placental production, relaxin facilitates pelvic ligaments and skin of the birth canal to relax, widen, and become more flexible. This increased motility expedites birth passage, for which baby and mom are both thankful.

While baby was still in the womb, placental hormones helped prepare mom's breasts to produce milk. After delivery, newborn suckling induces episodic oxytocin secretion by mom, which acts on breast ducts to cause milk let-down.

The reality clearly emerges that it is mother who is in many ways passive, detecting and responding to signals emanating from the baby—even at times to her own detriment. Scientific research has shown that while mom's reproductive organs and body are indispensable, they are not enough. It takes a baby…to make a baby. This evidence is pretty compelling of all-or-nothing unity and should preclude wild evolutionary speculations about a step-by-step evolutionary process over many generations leading to the systems that produce a baby.

Evolutionists Supply Insufficient Explanations

When reading evolutionary literature or listening to their programs, note that evolutionists will fail to explain the *origins* of biological information and reproduction. They simply start with reproducing entities. This is true not just for humans, but for any organism—even one-cell creatures.

Researchers with a prior bias forbidding consideration of non-natural explanations have addressed all-or-nothing unity in the best evolution-based journals,[3] but the argument has not been defeated.[4] These articles have *all* claimed that the solution to all-or-nothing unity is if researchers can imagine where similar—not always identical—parts could be borrowed ("co-opted," "pre-adapted," or "recruited") from existing objects. Even if borrowed parts could work, which is doubtful, only condition 1—availability—is satisfied. The necessary information and the other four conditions are not even addressed. Thus, by taking an *indirect* path to all-or-nothing unity, these responses fail to engage the true issue and demonstrate how imagination cannot substitute for testable findings.

All-or-nothing unity, particularly in reproduction, is powerful in confronting evolution's attempt to chip away at prohibitive improbability and explain biological design.

- Reproduction is one of many entities revealing that *all* necessary conditions, parts, and information must come together *or nothing* of the function is achieved—an event distinctive of real design.

- Scenarios depicting organisms arising incrementally are implausible,

since the minimum parts necessary for an organism to reproduce—
are the organism itself.

- Evolutionary explanations cheat. Reproductive origins are not explained; they start with replicating life.

Why should anyone believe that the living world only looks like it is designed, but really isn't? The design in the living world is such that it *resists*
being explained by natural causes. All scientific evidence shows that creatures
come programmed with innate abilities to reproduce after their kind, but not
strictly identical offspring, in order to divide, multiply, and fill the earth.

The Bible not only clearly says that the Lord Jesus Christ designed life, but
it also reveals how He did it: The chicken came "whose seed [egg or sperm] is
in itself"—all at one time. These things were placed by the Lord in our first
parents, Adam and Eve, fully functional right from the beginning.[5]

Notes

1. Behe, M. 1996. *Darwin's Black Box*. New York: The Free Press.

2. See Thomas, B. Have Scientists Created a Synthetic Cell? *Creation Science Update*. Posted on icr.org May 27, 2010.

3. See Clements, A. 2009. The reducible complexity of a mitochondrial molecular machine. *Proceedings of the National Academy of Sciences*. 106 (37): 15791–15795.

4. See Thomas, B. 2009. Preadaptation: A Blow to Irreducible Complexity? *Acts & Facts*. 38 (11): 15; and Thomas, B. Pseudo-science Attacks Irreducible Complexity. *Creation Science Update*. Posted on icr.org September 10, 2009.

5. Guliuzza, R. 2009. *Made in His Image: Examining the complexities of the human body*. Dallas, TX: Institute for Creation Research.

15

THE MISTAKES IN EVOLUTIONARY ARGUMENTS AGAINST LIFE'S DESIGN

Randy J. Guliuzza, P.E., M.D.

In the next chapter, obvious attributes of design in living things are detailed. The Bible says, "For since the creation of the world His invisible attributes are clearly seen, being understood by the things that are made" (Romans 1:20).

Is design clear even to atheists? It certainly is. Consider the remarks of the atheist Dr. Jerry Coyne of the University of Chicago:

> If anything is true about nature, it is that plants and animals seem intricately and almost perfectly designed for living their lives.... Nature resembles a well-oiled machine, with every species an intricate cog or gear. What does all this seem to imply? A master mechanic, of course.[1]

However, when Coyne says that animals "seem" intricately designed, he means they *look* or *appear* like they were designed, but really weren't. Thus, life's "design" is only an illusion. What arguments do evolutionists use to dismiss design?

The Argument of "Bad Design" Is an Assertion from Ignorance

Evolutionists argue that all sorts of creatures' parts are poorly designed, ranging from nerves, the retina found in vertebrate eyes, to even the way testicles descend from the abdomen in the human male fetus. They contend that these could not be designed by an infinitely wise deity. However, this argument against design reveals ignorance, which doesn't mean these evolutionists are stupid; it means they generally are ignorant of the full function of the parts they criticize and are ignorant of principles governing design.

111

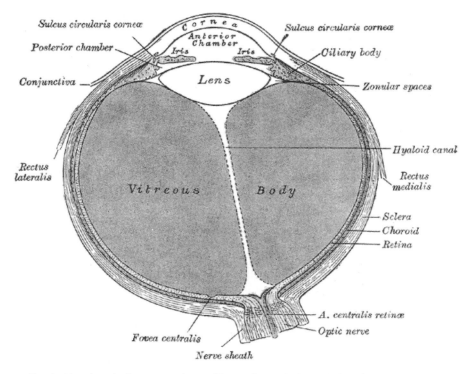

You decide—does the human eye show evidence of great design, or is it a classic example of poor design that argues against an all-wise Creator? That debate is theological in nature, but the main question really is, does the eye show evidence of design? Credit: *Grey's Anatomy* plate 869

There is absolutely no need from the outset to ever concede that any part of a creature is poorly designed. In reality, creatures in their prime normally do exhibit breathtaking fit and finish. For most people, the complexity and near-perfect function in living things are amazing. It would be one thing if evolutionists could show a single loss of function in the origins of the parts they criticize, but they cannot. So, claims that something is poorly designed are not equivalent to data-supported facts.

Critics usually demonstrate a profound lack of knowledge of the parts they fault, since that criticism is not backed up by other people who conduct research on those parts. For example, evolutionary biologist Frank Zindler claims, "Although the human eye would be a scandal if it were the result of divine deliberation, a plausible evolutionary explanation of its absurd construction can be obtained quite easily"[2] from evolutionary trial-and-error. However, a biophysicist eye researcher noted:

Yet for all these apparent flaws, the basic building blocks of human eyesight turn out to be practically perfect. Scientists have learned that the fundamental units of vision, the photoreceptor… are not just good or great or phabulous [*sic*] at their job. They are not merely exceptionally impressive by the standards of biology….Photoreceptors operate at the outermost boundary allowed by the laws of physics, which means they are as good as they can be, period.[3]

Another similar criticism is summed up in "I think it would make more sense to design [whatever] another way; thus, an infinitely wise deity could not have designed it." The late evolutionary biologist George Williams argued that there is no functional explanation for humans having specifically two eyes. "To begin at the grossest level, is there a good functional reason for having two eyes? Why not one or three or some other number?"[4] He's convinced that since humans do not have a third eye on the back of their heads, the visual system was clearly not designed.

Though these critics may not know what they are talking about in regard to function, there are other problems with their arguments. First, their attack is not scientific but theological. Their perception of a design does not fit their perception of a deity. Meaning what? They could be in error on both accounts. Questioning *how* something was designed has nothing to do with the question of *whether* it was designed.

Second, they may be ignorant, from a design perspective, of the need to balance several competing interests—i.e., obtaining an optimized design that satisfies conflicting needs-based design requirements. Whether a design maximizes performance of the one particular trait capturing their interest is irrelevant to the question of whether the entity as a whole was designed. They may be ignorant of good reasons for design tradeoffs between various traits, and others may yet be discovered. Design tradeoffs are actually a better indicator of intelligence behind a design.

Third, the claim of poor *quality* does not disestablish design. Items designed by humans range in quality from careless to extremely fine. Words describing quality such as "seamless," "blemish free," "consistent," or "durable" are qualifiers that add weight to correctly perceiving patterns of design—but so do words like "crude" or "sloppy." Quality in itself is not the sign of intellectual activity. Genuine design does not demand anything be of the best quality.

Finally, none of the arguments against design are actually arguments *for* evolution. From the most current experimental understanding of environments, environmental elements alone do not achieve even shoddy design— since they have not been shown to produce *any* design.

The Argument That Nature Designs by Repurposed Pre-existing Parts Is Pure Imagination

How do evolutionists explain the arrival of fundamentally distinct parts in molecular machines? They turn to imaginatively simplistic scenarios where "the necessary pieces for one particular cellular machine...were lying around long ago. It was simply a matter of time before they came together into a more complex entity"[5] upon which "natural selection" tinkered away at cobbling together borrowed parts for millions of years. Aside from the magical whimsy, this explanation is like saying cars originated when an engine was coupled to a transmission that was mounted to a chassis and so forth, leaving another major unanswered question—where did the engine, transmission, and chassis come from?

Individual parts between molecular machines may be almost like each other, but each *fits precisely* into each specific machine to maintain function. There are great gaps of information in the evolutionary path that depicts molecular parts as stripped from their primary original functions to self-assemble as new machines—making a plausible iterative evolutionary transition unbelievable.

These weaknesses are merely dismissed. Lacking experimental evidence supporting their explanations, evolutionists turn to a firm belief that if it can be imagined, it could happen. Dr. Coyne says, "It is not valid, however, to assume that, because one man cannot imagine such pathways, they could not have existed."[6] In conversation, highlight this disconnect, but be content in recognizing that Coyne's type of response cannot be satisfied with scientific answers.

The Argument That Nature Generates Complex Entities Is Irrelevant

Meteorologists and geologists analyze naturally occurring convoluted relationships that puzzle human understanding, such as the interplay of atmosphere and ocean conditions that produce hurricanes, or processes underlying the current understanding of plate tectonics and mountain building. While some natural processes might indeed be intricate, using them as illustrations to validate a natural origin for biological complexity is off-target, since they do not produce any precisely arranged parts and their interrelationships are not close to what is found in biological complexity.

The Argument That Order Spontaneously Arises from Chaotic States Is Irrelevant

Evolutionists correctly assert that natural processes alone can produce *ordered* arrangements. After molten aluminum cools, atoms do naturally align into ordered lattices. But only after being worked into specifically shaped and precisely arranged parts could aluminum become a *complex* engine. While an ordered status does have more structure than a chaotic one, it is far from the status of many intricately arranged parts. Thus, comparing order to biological complexity is inappropriate.

The Argument of "Vestigial Structures" Is an Assertion from Ignorance

The term "*vestigial structure*" is applied by evolutionists to a part in an organism they consider to be an evolutionary "leftover" whose function is diminished or totally lost from the part's original function in ancestors of that organism. The main point to make in replying to this argument is that the list of vestigial organs used today to support evolution is only useful as a historical record of today's current knowledge and ignorance. "Vestigiality" is not a real thing; rather, it is a concept that exists only in the mind of the beholder.

Given the fact that many organs on these lists have been an embarrassment to evolutionists since they have been found to have important functions (e.g., spleen, tonsils, appendix), one would think this argument would be abandoned. As addressed in creationist literature,[7] certain organs may not be vital for life, but they still perform important functions. (As a medical doctor discussing organ donation with patients, I wondered if I could accentuate that fact by asking them if they would like to donate their "vestigial organs" today.)

Be on Guard for Other Ploys Related to Design

Changing designs is "simple." The approach that evolutionists would have everyone adopt is this: Attach the word "simple" to biological processes, anatomy, and, especially, presumed evolutionary changes. Why? Because simple changes made to simple creatures are more easily believed.

Note this approach toward nature, starting in 1859 with Charles Darwin, who said:

> I can see no very great difficulty...in believing that natural selection has converted the simple apparatus of an optic nerve merely coated with pigment and invested with transparent membrane, into an optical instrument.[8]

In May 2010, the current authority, Dr. Coyne, stated:

> Bats evolved from small four-legged mammals, probably resembling shrews....How could they possibly evolve wings? And yet they did: selection simply retooled the forelegs into wings, along with modifying the animal's weight, shape, musculature, nervous system and bones for flying (no feathers needed). One of the great joys of being a biologist is learning about the many species in nature whose evolution would appear, a priori, impossible.[9]

That bats are designed to fly is clearly seen, but seeing that is not the challenge. Evolutionists would have people replace their natural understanding that bats are very complicated—and thus, designed—with a belief that changing shrews to bats is simple, meaning bats only look designed, but really aren't.[10]

Appealing to an organism's design to explain its own origination. The existence of complex biological features allows a test for their origins. This test only needs careful observation. However, it must be done right. Since the origination of how living things operate—especially their ability to generate diverse offspring—is the issue in dispute, ensure that the ability in question isn't used as part of the explanation in any way. Thus, for creationists the *original cause* of biological complexity is an intelligent mind, versus the chance coupled to environmental elements (sunlight, wind, rain, gravity, etc.) claimed by evolutionists. They can't start by using already-existing DNA, proteins, etc., in the context of a cell...that's cheating.

Extraordinary extrapolations. When looking at the evolutionist's best scientific journals for explanations on origins (e.g., molecular machines), stay alert for conclusions extrapolated far beyond what the evidence will bear.[11] The exaggeration is assured. Why? Since researchers find only one fully functioning machine or another, evolutionary *conclusions* of how, in the remote past, parts from one molecular machine morphed into another will always be conjectures inferred greatly beyond what the findings support.[12]

Notes

The Mistakes in Evolutionary Arguments Against Life's Design

1. Coyne, J. 2009. *Why Evolution Is True*. New York: Viking Press, 1.

2. Quoted in "Does an Objective look at the human eye show evidence of creation?" posted on 2think.org/eye.shtml. See also Sherwin, F. 2005. That Troubling Laryngeal Nerve? *Acts & Facts*. 34 (5).

3. Angier, N. Seeing the Natural World With a Physicist's Lens. *The New York Times*. Posted on nytimes.com November 1, 2010. See also Thomas, B. Eye Optimization in Creation. *Creation Science Update*. Posted on icr.org November 23, 2010..

4. Williams, G. 1998. *The Pony Fish's Glow: And Other Clues to Plan and Purpose in Nature*. New York: Basic Books, 9.

5. Report on reference 1 in Keim, B. More 'Evidence' of Intelligent Design Shot Down by Science. *Wired Science*. Posted on wired.com August 27, 2009.

6. Coyne, J. A. 1996. God in the details. *Nature*. 383 (6597): 227-228.

7. See Thomas, B. A Vocal Vestigial Organ? *Creation Science Update*. Posted on icr.org July 25, 2008; Bergman, J. and G. Howe. 1990. *"Vestigial Organs" Are Fully Functional*. Terre Haute, IN: Creation Research Society Books.

8. Darwin, C. 1859. *On the origin of species by means of natural selection, or the preservation of favoured races in the struggle for life*. London: John Murray, 218

9. Coyne, J. The Improbability Pump: Why has natural selection always been the most contested part of evolutionary theory? *The Nation,* May 10, 2010.

10. For a reality check, see Madrigal, A. C. To Model the Simplest Microbe in the World, You Need 128 Computers. *The Atlantic*. Posted on theatlantic.com July 23, 2012.

11. For example, Clements, A. 2009. The reducible complexity of a mitochondrial molecular machine. *Proceedings of the National Academy of Sciences*. 106 (37): 15791–15795.

12. For further information, see Guliuzza, R. 2012. *Clearly Seen: Constructing Solid Arguments for Design*. Dallas, TX: Institute for Creation Research.

16

UNMISTAKABLE EVIDENCE FOR GOD'S DESIGN: CELLS LEAD THE WAY

Nathaniel Jeanson, Ph.D., and Brian Thomas, M.S.

Did you know that the inner workings of the cell point toward God's design like nothing else in biology? Do you know *how* it does so? A review of Scripture will help, and then we'll dive into just a sampling of cell function to begin answering these questions.

Scripture clearly teaches God's unfathomably majestic design right from the start. In Genesis 1:1, the statement "in the beginning God created the heavens and the earth" assumes that before anything was, God was. He is eternal, and nothing and no one existed in the beginning except God. No one was present to compel Him to create or to give Him any ideas. Before the universe was, it existed only in *His* mind. Therefore, He alone knows everything about every molecule in every place. Furthermore, the way He intended each creation is exactly how it became. God repeatedly looked on the results of His creative acts and proclaimed them *good*. There were no mistakes, prototypes, or second tries when God designed. Genesis loudly declares the incomparable glory of God in designing the universe!

In light of God's creative acts in Genesis 1, Scripture teaches us to expect abundant evidence of His design in creation. Since man was made "in the image of God" and was commanded to engage in acts ("have dominion") that require creative design and engineering, we can anticipate that we will have the ability to recognize the design of the One whose ultimate design we are to mimic. The New Testament makes this expectation explicit. "For since the creation of the world His invisible attributes are clearly seen, being understood by the things that are made, even His eternal power and Godhead" (Romans 1:20). Thus, it is very biblical to expect unmistakable evidence in nature for divine design—design more ingenious than any human achievement.

Skyscraper Construction Requires Specific Steps

Perhaps the easiest way to recognize the astounding evidence in the cell is by analogy to human engineering. The human body can be viewed as a very large and complicated biological construction project that parallels human construction projects in many ways. A close examination of the intelligence required to build a skyscraper sets the stage for understanding the intelligence required to build the human body from a single cell.

At least four steps in skyscraper construction require intelligent intervention. First, the energy (i.e., sunlight) and raw materials (i.e., iron ore) must be transformed before they can participate in the construction process. For example, despite enormous amounts of energy streaming down from the sun and sitting below the desert surface in the form of oil, and despite plenty of raw materials present in the earth's crust, the hottest deserts in the Middle East do not spontaneously spawn skyscrapers. Why not? For work to be accomplished, the energy and raw materials must be converted into useful forms, sizes, and shapes—such as electricity, gasoline, glass, or steel. Thus, intelligent human beings build solar panels, oil refineries, and glass and steel plants to transform energy and raw materials into forms useful to the construction project. Sunlight does not build steel from rock.

The second step requires the transformed energy and materials to be harnessed to useful work. Even if the raw materials are nearby, they cannot begin to assemble themselves. A pile of steel and glass next to an electrical outlet will, if left alone, never change into the Sears Tower. Rather, intelligent humans must build tools (i.e., welders, cranes, etc.) that will harness the transformed energy to accomplish useful work.

The third step at which intelligence is absolutely required is organizing the useful work according to a plan that will lead to the final structure. Even if human workers are assigned tools and given raw materials, they will not automatically construct a skyscraper unless they are given a specified plan. Imagine the chaos that would ensue at a construction site not governed by an organized blueprint—without clear directions, one set of workers might begin to randomly connect steel beams, another would lay the wrong-size foundation, and another would wire the electricity however he saw fit!

The fourth step has already been assumed in the example above—the plan laid out in the blueprint must be enforced. Even if a blueprint is present at the construction site, it will never govern the process without intelligent human beings to read, interpret, and execute the plan. This step also assumes a means of communicating the steps to all involved. Without intelligent execution of the blueprint, the Empire State Building would still be a fancy drawing and not a reality.

Thus, skyscrapers exist only because creative and powerful humans do. Even evolutionists must concede this point. Whoever objects to this needs to explain why, in the history of the universe (a very long history, by evolutionary standards!), energy and raw materials did not bring skyscrapers into existence on their own. Alternatively, if they insist that skyscrapers *did* exist in the deep past, they must explain why they left no trace. Either way, it is undeniable that the world's tallest buildings came about only by intelligent planning and design.

"Constructing" a Human Requires the Same Steps

The same four problems must be overcome in order for a single cell to build the biological construction project we recognize as the human body. When sperm meets egg to form the first cell (the *zygote*), development will not proceed unless there is some means to (1) transform energy into something useful for cell growth, (2) harness the energy to useful work, (3) organize the work according to a plan, and (4) enforce the plan.

Though humans are involved in the initial act of procreation, Mom and Dad do not consciously instruct the zygote at any step of the developmental process. The cell solves these problems without human intervention. How?

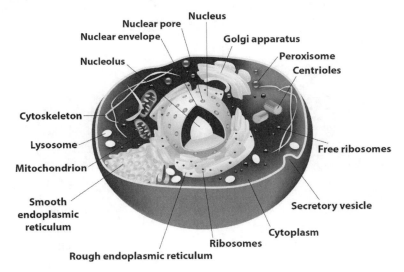

The cell maintains its own miniature power plants, called mitochondria, to overcome the problem of energy transformation. Inside the mitochondria, tiny protein machines harvest the energy present in chemical bonds of carbohydrates, fats, and proteins—energy-rich molecules that come from the foods that the mother consumes, digests, and provides to the developing baby. The baby's growing cells transform raw chemical food energy into a mobile and useful chemical energy called adenosine triphosphate (ATP). In the cell, ATP functions as cellular "electricity," fueling many other processes. Just like a power saw or drill is a machine designed to run on electricity, most of the machines and tools inside cells are designed to run on ATP. The mitochondria solve the problem of converting energy into a proper form.

The cell also possesses tiny factories in which the cell's own chemical building blocks (proteins, phospholipids, DNA, etc.) are made. Like any manufacturing facility, the cell's products are manufactured according to stringent quality control standards, and are produced in accordance with the needs of the relevant building project. Construction engineers do not order ten times the required number of bricks for a building, because that would clog the construction process. Similarly, cells manufacture or import just the right amounts of just what is needed. The chemical synthesis machinery solves the problem of raw material transformation.

Much of the work in the cell is performed by two major types of "tools"—proteins and RNA. Both of these classes of molecules are involved in everything from fat synthesis to cell division to information processing. The cell is well-equipped with many molecular tools to execute a wide variety of biological tasks, including materials transport, waste export, and intra- and extra-cellular communication.

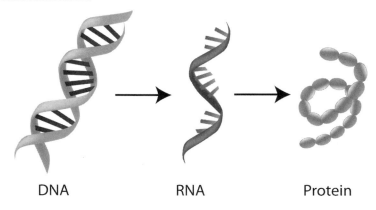

DNA   RNA   Protein

The cell organizes the work of development according to the "blueprint" found in DNA. Prior to division, a cell builds a complete complement of DNA, which for humans is 46 chromosomes. The information contained in these 46 chromosomes specifies nearly all the instructions for our anatomy and physiology. Thus, the information contained in the DNA sequence contains the "plan" that a single cell follows to become an adult body.

Last, the cell enforces and manages that plan. How? RNA and proteins read and translate the DNA-encoded plan into just the right RNA and proteins at just the right times to build more cell components at just the right production rate. These molecules recognize specific sequences of DNA and "know" where to begin "reading" and interpreting a particular sequence, partly by being "informed" and regulated by dozens of additional associated molecules.[1] Hence, a complex interplay among these three major classes of cellular molecules does the foreman's work of interpreting and enforcing the building plans stored in DNA sequences.

Does the absence of human intervention during the development process imply that intelligence is *not* required to construct the human body? Return to the skyscraper analogy. Everyone should recognize that designers and builders of the Empire State Building were intelligent and capable. If the designers instead programmed robots to perform all the tasks of the entire construction crew, would this have required more intelligence, or less, on the part of the designers? Clearly, this would require much more. They would not only have had to specify the solutions for energy and raw material conversion, as well as a building blueprint and means to enforce it, but they would also have had to specify similar solutions for each robot! In one sense, cell systems act like robots, following instructions in the DNA without human intervention. Yet the intelligence behind the workings of the cell goes beyond this analogy.

The Super-Intelligence Behind the Cell

To make our analogy more accurately reflect cellular reality, let's change it to something even more complicated. What if, this time, the designers programmed a computer chip with all the instructions for creating a skyscraper? What if all they would need to do is drop the chip on the construction site, after which the chip itself would use the surrounding raw materials and energy to build itself into the Empire State Building? Would this require more intelligence or less? Clearly, this would require intelligence that no human now possesses! But the intelligence in the cell exceeds even this analogy.

Extend the analogy beyond any conceivable human achievement to date. What if our designers programmed a computer chip, not only to build the Empire State Building, but to build an Empire State Building that possessed, *within itself,* the instructions to make *another computer chip* and begin the process all over again? What if the designers also hard-wired an error detection and correction program into the same chip, so that any mistakes at any step of the construction process would be identified and corrected? Clearly, we have far exceeded anything humanly realistic. Yet the cell possesses, within itself, the instructions to make the next generation of cells, to detect errors, *and to correct* problems. God's designs are not limited by man's finiteness—He creates systems with efficiencies, capacities, and tiny scales that exceed our wildest imaginations! The cell unambiguously points towards an Intelligence whose designs outpace anything within the realm of the best human achievements—it must have been created by a Super-Designer![2]

The observations we have made are not isolated. Rather, since every multicellular species on Earth is made up of cells, and since multicellular species populate every continent on Earth, the *entire planet* loudly proclaims unmistakable evidence for God's immeasurable, omnipotent, and omniscient design!

The cell bears remarkable testimony to the plain teaching of Scripture: The transcendent, omniscient, and sovereign God exercised His goodness and supreme intelligence in creating the entire universe, and in creating biological creatures that are made of cells.[3]

Notes

1. Thomas, B. 2010. Cell systems—what's really under the hood continues to drop jaws. *Journal of Creation.* 24 (2): 13-15.

2. Special thanks to A. E. Wilder-Smith for stimulating and extending some of the analogies in this chapter.

3. Tomkins, J. 2012. *Design and Complexity of the Cell.* Dallas, TX: Institute for Creation Research.

17

THE ORIGIN OF SPECIES: DID DARWIN GET IT RIGHT?

Nathaniel Jeanson, Ph.D.

Where do species come from? Did God create them in place? Does evolution happen? The answers to these questions may surprise you. Let's first consider what Scripture says about species, and then consider what science has shown about species' change.

Scripture and Species' Change

The first and most fundamental observation we can make from Scripture about the origin of species is that the term *species* never occurs in the Bible. Technically speaking, since the Old and New Testaments were written in Hebrew and Greek, respectively, the precise word for species does not appear in the original text. Some English Bibles occasionally translate the Hebrew or Greek with this term (i.e., Genesis 7:3 in the NKJV and James 3:7 in the NASB), but there is no word in the biblical text equivalent to our English term species.

Does this mean that Scripture is silent on species' formation and change? No.

The second key scriptural observation we can make is that the biblical text repeatedly uses the Hebrew word *min*, translated as *kind* in most English Bibles, to describe biological life. *Min* appears 31 times in Scripture—in the creation and Flood accounts (Genesis 1, 6–7), in the Mosaic law (Leviticus 11; Deuteronomy 14), and once in the Prophets (Ezekiel 47). The use of *min* in these contexts discloses profound insights to species' origin.

The use of *min* in Genesis is the most revealing as to its meaning. In Genesis 1, *min* denotes a type of created category of creature. For example, in

Genesis 1:25, "God made the beast of the earth according to its kind, cattle according to its kind, and everything that creeps on the earth according to its kind." Whatever *kind* ultimately denotes, in this passage it describes some sort of created group.

Careful examination of the use of *min* in Genesis 6 leads to a more precise definition of the term. In verses 19-20, God commands Noah, "And of every living thing of all flesh you shall bring…male and female. Of the birds after their kind, of animals after their kind, and of every creeping thing of the earth after its kind, two of every kind will come to you to keep them alive." Why would God command Noah to bring *male and female* of every kind on the Ark for the purpose of propagating them after the Flood? For sexually reproducing creatures, male and female is the minimum requirement for perpetuating the species. Why would God require this minimum to be met for *every* kind of land-dwelling, air-breathing creature? Why not command Noah to take one male of one kind and several female representatives of other kinds so that kinds could interbreed after the Flood? God's strict stipulation implies that individuals within a kind can breed only with other members of the same kind—that reproductive boundaries define the limits of each kind. Thus, members of the same kind can be recognized by their ability to interbreed.

This definition of kind—reproductive compatibility—has stunning implications for ancestry and biological change. First, based on current reproductive data, the term kind is best approximated by the traditional classification rank of family (kingdom-phylum-class-order-family-genus-species), not species. For example, horses, donkeys, and zebras can mate and produce live offspring.[1] Though these three creatures are classified as separate species, they belong to the same family, Equidae. Also, housecats, tigers, and lions can be connected in a reproductive continuum.[2] Though the housecat cannot breed with the big cats, the smaller cats can be linked to the larger ones through successive breeding via smaller-size steps; the major link between large and small is puma-ocelot hybridization. Thus, all cats, though classified as separate species, belong to the same family, Felidae, and are part of the same kind. *Family*, not *species*, best approximates the biblical term kind.

Second, approximating kind with the classification category of family means that many new species have formed in the last several thousand years. Recall that God commanded Noah to take *kinds*, not *species*, on board the Ark. Hence, there were not horses, donkeys, zebras, housecats, tigers, and lions all on board the Ark. Rather, Noah took two representatives of each kind/family—two of the Equidae kind, two of the Felidae kind, etc.—and from these ancestors have descended all the equid and felid species that we see today. This is an enormous amount of diversification and speciation in just a few thousand years!

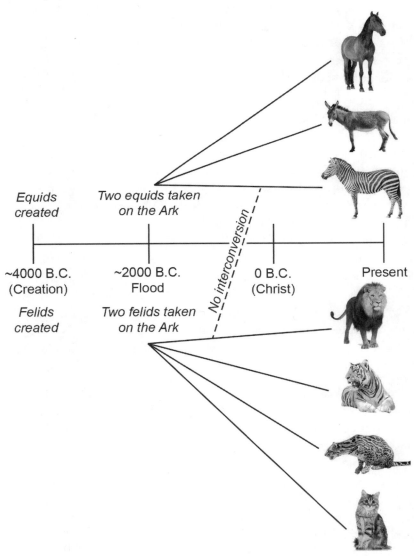

> ## Does the Classification Rank of Family Approximate the Created "Kind" for Humans?
>
> If we apply the classification level of family to humans, this would imply that humans and the great apes—chimpanzee, orangutan, gorilla—all have a common created *kind* ancestor since they all belong to the family Hominidae. We know this is not so because Scripture teaches that it is not so—God created Adam and Eve, not two cave-dwelling, knuckle-walking, ape-like ancestors. Is this an exception to our rule of thumb that kind is best approximated by family? No—because God did not create man "after their kind" but "in His own image"; and because family is simply a first approximation of the kind boundaries, not an absolute rule.

Third, since Scripture implies that kinds cannot be interconverted, there is a limit to biological change and speciation, and the limit corresponds to the family level in most cases, not species. The barrier to kind interconversion is implied in Genesis 6:19-20 (see above) when God commands *every* land-dwelling, air-breathing kind to be brought on the Ark. Why? "To keep seed alive upon the face of all the earth" (Genesis 7:3, KJV). Clearly, if one of the land kinds had failed to board the Ark, they would have died in the Flood and they would have no offspring—extinction! If kinds could be interconverted, there would be no need to load *every* kind on the Ark—just a few would have sufficed, and all those kinds not boarding the Ark could have been recovered via interconverting the kinds after the Flood. Since kind is approximated by family, new species can form within a family, but families cannot be interconverted. There is a hard limit to speciation and to biological change.

Why do we find species distributed in a particular pattern around the globe? Clearly, the ancestors to today's land species began their colonization of the planet from the Middle East after disembarking the Ark at Ararat (Genesis 8:4); God did not create *species* in their present locations. Furthermore, with an ice age immediately following the Flood (see chapter 34), the resultant land bridges would have opened up nearly every continent to colonization by the Ark kinds. Combined with the possibility of transport via plant rafts on prevailing ocean currents and with the possibility of human transport as mankind migrated away from Babel (Genesis 11:1-9), the Ark kinds would have easily found their way to the farthest reaches of every continent.[3,4] The precise mechanistic factors controlling the timing and geography of the kind diversification are not yet clear, but drive current research efforts at the Institute for Creation Research.

How did God hardwire the limit to inter-kind conversion into the DNA of each kind? What caused new species to form from the original kinds on board the Ark? Is family the best approximation of kind for all the kinds on earth? These questions are the current focus of the Bio-Origins project at ICR.[5]

Is "Reproductive Compatibility" Contradicted by Production of Sterile Offspring?

Some might object to placing horses, donkeys, and zebras in the same kind since some of their offspring (mules, hinnies, etc.) are sterile. However, a broader perspective on reproductive failure supports the original conclusion of including them in the same kind. Reproductive incompatibility can arise at nearly every step of the reproductive process—from incompatible mating rituals, to incompatible proteins on the surface of sperm and egg, to failure of the embryo to reach full term. Hence, to reach the step of live (but sterile) offspring is a significant biological feat. Furthermore, evidence is accumulating that it is possible for an originally reproductively compatible population of creatures to become reproductively incompatible over time. Given the ~4,000 years since the Flood, there has been much opportunity for reproductive failure to arise, and the ability to still produce a live offspring represents a tremendous preservation of reproductive compatibility. Hence, production of live offspring still functions as an excellent criterion by which to identify members of a common kind.

Science and Species' Change

All scientific observations to date are consistent with the model of speciation outlined above. All the changes observed in the lab or in the field correspond to changes within kinds. For example, the textbook example of change in the size and shapes of the beaks of the finches on the Galapagos Islands represents changes within the finch/sparrow kind.[6] Darwin did not propose a new idea when he hypothesized that the 13 species of finches on the Galapagos have a common ancestor; Scripture teaches the same thing—that these finch species descended from the finch kind on the Ark!

In fact, recent breeding data argue that, not just the Galapagos finches, but nearly *1,000* species of finches and sparrows arose from a common ancestor on the Ark.[7] All other examples of change—including the classic textbook examples of *E. coli* bacteria developing resistance to antibiotics and HIV developing resistance to the immune system—depict change within a kind. No documented examples of one kind changing into another kind exist. Science confirms the biblical account of species' origins.

What about evolution? Have we observed it? The answers to these questions depend on how we define the term evolution. If evolution simply denotes *change*, then, yes, evolution has been and continues to be observed. If evolution means *microevolution*—a term evolutionists use to refer to small changes, or those changes we can observe—then, yes, evolution happens. When evolution is used synonymously with the phrase *survival of the fittest to reproduce* (a process Darwin referred to as *natural selection*),[8] then it is fair to say that evolution has happened; we observe survival of the fittest commonly—the changes in the sizes and shapes of the Galapagos finch beaks illustrate this well. If evolution is defined in any of these ways, it depicts real phenomena—but phenomena the Bible explains equally well as change within kinds.

When evolution is equated with *macroevolution*, then it depicts a fanciful hypothesis and not an observable fact. Macroevolution is the term evolutionists use to refer to large changes, and even evolutionists themselves admit that large-scale changes would occur too slowly for human observation. For example, Richard Dawkins admits that "we can't see evolution happening because we don't live long enough."[9] We know from Scripture that change from one kind into another kind—in evolutionists' parlance, macroevolutionary change—cannot happen; hence, this sort of evolution has not, cannot, and will not happen. Evolution in this sense is not an observable fact.

Was Darwin right in his explanation of the origin of species from a common ancestor? To the extent that members of the same kind share a common ancestor, Darwin correctly hypothesized that new species arise from pre-existing species. However, in hypothesizing that all species came from a single or a few primordial species millions of years ago, Darwin directly contradicted Scripture, and we have no scientific observations that would support his grandiose hypothesis.

Notes

1. Batten, D. 2000. Ligers and wholphins? What next? *Creation.* 22 (3): 28-33.
2. Pendragon, B. and N. Winkler. 2011. The family of cats—delineation of the feline basic type. *Journal of*

Creation. 25 (2): 118–124.

3. Statham, D. 2010. Biogeography. *Journal of Creation.* 24 (1): 82-87.

4. Johnson, B. 2012. Biogeography: A Creationist Perspective. *Creation Research Society Quarterly.* 48 (3): 212-223.

5. ICR's Bio-Origins Research Initiative. Institute for Creation Research fact sheet. Posted on icr.org.

6. Thomas, B. New Finch Species Shows Conservation, Not Macroevolution. *Creation Science Update.* Posted on icr.org.

7. Lightner, J. K. 2010. Identification of a large sparrow-finch monobaramin in perching birds (Aves: Passeriformes). *Journal of Creation.* 24 (3): 117–121.

8. Darwin, C. 1859. *On the Origin of Species.* London: John Murray.

9. The Hour S6: Episode 5—Richard Dawkins & Drew Barrymore. *George Stroumboulopoulos Tonight.* Posted on cbc.ca September 29, 2009.

18

DOES BIOLOGICAL SIMILARITY PROVE EVOLUTIONARY ANCESTRY?

Nathaniel Jeanson, Ph.D.

Did you know that you share DNA with a worm? Does this prove that you both shared an ancestor in the distant past? Evolutionists think so. Does the evidence support this conclusion? Let's consider first what evolution claims, and then evaluate the science used to support it.

Evolution is founded on the hypothesis that all species on Earth trace their ancestry back to a shared great-great-great-(etc.)-grandparent. Darwin claimed "There is grandeur in this [evolutionary] view of life...having been originally breathed into a few forms or into one."[1] Textbook diagrams depict the same—all of today's species connected through an unbroken genealogical tree back to a common ancestor (Figure 1). According to evolution, you are related to worms—and to every other species on this planet, plants, fungi, and bacteria included.

Based on the hypothesis of common ancestry, evolutionists predict that life will display unmistakable evidence

Figure 1. The "tree of life" embodies the evolutionary idea that all of life came from a common ancestor.

133

of its underlying genealogical connection. Though species can vary each generation, evolutionists expect that they will retain a signature of their common heritage. For example, there is variation in the human species each generation; human children never look exactly like their parents. However, children still retain features that are signatures of their parents—you can often identify parent-child relationships by appearance and, with modern technology, by DNA comparisons. Evolutionists extrapolate this sort of thinking from human family trees to all of life—since they hypothesize that all of life shares a family tree.

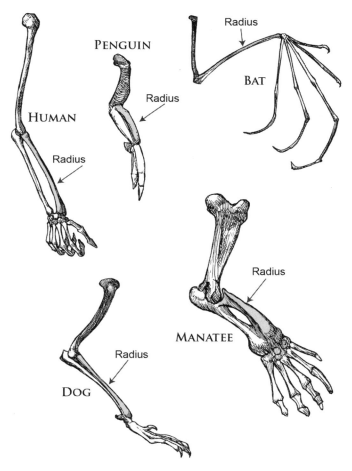

Figure 2. Human and animal forelimbs share an underlying structure.

Of all the lines of evidence evolutionists use to support common ancestry among all species, three stand out in popularity and prominence. First, evolutionists point toward the underlying gross similarity in anatomical structure across diverse animal species. For example, the forelimbs of humans, mammals, reptiles, birds, and salamanders all bear an underlying shared pattern in the structure and order of their bones (Figure 2). This shared pattern across vast classifications—at least four classes (kingdom-phylum-*class*-order-family-genus-species)—compels evolutionists to conclude that all these species (and their corresponding classes, by extension) inherited this forelimb pattern from a shared ancestor millions of years ago.

Second, evolutionists cite similarities in developmental stages as harkening back to former relatives. For instance, during human development, pharyngeal pouches form temporarily before eventually giving rise to tonsils, Eustachian tube, and thymus.[2] The resemblance between the pharyngeal pouches of humans and those of fish (which give rise to gills) is, according to evolutionary thinking, a convincing demonstration that humans have a distant fish ancestor (Figure 3).

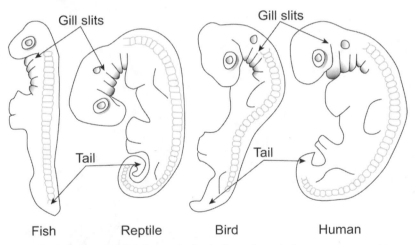

Gill slits

Gill slits

Tail

Tail

Fish   Reptile   Bird   Human

Figure 3. Evolutionists try to link features in developing embryos to show common ancestry.

Third, the growing body of evidence from molecular biology and DNA sequencing is, for many evolutionists, the final proof of Darwin's hypothesis (inconsistencies in the tree of life notwithstanding—see chapter 20). By comparing the DNA sequence across diverse species, evolutionists find two proofs of common heritage. First, the simple fact that nearly every species' DNA is built on the same underlying genetic code leads them to believe that all species derived from a single original ancestor that evolved this code. Second, by comparing subsequences of shared DNA across the biological kingdoms, evolutionists see a hierarchy that fits their expectations of evolutionary divergence over time (Figure 4). The well-known evolutionist Richard Dawkins claims that the most persuasive proof of evolution is, for him, "comparing the genes [subsets of DNA sequence] molecularly across all animals and plants. It falls on a precise hierarchical pattern which is obviously best interpreted as a family tree."[3] Thus, evolutionists take what is known from human genetic testing—that the degree of DNA similarity and difference among individuals reflects ancestry—and extrapolate far beyond human genealogies to all of life, and they claim to find patterns reflective of a common evolutionary heritage.[4]

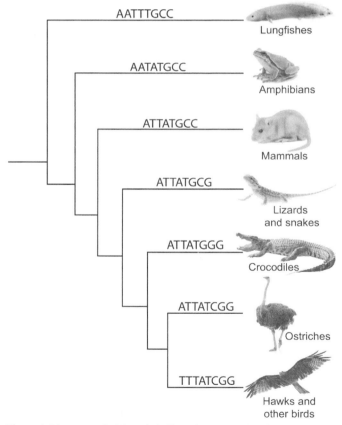

Figure 4. Diverse species' DNA is built on the same underlying genetic code. Does this show a "family tree"?

Is the evidence as convincing as evolutionists claim?

The first and most significant line of evidence contradicting these claims is the testimony of Scripture. As discussed in chapter 17, the scriptural teaching on the origin of species permits the formation of new species from a common created kind but prohibits the transmutation of one kind into another. For example, horses, donkeys, and zebras belong to the same kind and, thus, share a common ancestor (the equid pair on the Ark), but these species do not share an ancestor with cats. In contrast to the evolutionary tree of life (Figure 1), Scripture gives rise to a model that has been termed the creationist "orchard" (Figure 5), with every species' ancestry traced back to the *kinds* that were created separate and distinct in Genesis 1. Scripture denies universal common ancestry.

Figure 5. Scripture teaches that all living creatures are descendants of "kinds" that were created separate and distinct.

The written testimony of Scripture invalidates not only the evolutionary model of ancestry, but also the basis for the analogy evolutionists use to justify DNA comparisons as evidence for common ancestry. Recall that DNA comparisons are used to establish human paternity. How do we know that this method works? Because we have written historical records of human genealogies to independently verify the DNA results! How do evolutionists know that DNA comparisons for species other than humans works? Evolutionists have no independent verification (i.e., written historical records) of their extrapolation from human paternity testing to universal common ancestry testing. According to standard evolutionary thought, 99.9 percent of the universe's history passed without a single human observer to record it. Furthermore, the only reliable independent confirmation of species ancestry that we *do* have— Genesis 1–11—explicitly limits species' ancestry to the kinds of Genesis 1.

Thus, the evolutionary analogy has no justification either in Scripture or in evolution itself.

The second major line of evidence contradicting evolutionary claims is the pervasive pattern of discontinuity that distinguishes all created kinds. The first level of discontinuity is morphological/anatomical (see chapter 32 for a discussion of discontinuity in the fossil record). Not just created kinds, but many species are recognizable by appearance and can be classified into logical groups.[5] Even children readily recognize different types of creatures (dog, cat, giraffe, elephant, etc.) with very little training. This elementary observation points towards a startling underlying reality—created kinds are discrete and discontinuous from one another. If evolution were true, we might expect to find a number of organisms on this planet that resist classification—for example, a cat-dog that hasn't yet completed the evolutionary transition between the two species. Yet we find that life is very distinct and recognizable. This points away from evolution and toward the biblical "created after their kind" model.

The second level of discontinuity is found during development/embryogenesis. Given the underlying similarity in the pattern of the forelimb in reptiles, amphibians, mammals, and birds, one might expect to find very similar patterns in the process that ultimately builds this structure. However, profound and obvious differences are present at the four-cell stage—two cell divisions after fertilization![6] Such a deep divide among classes of species at such an early stage of development clashes with the predictions of universal common ancestry.

The third line of discontinuity—and the most striking—derives from DNA and protein comparisons across species. Unlike morphology and embryology, molecular biology is rigorously quantitative; DNA and protein sequences can be lined up letter-by-letter and scored for matches and mismatches. Using some of the same molecular data that evolutionists use, Michael Denton discovered the phenomenon of "equidistance"—that some species are the same genetic distance from *all other species.*[7] For example, Denton found that bacteria are as different from horses as they are from yeast! These molecular gaps among species point toward an underlying "disconnected-ness" in nature and not toward a uniform link across all species.

Clearly, this evidence points toward a devastating conclusion for evolution. The smooth genealogical thread connecting all species to one another is not supported by the evidence. Data from multiple fields describe a broken and disconnected thread across the kingdoms of life.

What evidences do evolutionists have left to buttress Darwin's hypothesis?

For those committed to evolution, evidence still exists in support of the evolutionary tree of life. While acknowledging the gaps in nature, evolutionists still point toward the shared *patterns* across diverse species. For example, while admitting that the forelimb is unique in each species and that it points toward gaps in nature, evolutionists would appeal to so-called "transitional forms" in the fossil record to explain the gaps (see chapter 32 for a refutation of this claim), and then point toward the basic *pattern* behind the forelimb structure as indicative of a common heritage.

Is this claim justified? Or is there a better explanation for these similarities?

Shared *patterns* in nature fit exactly what we would expect from the testimony of Genesis 1 and from the nature of God. Since Genesis 1 identifies God as the Creator and since God is omniscient and omnipotent, we would expect to find the results of creation to be *optimally designed*.[8] What would optimal design look like?

Consider the results of human design in the realm of transportation vehicles—cars, trucks, semi-trailers, tractors, motorcycles, etc. All of these vehicles could be classified and arranged in a hierarchy based on their features—number of wheels, size of the engine, etc. If this exercise were performed, we would quickly begin to see shared patterns across diverse classification categories: Many cars, trucks, and tractors would share the pattern of four wheels, many small cars would share the pattern of four-cylinder engines, etc. Furthermore, if we observed the manufacturing plants where these vehicles were constructed, we would likely find similar plans and assembly schemes.

Why would all these design patterns be shared? Because good engineering and design principles dictate that if a pattern works well in a certain environment and with certain resources, it should be used again! Four wheels appear in so many car and truck designs because they work well on the paved roads that stretch across much of the developed world. What do we see in nature when looking at shared patterns in the structure (anatomy), function (physiology), and construction (development, DNA) of each species? We see optimal design and the general re-use of effective design patterns! Four limbs are present in many reptiles, amphibians, mammals, and birds because this pattern works well. Thus, evolutionists miss the obvious explanation for shared patterns when they invoke common ancestry. Optimal design is what every person should immediately recognize instead.

In summary, Darwin hypothesized that all species descended from a common ancestor in the distant past, and that this process would have littered life with many evidences of this common heritage. Darwin's speculation is strongly contradicted by the ubiquitous evidence for discontinuity. The evidence for similarity or shared patterns in DNA and body plans depicts exactly what we would expect from a plain reading of Scripture—namely, (near) optimal design and the general re-use of effective design principles. Thus, the comparison of organisms on many levels denies evolution and confirms creation.

Notes

1. Darwin, C. 1859. *On the Origin of Species*. London: John Murray, 490.

2. Gilbert, S. F. 2003. *Developmental Biology*. Sunderland, MA: Sinauer Associates, Inc., 511.

3. The Hour S6: Episode 5—Richard Dawkins & Drew Barrymore. *George Stroumboulopoulos Tonight*. Posted on cbc.ca September 29, 2009.

4. Carroll, S. B. 2006. *The Making of the Fittest: DNA and the Ultimate Forensic Record of Evolution*. New York: W. W. Norton & Company, Inc., 99.

5. Jones, A. 1982. A creationist critique of homology. *Creation Research Society Quarterly*. 19 (3): 156-175.

6. Gilbert, *Developmental Biology*, 225.

7. Denton, M. 1985. *Evolution: A Theory in Crisis*. Bethesda, MD: Adler & Adler, Publishers, Inc., 279.

8. Since the Bible indicates that we live in a cursed and fallen world (Genesis 3; Romans 8), we should modify our expectation to *(near) optimally designed*. Jones, A creationist critique of homology.

19

THE EROSION OF GENES CONFIRMS GENESIS HISTORY

Brian Thomas, M.S.

Nobody lives forever. Most of us are aware that our individual bodies are engaged in a relentless countdown called aging. If we are fortunate enough to avoid lethal violence and disease, our biological countdown will eventually reach zero and our bodies will simply stop working.

The death of an individual is a sad fact of life, but it gets worse. Many are unaware that biological decay overtakes not just individuals, but whole species. The entire human race is on a countdown to zero. And the countdown is occurring rapidly. The only reason we have not yet reached the end must be because we began our journey as a species recently—only thousands of years ago.

Let's examine how this genetic countdown happens. DNA contains densely packed, highly regulated, and mind-bogglingly complicated biological information. That kind of functioning intricacy could only come from an ingenious Creator, and it matches a creation that was originally "very good" (Genesis 1:31).

The world we live in is no longer very good. Genesis 3 tells why the world was cursed—the reader learns that the penalty for Adam's sin is death. And sure enough, each new body cell undergoes a process of programmed death.[1] When enough cells in any vital system die, then the whole body ceases to function.[2]

Even without programmed cell death, another process would eventually cause bodily death. Every time a cell divides, a small number of its 3.2 billion DNA chemical building blocks fails to copy correctly. These copying errors, or mutations, build up over time. Not only do they accumulate in an individual's body during their one lifetime, contributing to system failure leading to diseases and death, but they also accumulate over many lifetimes, passing from generation to generation. Fortunately, the believer in Christ will receive a new body, and its "flesh shall be young like a child's, He shall return to the days of his youth" (Job 33:25).

Geneticists use powerful new technology to count the exact number of single DNA differences, often called "single-nucleotide variants" (SNVs), between two individuals. This permits them to track mutations, many of which occur as SNVs. A few recent studies counted the accumulation of SNVs within direct descendants. Their results confirm what geneticists had suspected. Over 100 brand-new SNVs occur every generation. That means every person alive today is a mutant! It also means that every person alive today carries more mutations than their parents, grandparents, and all ancestors all the way back to Adam, whose genes were perfect. Fortunately, the vast majority of these SNVs have an immeasurably small effect. But over hundreds of generations, thousands of nearly harmless individual mutations add up to become harmful in total. And these mutations are counting down to the end of the entire human race. The fact they're still "counting" must mean that we are still young.

Nearly neutral mutations accumulate and slightly garble genetic information. This type of mutation far outnumbers any that could in theory construct new and useful information, and likewise those few that cause severe harm.[3]

This process is like copying an encyclopedia every 20 years (the approximate length of a human generation) by hand. Each time the encyclopedia is copied, only a few errors—simple typos—creep into the text. At first, and for thousands of years, the information in each article can still be understood, even with the copying errors. But eventually, after many thousands of years, the articles become so riddled with mistakes that the encyclopedia becomes totally useless.

Similarly, cells are left to interpret the damaged genetic information like scholars who must try to reconstruct text from tattered and marred ancient scrolls. Cells can decipher enough information even from inferior DNA sequences to continue functioning for many generations, but eventually core coding will become corrupted. Genetic information is garbled just a tiny bit more with each generation. This ongoing "erosion" of genes and supporting DNA sequences confirms a corrupted creation, just like Paul described in Romans 8:22, saying, "For we know that the whole creation groans and labors with birth pangs together until now."

The decay of DNA's biological data also confirms biblical creation by limiting the total possible number of human generations to far fewer than evolutionary history requires. Since each generation accumulates about 100 more mutations than the prior generation—and since each mutation is so nearly harmless that no cellular or natural process can detect or remove it—the total number of mutations continues to mount unimpeded. This sets a finite total threshold for number of generations. Currently, the best estimates show that mutational overload will doom the whole of humanity in fewer than 500 generations.[4]

According to the genealogy of Jesus through Mary provided in Luke 3, and the genealogy of Jesus through Joseph as shown in Matthew 1, the total number of human generations from creation to Christ averaged about 100. Assuming a new generation every 20 years, the 2,000 years that have elapsed since Christ should have yielded another 100 or so generations.

Two hundred total generations multiplied by 100 mutations per generation equals 20,000 more mutations than were in the genome of Adam, who had none.[5] Evolutionary ideas insist that modern humans evolved about 2.5 million years ago. Such a vast time would have produced about 125,000 generations and many thousands of mutations. Where are all the expected human SNVs? Or, as one evolutionary human population geneticists candidly asked, "Why have we not died 100 times over?"[6]

One recent genetics study has provided particularly clear confirmation of biblical history. In it, the authors counted genetic diversity within a group of over 2,400 people.[7] They discovered that each person harbors very recently formed DNA differences (SNVs) within their genes. The study authors modeled the rise of genetic diversity through time, finding that it exactly paralleled historical population growth. Their data indicated that human genetic diversity began to accelerate only about 5,100 years ago.

Of course, 5,100 years falls right in line with biblical creation, but presents big problems for evolutionary history. Anyone who defends human evolution now needs to explain why the human population failed to grow for 2.5 million years, only to begin exponential growth in just the last 5,100 years. In other words, they should explain how each family produced, and how nature maintained, no more or less than two children per generation—one to replace the father and one to replace the mother—for about 125,000 consecutive generations!

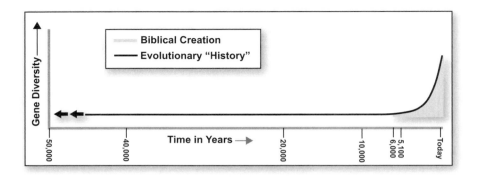

Figure 1. Human gene diversity over time, after Tennessen et al. Genetic data show that genes diversified beginning about 5,100 years ago. This presents a significant challenge to an evolutionary timeline, which must now explain why humans waited for millions of years before beginning to diversify. The results, however, are quite consistent with a biblical timeline.

Evolutionists reason that mankind's long delay before the population exploded stemmed from his supposedly long wait until agriculture had evolved. But this merely begs the question—it assumes evolution to prove evolution. In reality, the weight of archaeological evidence shows that mankind has always been as smart, or smarter, in the past than today. For example, the world's oldest temple, Gobekli Tepe in Turkey, has expertly carved animal and human figures on its still-straight stone pillars. And artifacts that include spears in an Ice Age German coal mine, Neandertal jewelry, axe glue, butchered bones in Africa, and ancient stone animal pens in Arabia all show that people have always been fully capable of manipulating their environments much like today's people do. Thus, in contrast to the false picture of human evolution that invokes invented "rescuing" devices like agriculture evolving, biblical history fits the genetic diversity and archaeological data straightforwardly.

Overall, genetics clearly confirms biblical creation in at least three ways. First, high-tech gene organization could only be the product of a Mastermind. Second, the breakdown of genes both within and between generations is consistent with the Bible's description of a fallen creation. Last, two observations from genetics confirm the Bible's timeline: The human genome would accumulate too many copying errors to survive more than 500 generations, fitting well with the Bible's inferred 200 or so elapsed generations. Also, genetic diversity only began accelerating about 5,100 years ago, a scientific finding that is in lock-step with the biblical record.

Notes

1. Specifically, the cell division process has a counting mechanism that appears to be related to the fact that telomeric DNA shortens after each cell division. After about 40 divisions, cells cease dividing and eventually turn themselves off through a process called apoptosis. See Hayflick L, P. S. Moorhead. 1961. The serial cultivation of human diploid cell strains. *Experimental Cell Research*. 25: 585-621.

2. "When the same kind of molecular mischief occurs in the cells of vital organs, leading to an increase in vulnerability to disease or pathology, treatment is required because life may be threatened." Hayflick, L. 2007. Entropy Explains Aging, Genetic Determinism Explains Longevity, and Undefined Terminology Explains Misunderstanding Both. *PLoS Genetics*. 3 (12): e220.

3. Sanford, J. S. 2005. *Genetic Entropy and the Mystery of the Genome*. Lima, NY: Ivan Press, 150.

4. "Assuming an additive model, the result is that our species goes extinct in roughly 300 generations." Ibid, 113.

5. Actually, any two people have many more than 20,000 SNVs. But the majority of DNA differences were likely placed into Adam's genome on purpose. After all, Adam had two each of 23 chromosomes, one with certain gene variations and the matching chromosome with other variations. God designed Adam's body to produce future generations that could produce trait variations that would successfully multiply and fill the earth's ever-changing environments. God "has made from one blood every nation of men to dwell on all the face of the earth" (Acts 17:26).

6. Kondrashov, A. 1995. Contamination of the genome by very slightly deleterious mutations: why have we not died 100 times over? *Journal of Theoretical Biology*. 175 (4): 583-594.

7. Tennessen, J. et al. 2012. Evolution and Functional Impact of Rare Coding Variation from Deep Sequencing of Human Exomes. *Science*. 337 (6090): 64-69.

20

IS THE EVOLUTIONARY TREE OF LIFE REAL?

Jeffrey Tomkins, Ph.D., Frank Sherwin, M.A., and Brian Thomas, M.S.

Evolution is often depicted in a tree-like structure with single-cell organisms at the bottom and more complex forms of life progressively emerging as the tree branches upward. The individual branches represent lineages and new lines of evolution that terminate with either living organisms or organisms that are now extinct (Figure 1). This tree represents the supposed evolution of increasingly complex organisms during millions and billions of years of "deep time."

Evolutionary trees were first popularized by Charles Darwin, who drew a picture of one in 1837 in what is known as his B notebook, along

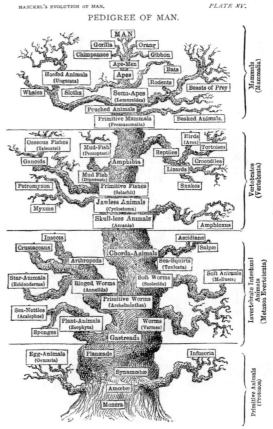

Figure 1. A graphical illustration of an evolutionary tree showing what is often called macroevolution, or vertical evolution.

147

with the comment "I think" (see Figure 2). This drawing visually depicted his idea that all of today's species arose from a single common ancestor. Darwin's thinking lies at the heart of evolutionary dogma, and his fictional tree-like images have since been embellished, making them effective indoctrination tools.

There are both biblical and scientific problems with this concept. If today's creatures (as well as those that are now extinct) evolved from other creatures millions or billions of years ago, then the biblical account in Genesis must be abandoned. Scripture indicates that the creation of all the "kinds" of biological life occurred in the latter days of the creation week. Thus, millions of years were *not* involved in their creation. The Bible does not support the concept of vertical Darwinian "descent with modification" with one kind changing into another.

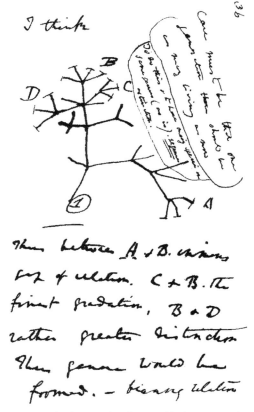

Figure 2. Charles Darwin's first graphical representation of vertical evolution.

Interestingly, many scientific discoveries since the time of Darwin now fully support and confirm the biblical concepts outlined in Genesis. These discoveries have been bad news for both evolutionary trees and evolutionary theory in general. Attempts to mathematically build evolutionary trees (also known as phylogenetic trees) have resulted in many inconsistencies that are casting doubt on the Darwinian paradigm. An article in *New Scientist* magazine titled "Why Darwin Was Wrong About the Tree of Life" reflected this frustration among evolutionists.[1]

Molecular vs. Morphological Trees

Traditional phylogenetic trees show the relatedness of organisms to possible ancestors based on data measurements taken from morphology. Morphology refers to observable physical traits that can be measured, like brain size, skull shape, or arm length. Measurements of such features are taken from multiple organisms. Scientists use a computer algorithm to compare similarities between these measurements, then position each organism in an evolutionary hierarchy. The result is then graphically represented by a tree diagram, similar to Darwin's original concept.

Several serious problems immediately became apparent with this type of evolutionary analysis. First, evolutionists quickly realized that the phylogenetic trees they obtained depended upon the trait being measured, and that these trees often contradicted the expected evolutionary lineage.

For example, no evolutionist suggests that octopi are closely related to mammals. And yet, both have very similar eyeball structure and function. Did mammals inherit octopus eyes, but not their tentacles? A phylogenetic tree based only on eyes would place mammals and octopi on very close branches. But another analysis based on body structure, counting the fact that octopi have no skeleton, would place them on opposite sides of the tree!

This paradox was initially termed *incomplete lineage sorting*, and the conflicting trees were labeled as *discordant*.[2,3] Furthermore, many researchers had differing opinions as to which phylogenetic trees were correct based upon the organisms they studied in their own research.[4]

Contradictory Trees from DNA and Proteins

In an attempt to settle the issue of conflicting phylogenetic trees, evolutionists began using protein and DNA sequences instead of morphological data. Researchers had hoped that digital comparisons of protein or DNA sequences would result in the construction of authoritative phylogenetic trees that would finally show consistent evolutionary patterns among the categories of life. However, these new techniques only solidified the problem of incomplete lineage sorting and discordant trees.

Study after study has revealed even more problems with the evolutionary lineages derived from molecular data than with lineages derived from morphological data.[2,3] Furthermore, lineages based upon biological sequence data often contradict lineages based upon morphological data.[4] In these studies, evolutionists will select sequences that lend themselves to evolutionary interpretations and reject sequences that have no apparent evolutionary explanation. However, even this technique still produces discordant phylogenetic trees.

For example, in one study on human evolution, a large pool of human, chimp, orangutan, rhesus, and gorilla DNA sequences were fitted into an evolutionary tree format.[5] The original pool of DNA sequences went through several levels of selection for optimal DNA comparisons. First, a set of 30,112 sequences that shared similarity between humans and all the apes were selected. Dissimilar sequences were ignored. These hand-picked sequences were further evaluated for their evolutionary utility. Only those which produced ≥300 base alignments were retained for another series of alignments, and only the sequences that produced superior statistical probabilities (>95 percent) were used in the final analysis. This filtering process removed over 22 percent of predetermined, highly similar DNA sequence. Despite this DNA cherry-picking designed to produce the most favorable evolutionary trees, the results did not show any clear evolutionary connection between humans and chimps (nor with any of the other apes). Instead, the data showed a mosaic of unique human and ape DNA sequences. Perhaps the most revealing features of the research are found in the author's own words:

> For about 23% of our genome, we share no immediate genetic ancestry with our closest living relative, the chimpanzee. Thus, in two-thirds of the cases a genealogy results in which humans and chimpanzees are *not* each other's closest genetic relatives. The corresponding genealogies are incongruent with the species tree. In accordance with the experimental evidences, this implies that there is no such thing as a unique evolutionary history of the human genome. Rather, it resembles a patchwork of individual regions following their own genealogy.[5] (emphasis added)

The authors added that the lack of support for a consistent and clear evolutionary relationship between humans and apes is due to the "inclusion of alignments with no clear phylogenetic signal." This is a remarkable admission, given that the researchers did a great deal of data filtering and "cherry-picking" in an attempt to show a relationship between humans and apes. However, even with this biased selection of the data, they could find no clear evidence of such a relationship!

Indeed, the situation is prevalent across the spectrum of life. British evo-lutionist Michael Benton, when comparing evolutionary rates based on fos-sils with the rates of DNA change evaluated in live specimens, commented, "Lungfishes show significantly higher rates of evolution of the 28S rRNA gene sequences than coelacanths, other fishes and tetrapods, and this makes it hard to discriminate their correct position in the tree." Addressing supposed evo-lutionary relationships from vertebrates' supposed distant past, Benton states, "There is, however, a major discrepancy between this result and current mo-lecular phylogenies."[6]

Evolutionary biologists Andrea Feller and S. Blair Hedges compared the DNA sequences of four mitochondrial genes and found a sister-group rela-tionship of salamanders and caecilians, with frogs as the outgroup.[7] This con-tradicts the pairing of frogs and salamanders, based on their similarly amphib-ian life cycles. Olivier Rieppel has found very little morphological support for the molecular pairing of turtles and archosaurs, an arbitrary grouping of birds and reptiles.[8] The same contradiction popped up when cartilaginous fish were investigated: "Molecular analyses of chondrichthyan phylogeny so far do not support the morphological tree."[9]

Examples of this widespread disharmony continuously emerge across all forms of animal life examined. Nor is this issue restricted to the animal king-dom: "Only rarely have phylogenetic studies of morphology and DNA data agreed in plant studies, even in well-studied groups."[10]

No Detected Evolutionary Relationship—the Implications

Evolutionary trees typically contradict one another. Examples are plenti-ful and many more could be shown. The best explanation for this observed discordance is that the data do not fit evolutionary origins. Evolutionists must force the data—whether it is physical traits or molecular sequence differenc-es—into their preconception, and then make excuses for why it produces so many problems.

This widespread embarrassment is still not widely acknowledged outside the secular scientific community. General biology texts still typically depict outdated and mythical evolutionary trees with smooth progressions of crea-tures evolving into "higher" forms. Of course, these fictional depictions com-pletely ignore the rampant disagreement found at every level in the technical literature. Perhaps this is because many scientists are unwilling to face the glaring implications of all these studies. They know they must find support for vertical Darwinian evolution to justify their denial of a Creator and His Word. The total lack of support for vertical evolution from actual creatures also refutes the erroneous idea that claims God used evolution as a means of "creation."

The fact that it has been impossible to objectively establish evolutionary relationships between so many creatures reflects an underlying reality: Evolution never occurred. Darwin's tree of life and the generations of more and more intricate versions of phylogenetic trees published over the past 150 years are merely man-made fictional illustrations of a long macroevolutionary past that never really happened.

Like junk DNA and vestigial organs, Darwin's tree of life was a roadblock, misleading students and scientists for over a century. Is it any wonder that evolutionist Michael Rose stated, "The tree of life is being politely buried—we all know that."[11] Instead, the science confirms what God's Word says. The progenitors of today's living creatures were created as distinct kinds around 6,000 years ago according to the biblical record—in strong agreement with the observed scientific data.

Notes

1. Lawton, G. 2009. Why Darwin Was Wrong About the Tree of Life. *New Scientist.* 2692: 34-39.
2. Degnan, J. H. and N. A. Rosenberg. 2009. Gene Tree Discordance, Phylogenetic Inference and the Multispecies Coalescent. *Trends In Ecology and Evolution.* 24: 332-340.
3. Dolgin, E. 2012. Phylogeny: Rewriting Evolution. *Nature.* 486 (7404): 460-462.
4. Patterson, C., D. M. Williams, and C. J. Humphries. 1993. Congruence Between Molecular and Morphological Phylogenies. *Annual Review of Ecology and Systematics.* 24: 153-188.
5. Ebersberger, I. et al. 2007. Mapping human genetic ancestry. *Molecular Biology and Evolution.* 24 (10): 2266-2276.
6. Benton, M. J. 2005. *Vertebrate Paleontology.* Malden, MA: Blackwell Publishing, 69.
7. Feller, A. E. and S. B. Hedges. 1998. Molecular evidence for the early history of living amphibians. *Molecular Phylogenetics and Evolution.* 9 (3): 509-516.
8. Benton, *Vertebrate Paleontology,* 144.
9. Ibid, 165.
10. Frohlch, M. W and M. W. Chase. 2007. After a dozen years of progress the origin of angiosperms is still a great mystery. *Nature.* 450 (7173): 1184-1190.
11. Lawton, Why Darwin Was Wrong About the Tree of Life.

21

THE JUNK DNA SCAM

Jeffrey Tomkins, Ph.D.

One of the greatest evolutionary frauds in biology is the idea that plant and animal genomes contain vast amounts of meaningless "junk" DNA sequences that serve no practical purpose. However, many researchers working in the vast field of genomics now realize that virtually the entire genome is functional in some respect.

Nevertheless, a handful of influential bio-science authors still authoritatively proclaim the fraudulent concept of junk DNA as a key component to perpetuate the overall myth of Darwinian evolution.

The general idea behind junk DNA is that the large percentage of the genome that does not directly code for protein represents the evolutionary vestiges of viruses, defunct genes, and other repetitive sequences dragged along through evolutionary history like some sort of excess baggage. These so-called junk DNA regions are postulated to be "neutral" in regard to natural selection as some sort of explanation as why they still exist.

One of the more common arguments from some of the evolutionary propagandists is that a Creator God would never have filled genomes with such large amounts of seemingly useless DNA. Of course, this presupposition is based on the false idea that these regions of the genome serve no purpose. However, as will be shown, science now abundantly proves that this is not the case.

Because literally hundreds of research citations would be required for this chapter, only a few key papers will be cited. For the advanced reader who is interested in exploring this material in more detail, please see the recent book on this subject by Jonathan Wells, *The Myth of Junk DNA*.[1]

The Coding of Non-Coding DNA

The non-protein-coding parts of genomes can be divided up into a number of categories. One category contains segments of so-called junk DNA that are very similar across a wide variety of creatures.[2,3,4] These are called highly conserved non-coding regions. According to evolutionary reasoning, these should be heavily mutated and variable. Since they are supposedly non-functional and not actively undergoing any type of natural selection, they should freely mutate. However, the high level of similarity in these non-coding DNA segments among many types of organisms is actually a strong indicator of the functionality of these sequences. They serve a common and important design purpose across various classes of life.

Another major argument indicating the functionality of so-called junk DNA is the fact that diverse classes of non-protein-coding DNA are used as templates to make a wide variety of RNA molecules that help regulate gene activity throughout the genome. These types of DNA sequences code for functional RNA molecules that are not used to make proteins and are broadly classified as regulatory RNA with many different types of sub-classes. There are a variety of ways that RNAs can be used to control gene activity.

Interestingly, many of these RNAs are transcribed from the reverse (anti-sense) strand of the double-stranded DNA helix to produce RNAs that will base-pair in a complementary fashion to protein-coding RNAs transcribed from the forward (sense) strand.[5,6] This can provide rapid regulation in several ways. First, it can keep messenger RNAs (mRNAs) from being degraded, preserving their presence in the nucleus. Secondly, it keeps messenger RNAs from being translated to make proteins.

In fact, the regulation of gene expression by a wide variety of RNAs produced from non-protein-coding DNA sequence is now also perceived as an important target of study in addition to the actual protein-coding sections of the genome. The wide diversity of non-coding RNAs (ncRNAs) in a cell affects virtually all aspects of growth, development, and physiology, and is one the key features of life.

For example, the protein-coding sections of the human genome, which comprise less than 5 percent of the DNA sequence, are somewhat analogous to the raw materials (bricks, boards, wire, etc.) used in a construction project. It is the intelligent oversight, implementation, and usage of these raw materials that makes the building take shape and function. To a major degree, that's what the non-coding parts of the genome do, and ncRNAs appear to play a major role in this.

The Amazing Splicing Code

Another major feature of the genome that destroys the junk-DNA scam is the splicing code. This genomic paradigm has been progressively developed over the past several decades but has recently come together in more detail. Researchers claim that the number of human protein-coding genes is about 21,500 to 23,000. However, the public databases currently contain about two million different human protein sequences.

The amazing thing is that the number of protein variants greatly outnumbers the total number of protein-coding genes. Obviously, something very complicated is going on in a regulatory sense, roughly akin to the way a computer programmer utilizes code optimization and re-use. However, what has been described through the discovery of the splicing code is much more complicated than any computer system developed by man.

Plant and animal genes are interrupted by non-coding areas that are spliced out after RNA transcripts of the gene are produced. These are called *introns*. The coding regions are called *exons*. Scientists discovered early on in the genomics era that some genes exhibit alternative splicing, where exons are either omitted or added in the linear sequence of a transcript, allowing for the production of different proteins from the same sequence (see the illustration in Figure 1). The great disparity between the number of protein-coding genes and the number of proteins produced appears to be the result of the amazing splicing code.

So-called junk DNA plays a comprehensive and immense regulatory role in the process of alternative splicing. Not only does non-coding DNA contribute to exon selection and placement decisions, but it also controls the recognition and usage of alternative transcriptional start sites, splice site recognition, transcriptional and translational cues, transcript processing and transport, genome architecture, and nuclear membrane architecture.

The actual triggers or predictors for the splicing code consist of a large list of protein, DNA, RNA, tissue type, and cell physiology factors combined in complex sets of configurations to produce different transcript and protein production activity in the cell. If there ever was a foolproof example from the world of biology to unequivocally prove intelligent design, the function of the genome is it.

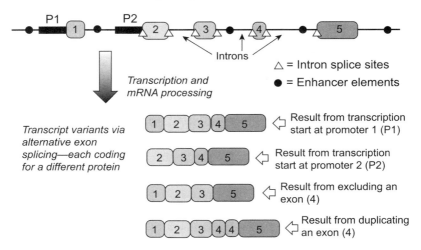

Figure 1. Diagram of a gene with five exons (protein-coding regions) showing some features that allow for the splicing code. The gene has alternate controlling (promoter regions) labeled P1 and P2. These provide variable control of the gene, along with alternative start sites for the production of a messenger RNA transcript. The different protein-coding regions (exons) can also be used to create different proteins. Special controlling sequences called enhancer elements also play an important role in up-regulating the gene.

Pseudogenes Are Functional

Another critical topic related to the whole junk-DNA scam is the commonly misunderstood subject of pseudogenes. The false idea that pseudogene regions of the genome represent dysfunctional genes or non-functional copies of genes has been a key argument in evolution.

Pseudogenes are supposedly partial or dysfunctional copies of genes that are fully functional in other parts of the genome. When these sequences were first discovered, evolutionists immediately assumed that they were the products of hypothetical naturalistic processes and served no immediate functional purpose. They were thought to be the cryptic remnants of once-functional genes or copies of genes that are in the process of evolving.

However, a slew of contemporary research is showing that pseudogenes are fully functional and critical control features of the genome.[8,9] Indeed, in some cases when they are disrupted in genetic studies, their mutation is lethal to the test organism. In fact, their disruption in many cases causes severe problems in gene expression and disease. Obviously, these are critical features of the genome required for life and changing their sequence causes problems.

Pseudogenes have also been proven to be actively transcribed via both the minus and plus strands of the DNA molecule, so their regulation in the genome is quite complex. These types of transcripts play a diversity of critical roles in both the up and down regulation of a wide variety of functional protein-coding genes with which they share similarity.

Transposable Elements

Another class of so-called junk DNA that has also been the target of evolutionary propagandists is the diverse group of DNA features called transposable elements (TEs), sometimes referred to as "jumping genes." Many scientists have stated that all of the subclasses in this diverse group of DNA elements were merely genomic baggage conferred by ancient ancestral viruses that maliciously infested our DNA and have served no other purpose than to bloat and expand our poor hapless genomes with meaningless DNA fragments. However, the past several decades of research now show that every identified class of TEs (LINEs, SINEs, ERVs and DNA-transposons) has an important role in the function of the genome during development, growth, and day-to-day physiological activity.[10,11,12,13]

In *The Myth of Junk DNA*, Jonathan Wells discusses the history of these discoveries, along with detailed information about each sub-class of TE and its currently known functional characteristics. Interestingly, all of these TEs are now known to have multiple functions depending on the type of cell and its activity. Rather than cryptic viral genome contaminants, it is now clear that TEs are absolutely critical to genome function and survival. TEs apparently also play important roles in cell stress responses and other protective measures. Wells' book clearly shows how the various classes of TEs present in the genome are not useless trash, but indispensable functional features that contain numerous critical control features that regulate gene expression and genome formatting.

Computer hard drives have specialized code to format the arrangement and function of files. One of the key functions of transposable elements has been described as serving a similar purpose.[14] They literally format the genome for proper gene function and expression.

Non-coding Structural Genomic Information

Another important aspect of non-coding DNA is the architectural purpose it serves in genome structure. It is now known that DNA is not randomly strewn about the nucleus, but packaged into distinct, highly controlled organizational areas depending on what type of cell it is and the genetic processes involved. [14,15,16]

Chemical modifications not associated with actual base changes also affect the DNA molecule itself. These include nucleotide methylation and histone protein acetylation and methylation. Histones are proteins that stabilize and package the DNA molecule. Histones can be modified as well as the DNA molecule to affect genome and gene function. This field of research is called epigenetics.

The levels of DNA packaging and chemical modification greatly affect gene function and access by a wide variety of regulatory molecules. These modifications can be localized (local genome topology) and also affect the whole shape of the genome (global configuration). In any given local region of the genome, it may contain looping structures, structural integration of RNA molecules, and specific nuclear matrix attachment sites. These local topological features and configurations influence gene function and are facilitated and made possible by the non-coding DNA regions of the genome. The global configuration of the genome is another key subcellular feature.

The dynamically configured overall three-dimensional structure of the genome depends on the cell type and its associated stimuli and cues.[17,18,19] In such a scenario, certain chromosomes and chromosomal regions are dynamically configured to occupy specific functional domains. These three-dimensional features and configurations are made possible by the non-coding DNA structural regions of the genome.

Conclusion: Not So Junky After All

Clearly, the genome is a masterful marvel of incredibly complex engineering and design. Every new discovery shows how functional and critical every single feature is to cell function, growth, and development. Just because a scientist cannot immediately determine the function of some aspect of the genome doesn't mean that it is junk. Science has proven this over and over again.

Notes

1. Wells, J. 2011. *The Myth of Junk DNA.* Seattle, WA: Discovery Institute Press.

2. Siepel, A. et al. 2005. Evolutionarily conserved elements in vertebrate, insect, worm, and yeast genomes. *Genome Research.* 15: 1034-1050.

3. Retelska, D. et al. 2007. Vertebrate conserved non coding DNA regions have a high persistence length and

a short persistence time. *BMC Genomics.* 8: 398.

4. Elgar, G. 2009. Pan-vertebrate conserved non-coding sequences associated with developmental regulation. *Briefings in Functional Genomics and Proteomics.* 8 (4): 256-265.

5. Lapidot, M. and Y. Pilpel. 2006. Genome-wide natural antisense transcription: coupling its regulation to its different regulatory mechanisms. *EMBO Reports.* 7: 1216-1222.

6. Li, K. and R. Ramchandran. 2010. Natural Antisense Transcript: A Concomitant Engagement with Protein-Coding Transcript. *Oncotarget* 1: 447-452.

7. The ENCODE Project Consortium. 2007. Identification and analysis of functional elements in 1% of the human genome by the ENCODE pilot project. *Nature.* 447 (7146):799-816.

8. Zheng, D. et al. 2007. Pseudogenes in the ENCODE regions: Consensus annotation, analysis of transcription, and evolution. *Genome Research.* 17: 839-851.

9. Pink, R.C. et al. 2011. Pseudogenes: Pseudo-functional or key regulators in health and disease? *RNA.* 17: 792-798.

10. Shapiro, J. A. and R. V. Sternberg. 2005. Why repetitive DNA is essential to genome function. *Biological Review.* 80: 1-24.

11. Hasler, J and K. Strub. 2006. Alu elements as regulators of gene expression. *Nucleic Acids Research.* 34: 5491-5497.

12. Bourque, G. 2010. Transposable elements in gene regulation and in the evolution of vertebrate genomes. *Current Opinion in Genetics and Development.* 19: 607-612.

13. Gong, C. and L. E. Maquat. 2011. lncRNAs transactivate STAU1-mediated mRNA decay by duplexing with 39 UTRs via Alu elements. *Nature.* 470 (7333): 284-290.

14. von Sternberg, R. and J.A. Shapiro. 2005. How repeated retroelements format genome function. *Cytogenetic and Genome Research.* 110: 108-116.

15. Lam, E. et al. 2009. Charting functional and physical properties of chromatin in living cells. *Genetics and Development.* 19:135-141.

16. Lieberman-Aiden, E. 2009. Comprehensive Mapping of Long-Range Interactions Reveals Folding Principles of the Human Genome. *Science.* 326 (5950): 289-293.

17. Zhao, R. et al. 2009. Nuclear neighborhoods and gene expression. *Genetics and Development.* 19: 172-179.

18. Schoenfelder, S. et al. 2009. The transcriptional interactome: gene expression in 3D. *Genetics and Development.* 20: 127-133.

19. Barash Y. et al. 2010. Deciphering the splicing code. *Nature.* 465 (7294): 53-59.

22

THE ORIGIN OF PREDATOR/PREY RELATIONSHIP AND PARASITES

Frank Sherwin, M.A.

Perhaps no area of biology has raised more questions than the issues of predator/prey relationships, hereditary diseases, and parasites in a world God created. This chapter will address some of these issues.

We start with the two opposing worldviews on origins. While evolutionists have their unscientific ideas regarding all life coming from a single cell that somehow developed from non-life, creationists turn to the book of beginnings—Genesis. In this historical, God-breathed document, we read of an idyllic creation, with God the Creator proclaiming, "It was very good" (Genesis 1:31).

Christians see the problem of natural evil and physical death as not being part of God's original plan (Deuteronomy 32:4). In Genesis 3, we read of the Fall of Adam and Eve, followed by God cursing the earth: "Both thorns and thistles it shall bring forth for you; and you shall eat the herb of the field" (Genesis 3:18). We can see that something changed at the Curse.

Thankfully, although Genesis 3 graphically shows the Curse and its effects on a world that fell into sin, it also gives the first prophecy of redemption. We read in verse 15 God's pronouncement to the serpent:

> And I will put enmity between you and the woman, and between
> your seed and her Seed; He shall bruise your head, and you shall
> bruise His heel.

Our creation and Curse are there in Genesis—but so is the blessed hope we have with the first promise of salvation and renewal in Christ.

Evolutionists see the evil and pain in the world and, not surprisingly, attribute it to the evolutionary paradigm. Darwin stated in the closing paragraphs of *Origin of Species*:

> Thus, from the war of nature, from famine and death...the production of higher animals, directly follows.[1]

We read in Romans 8:19-21 that the creation is subject to "futility" (vs. 20), and that the universe is subject to death and deterioration. In verse 21, Paul uses the word "corruption," which is equivalent to decay. But this dreadful cycle of disease and death was never part of God's original plan, despite evolutionists' attempt to make it seem a part of the "natural" order.

Thorns and Thistles

Creation scientists and theologians are researching this area called the Curse to understand the mechanisms by which this alteration from God's perfect creation occurred. It would not be theologically accurate to say that God created thistles and thorns at this time, since Genesis 2:2 indicates that "on the seventh day God ended His [creation] work." Perhaps He allowed the beneficent structures and processes He created previously from His "very good" creation to deteriorate. This deterioration was due to man's sin (Isaiah 53:6). Some animals and plants now have a physically changed form (such as thorns) that would have to have genetic modifications to pass on the changes to future generations.

Another theory regarding the function of thorns and thistles prior to the Fall involves a concept called exaptation. God could have designed a trait with a specific function that subsequently came to serve another purpose after the Fall.

Creation scientists also suggest there was hidden or latent genetic information contained within a person, plant, or animal's genome that could be phenotypically (physically) expressed at a later time.

Bacteria and Viruses

Today there are increasing discoveries indicating "bad" (pathogenic) bacteria, parasites, and viruses may have had a more neutral or even beneficial function prior to the Fall. For example, *Escherichia coli* (*E. coli*) bacteria can either be good or bad depending on the subspecies and where it is found in the body. In the colon, the bacteria make important B vitamins and vitamin K, but if the colon is ruptured, *E. coli* escaping into the body cavity can have fatal consequences.

If the creation science model of deterioration (or alteration) after the Fall is true, it raises the possibility that under different conditions, disease-causing bacteria in nature, for example, might have had beneficial applications. This can be seen with the Hawaiian bobtail squid, which hosts the otherwise pathogenic bacteria called *Vibrio cholera*. The bacteria secrete a deadly toxin that can cause cholera. Perhaps this toxin had an alternative function in the beginning?

A very similar toxin is produced by *V. fischeri*, a curious light-emitting symbiotic bacterium found in the Hawaiian bobtail squid. The creature uses the luminescent properties of the bacteria to evade predators in the clear water where it feeds. Although the squid are good hunters, they are preyed upon by large, nocturnal predators. Seen from below, the dark squid would ordinarily be framed against the moonlight, making an easy target. But the bottom (ventral) side of the squid contains a light organ containing *V. fischeri* surrounded by an ink sac that operates much like a camera's diaphragm. Light from the bacteria, plus a reflector, is radiated downward in a way that counters the moonlight, putting the squid in a "stealth mode." When the bacteria get hungry, they secrete the cholera-like toxin, which doesn't *sicken* the squid but rather *informs* it—they need food, which the squid then provides.

Indeed, one evolutionist suggested, "Maybe when we've been studying cholera pathogenesis we've been studying an aspect of a normal conversation that's gone wrong."[2] Creation scientists suggest this may be a result of the Curse. The example above indicates that biological compounds and organisms are not evil in themselves, but have different functions depending on the perspective.

Non-cellular viruses have the protein-DNA coding design showing they were created. Dr. Gary Parker suggests a non-Darwinian explanation for the originally created viruses:

> It seems to me that in God's originally perfect creation, the interlocking of docking and receptor proteins was designed to allow viruses to insert their DNA (or RNA) into only those cells in which gene transfer would be beneficial. In properly programmed receptor cells, some viruses can splice their DNA into the cell's genome, and the added (pre-existent, pre-programmed!) genetic information multiplies along with the cell....Perhaps God, the ultimate Genetic Engineer, designed viruses as gene carriers, especially for bacteria.[3]

Parasitism

A parasite is a type of animal (or plant) that lives together in close, non-mutual association with another, usually larger animal (or person) called the host. The word parasite comes from the Greek word meaning a person who eats at another's table. For example, malaria parasites are single-cell animals that live in the liver and red blood cells of a victim after the person is bitten by an infected mosquito. The tiny parasites eat the red pigment in the blood cells, reproduce, and are shielded from the person's immune system. Well over 650 million people are currently infected, with hundreds of thousands dying yearly.

Parasites may have been free-living in the environment as complete animals that became parasitic after the Fall and Curse. Their complexity as to how they evade our immune system, as well as their incredible life cycles, shows God's creative hand.

The evolutionary community knows very little regarding parasite origin, evolution, or their complex biology. "Complex life cycles remain one of the most baffling features of parasites, and there is still much to be learned about their evolution."[4] Creationists maintain evolutionists will never come to a full knowledge regarding parasites because they begin with a faulty premise—their supposed evolution.

Evolutionists ignore Genesis 1–3, so they ignore God's role in creation and the corruption of it due to sin. It is a given that parasites today such as malaria, along with genetic mutations, were not part of God's very good creation. At the Curse, could God have allowed beneficent structures in creatures that were non-parasitic to deteriorate into the devastating parasites we have today (including weeds, poisons, and pathogens)?

Creation scientists have some intriguing ideas regarding the origin of parasites from a biblical context. Could parasites (post-Fall) such as the malaria organism be slight genetic variations of non-parasite ancestors (pre-Fall)? After Adam sinned, God cursed the animals possibly by design modification. Genesis 3:14 says that God told the serpent he is cursed above all cattle and above every beast of the field, the implication being that these animals were cursed as well, though to a reduced extent. God did this with plants (thorns and thistles) so that they now cause pain. The vector of malaria—the female mosquito—has needle-like structures (stylets) specifically designed to allow it to obtain a blood meal. God may have adjusted the design of creatures such as the mosquito at the time of the Curse to allow it to feed off of other creatures. The originally created malaria parasite itself seemed to have a photosynthetic capability (using sunlight to make food). Conceivably, at the time of the Fall the group lost this complex food production capacity and became parasitic.

The biblical perspective is that parasites as well as pathogens were possibly created as neutral or even beneficial, but became destructive. Because of sin, there was an easing of biological controls that would have kept them beneficial. Genetic mistakes (mutations) might have contributed to parasites and the suffering they cause. Creation zoologists do not have all the answers regarding parasite origin and their interesting, convoluted life cycles. However, we use *a priori* creation thinking to ask (or hypothesize) what the origin and advantage of, for example, parasite life cycles might be. Some creation zoologists suggest free-living creatures (i.e., non-parasitic) became parasitic after the Fall. This is hardly far-fetched. As one evolutionist stated, "Parasitic species have retained some morphological resemblance with their free-living counterparts."[5] The step to a parasitic mode after the Fall could have been a small one: "In fact, free-living species could become parasitic without substantial anatomical or physiological changes."[6]

Another concept to consider is that parasites may have had a beneficial function prior to the Fall (exaptation). One evolutionist stated:

> Parasitism usually implies that some harm is done to the host, but this interpretation must be qualified. Effects on the host range from almost none to severe illness and eventual death, but even where such obvious immediate harm accrues to the individual host it does not follow that the relationship is harmful to the host species in the long term.[7]

If the relationship may not have been harmful to the host in the long run, then perhaps this may point to a time prior to the Fall when there may have been commensalism (one party gains some benefit) or mutualism (both parties benefit, e.g., lichens).

Those who ignore Genesis 1 and 3 cannot understand the nature of disease and parasites.

Although parasites still show God's glory, before the Fall they were evidently a complete, non-parasitic animal. Many parasites today are little more than protoplasmic bags of reproductive structures with an attachment (hooks or suckers) on one end. It has been suggested they have lost much of their genetic information as a result of the Curse.

Creation scientists have an explanation for parasites based on the written record of One who was there. Parasites are mostly ugly reminders that the law of sin and death (the Curse) is operating today. Death is God's enemy, but death is doomed. As fallen creatures, we see parasites as a reminder of how today's world is still "good yet groaning" as we await the ultimate redemption of creation promised in Romans 8:20-22.

Conclusion

The Curse is the key to understanding the presence of disease and death in today's world. It is man, not God, who is to blame for sin and death. To say that God is the author of death and suffering is to say He either does not care to solve this dilemma, He is not powerful enough to do so, or that He doesn't exist at all. The Bible, however, teaches that natural evil and physical death came into existence only after the Fall. One should remember that the design came first, and disease and devastation are an example of a breakdown of these ingenious and created systems. Yes, there are details that require further research, but the model of creation, the Fall, and the Curse is superior to the strange science of Darwinism.

The Curse answers the accusation by secularists that a loving God could not have created the world we see today. It was God, however, who provided a means of total forgiveness in the sinful world into which man is born. Jesus Christ made the blood atonement for our sins for those who put their trust in Him, promoting them from a world groaning with sin to eternity with Him (Luke 23:43). Christians await the ultimate redemption of creation that is promised in Romans 8:20-22, when He will wipe away every tear (Revelation 21:4).

Notes

1. Darwin, C. 1964. *On the Origin of Species.* Cambridge, MA: Harvard University Press, 490.

2. University of Wisconsin-Madison biologist Margaret McFall-Ngai, quoted in Weird Wonders of Biology. The Why? Files. Posted on whyfiles.org December 29, 2011.

3. Parker, G. 2006. *Creation: Facts of Life.* Green Forest, AR: Master Books, 140.

4. Poulin, R. 2006. *Evolutionary Ecology of Parasites*, 2nd ed. Princeton, NJ: Princeton University Press, 40.

5. Ibid, 13.

6. Miller, S. and J. Harley. 2010. *Zoology*, 8th ed. New York: McGraw Hill, 226.

7. Allaby, M. 2009. *Oxford Dictionary of Zoology.* New York: Oxford University Press, 459.

23

CAIN, HIS WIFE, AND THE ORIGIN OF RACES

Frank Sherwin, M.A.

As Christians, our thinking about the past is based on the events listed in the critical opening chapters of Genesis—the book of beginnings. Scripture presents us with the proper interpretation of the past, versus the fictitious view of evolution and uniformity that rejects the biblical record. The origin of people groups and nations are critical events, so we must get it right.

One of the premier questions the materialist often asks the Christian is, "Who was Cain's wife?" This trivial question was presented in the movie *Inherit the Wind*, a fictionalized portrayal of the Scopes "Monkey" Trial with Spencer Tracy playing Henry Drummond, a character patterned after the infamous Chicago lawyer Clarence Darrow. A frustrated Matthew Harrison Brady (based on William Jennings Bryan and played by Fredric March) was not surprisingly unable to answer Drummond's bullying query. At the end of the film, secular reason prevailed and audiences through the decades have been left with the impression that the Bible had—and has—no answer, or that it supports immorality by condoning incest.

This is a typical "heads I win, tails you lose" argument supposedly with no decent possible answer. So how is a Christian to respond to this challenge?

We should start "in the beginning." Eve was the first woman, the mother of all peoples, and there were no other women at the start of creation. Genesis 3:20 states, "And Adam called his wife's name Eve, because she was the mother of all living." They were commanded by God to "be fruitful and multiply" (Genesis 1:28), so it is not beyond reason to suppose they had many children—especially when Adam lived for 930 years, and Eve for a presumably similar period. Indeed, the Jewish historian Josephus said, "The number of Adam's children, as says the old tradition, was thirty-three sons and twen-

167

ty-three daughters."

Cain was Eve and Adam's first child (Genesis 4:1), and he had two recorded brothers, Abel and Seth. It should be noted that Adam and Eve also had other offspring. Genesis 5:4 says, "After he begot Seth, the days of Adam were eight hundred years; and he had sons and daughters." So who was Cain's wife? She was a descendant of Adam/man—or, Cain's sister.

Skeptics maintain there must have been people other than Adam and Eve, because Cain went to the land of Nod after killing Abel. But the Bible makes it clear there was only one man and one woman from whom came all other human beings. In the pre-Flood world, women and men lived to be hundreds of years old and populations grew rapidly. Cain had enough time to marry his sister (or a niece perhaps), move to Nod, and build a city for his own descendants and others. Originally, there was nothing wrong with marriage between sister and brother. Indeed, how else was the world going to be populated except by these unions? God did not condemn the marriage of Abraham and his half-sister, although this was later forbidden in the Levitical laws.

Today, interbreeding is dangerous because of the genetic load or genetic burden that a species carries.[1] Purebred dogs, for example, always carry a hidden genetic defect (deafness, hip dysplasia, and other imperfections) that often manifests itself physically (called "phenotypic expression"). In the days of Adam and Eve, there were virtually no mutations built up, and intermarrying could occur without genetic harm. Indeed, in that first generation all marriages had to be brother/sister marriages. As the centuries progressed, mutations began to accumulate in the human genome. Therefore God, in His infinite wisdom, prohibited incest, as we read in the Mosaic laws (Leviticus 18–20). For example, "none of you shall approach anyone who is near of kin to him" (Leviticus 18:6). These new laws were introduced by God for our sake, because of our sin. Today, the more closely related two people are, the greater the chances that they will have the same mutation on the same chromosome. With a brother/sister union—even first cousins—the offspring would inherit the two gene sets (for example, Aa in the sperm and Bb from the egg) and very likely phenotypically express one or more of the mutations. Today, people are now subject to at least 5,000 mutational conditions that our first parents and their offspring didn't encounter. It is no wonder God implemented the Levitical laws.

The Origin of People-Groups

> And He has made from one blood every nation of men to dwell on all the face of the earth, and has determined their preappointed times and the boundaries of their dwellings. (Acts 17:26)

Genesis 1–11 takes the reader through creation, the Curse, and the global Flood (catastrophe) of Noah's day. We will never comprehend human origins, migrations, genetics, or languages without considering Babel. "From there the Lord scatter them abroad over the face of all the earth" (Genesis 11:9). The events at Babel give us the key to understanding the origin of modern nations and peoples. We are descended from those confused and scattered at Babel after the Flood. Babel was the breakup of the languages and the dispersion of families into all parts of the world.

After the Flood, God instructed Noah and his family (eight people in all) to "be fruitful and multiply, and fill the earth" (Genesis 9:1). Instead, in the years to follow their descendants assembled at Babel under the leadership of a defiant Nimrod, who no doubt was under demonic influence.

They proceeded to build a tower "lest we be scattered abroad over the face of the whole earth" (Genesis 11:4), and it became an astrological worship center to praise the creation rather than the Creator (Romans 1). Except for a faithful remnant (e.g., Noah, Shem), the disobedient populace had united in rebellion against God.

But God separated their one language into many, preventing their communication (and therefore cooperation). This confusion of language caused them to disperse throughout the earth (Genesis 11:6), as He had commanded earlier (Genesis 9:1).

In the Table of Nations (Genesis 10), we discover a documentation of 70 nations/family groups migrating to fill the earth after Babel. Not surprisingly, linguists have found the number of separate language groups is basically the same as the 70 listed in Scripture. The Ice Age that extended for centuries after the Flood resulted in global changes such as severe climates in Europe, a lush Egypt, and a reduced sea level that allowed migration across the Siberia/Alaska land bridge, as well as others. Genesis 13–50 mentions physical locales, towns, and cities that have been verified through the centuries by archaeology, confirming these basic details and identifying major locations and people groups. Sadly, history has been rife with conquests of uninhabited lands and wars between tribes who spoke different tongues.

Regardless, since the dispersion at Babel we have seen only variation within the created kind of people. If this is true, then there are no separate races, but only one race—the human race (as we read in Acts 17:26). Creationists would call the different groups of people we see throughout the world not "races," but people groups. We are all humans, but quite variable in function and form.

One creation scientist has called this the law of conservation of genetic variability. The human genome is composed of at least six billion nucleotides (a nucleotide is the functional unit of DNA composed of a sugar molecule, a phosphate molecule, and a nitrogenous base). Evolutionist Francisco Ayala has said the human genome is 6.7 percent heterozygous (different alleles at a specific gene locus or location) for a variety of the genes.[2] Translated, this means that of every hundred genes, six or seven pairs of genes for a given trait differ, such as eye color or the ability to roll the tongue. So, a human couple with this kind of variety can—according to Ayala—produce ten to the 2,017th power children that would be unique before producing an identical twin. How big is that number? Physicists estimate there are "only" ten to the 80th power atoms in the universe. God has created us with an amazing variation potential.

Take skin color, for example. Physically and genetically, we find people of the world with different skin colors and shades. In fact, we all have the same pigments or skin-coloring agents—just different shades or combinations of them. This is due to cells called melanocytes located in the lower epidermis (skin) that produce melanin (dark pigment) granules. Melanin is injected by the melanocytes into adjacent cells. The question is, how long would it take to get all the skin color variation we see in people today? The answer is—a single generation. In 2006, the mother of a medium-dark-skinned couple produced fraternal twins; one was quite light, while the other was quite dark. How could this be?

Geneticists have found that four to six genes (DNA) control the type and amount of melanin formed (melanin also gives us our different eye colors). Although Scripture doesn't say, the Punnet Square used in basic genetics indicates the skin color of Adam and Eve was very probably a middle-brown shade (AaBb). Each parent having these four alleles (different sequences of genetic material) could produce offspring from very dark (AABB) to very light (aabb) in just one generation due to crossing over of chromosomes and gene segregation. As people break up into isolated groups, some groups would develop limited variability—only dark (many parts of Africa), only medium (such as Orientals, Polynesians, and Native Americans), or only light (much of the Scandinavian population). This variation of skin color—as well as variation in height and all other forms of human function and form—has been built into humans by God starting with our first parents. Variation within the created kind is consistent with what we observe—not only with people since Babel, but also in plants and animals.

To conclude, the Christian should be equipped with biblical knowledge to "give a defense to everyone who asks you a reason for the hope that is in you, with meekness and fear" (1 Peter 3:15), whether it concerns Cain's wife, the origin of people groups, the Genesis Flood, or the resurrection of our Lord.

Notes

1. Sanford, J. C. 2008. *Genetic Entropy and the Mystery of the Genome.* Waterloo, NY: FMS Publications.
2. Ayala, F. 1978. The Mechanisms of Evolution. *Scientific American.* 239 (3): 56-69.

24

APE-MAN OR IMAGE OF GOD?

Jeffrey Tomkins, Ph.D.

A key part of evolutionary dogma is the "tree of life" paradigm, the claim that all creatures are descended from an original single-cell organism (see chapter 20 for reasons this paradigm is invalid). An important part of the evolutionary story is that humans and chimps shared a hypothetical common ancestor that lived three to six million years ago. (Of course, no fossil evidence exists for this hypothetical ancestor.) Since three to six million years is a relatively short time in the evolutionary story, evolutionists believe that the human and chimp genomes should have changed very little since humans and chimps "branched off" from this supposed ancestor. Evolutionists claim that humans and chimps are 98 to 99 percent genetically identical, and that this similarity is support for an evolutionary origin of man. However, as we will show, this similarity is not as great as is frequently claimed.

In 2004, it was announced that the human genome had been nearly completely sequenced, with just a few remaining areas that could not be finished because of limitations in DNA sequencing and computational technologies.[1] A less-complete "draft sequence" of the chimpanzee genome was announced in 2005.[2] Evolutionists quickly compared this draft sequence of the chimpanzee genome to the human genome, hoping that the comparison would provide clear-cut DNA similarity evidence for an ape-human common ancestry. The supposed similarity claimed in this report is frequently cited as proof of man's evolutionary origins, but a more objective analysis of this research, in addition to a more detailed analysis of other reports, tells a different story, one that is less supportive of evolution than scientists seem willing to admit.

One of the main problems with comparative analyses between human and chimp DNA is that sizeable portions of non-similar sequences are typically omitted, markedly enhancing the reported similarity data. Another problem is that researchers pre-select human and chimp DNA sequences that are already known to be quite similar, while non-similar DNA is omitted. As a result, estimates of similarity are inflated because of this "cherry-picking" of the data. An inflated human-chimp DNA similarity is then reported to the general public, bolstering the case for human evolution. Since most people are not equipped to investigate the details of DNA analysis, these claims go largely unchallenged. Thus, the claim that human DNA is 98 to 99 percent similar to chimpanzee DNA is very misleading because it is based upon biased data.

One of the best illustrations of biased use of the data is the 2005 research report describing the chimp genome sequence; this is one of the most cited research papers for the claim of nearly identical human-chimp DNA.[2] First, it should be noted that the chimp genome was sequenced to a much less stringent level than was the human genome, and when completed, it consisted of a large set of small un-oriented, random DNA fragments.[3] When these DNA fragments were assembled into properly ordered sections representing various regions of chimp chromosomes, the human genome was used as a guide or framework to anchor and orient the chimp sequence. In addition, the European genomics laboratory (ENSEMBL.org) where chimp DNA sequence was assembled and annotated openly admitted that they added human gene sequences to the chimp genome based on evolutionary assumptions.[3] Therefore, another reason that the chimp genome bears similarity to the human genome is because human DNA was added to the chimp DNA! The Darwinian assumption of a supposed ape-to-human transition was used to assemble, construct, and annotate the otherwise random chunks of chimp DNA sequence, making it appear more similar to human DNA than it really is.

The 2005 chimp genome publication largely focused on various types of hypothetical evolutionary analyses and only reported DNA similarity on highly filtered, cherry-picked data, thus avoiding the issue of genome-wide DNA similarity with human. However, one can determine a very conservative figure for overall genome similarity between humans and chimp by including concurrent information from the human genome project. In regard to the overall DNA alignment (sequence comparison), the authors give the following statistics.

> Best reciprocal nucleotide-level alignments of the chimpanzee and human genomes cover ~2.4 gigabases (Gb) of high-quality sequence.[2]

And:

> The indel [insertions and deletions of bases] differences between the genomes thus total ~90 Mb. This difference corresponds to ~3% of both genomes and dwarfs the 1.23% difference resulting from nucleotide substitutions.[2]

It is important to note that the human-chimp DNA alignments did *not* include segments in regions called "low complexity sequences" that are typically omitted by the computer algorithm that does the comparison (using a function called "sequence masking"). These omitted "masked" segments contain repetitive DNA regions, as well as many important sequences that are critical for the control of gene function. The fact that these segments were excluded from the comparison is important to consider. For the chimp sequence that actually *did* align, the data for base substitutions and indels (insertions and deletions) indicates 95.8 percent similarity, a figure that excludes the masked regions.

As of 2005, the human genome was estimated to be virtually (99 percent) complete at 2.85 billion bases (2.85 Gb) of DNA. All of this information taken together makes it possible to estimate the genome-wide similarity between human and chimp DNA. The 95.8 percent of the 2.4 Gb of chimp DNA that actually aligned with the human genome is 2.3 Gb ($0.958 \times 2.4 = 2.3$). When we use this estimate of 2.3 Gb of chimp DNA that is similar to the 2.85 Gb of human DNA, we get an overall similarity of 81 percent ($2.2/2.85 \times 100\% = 81\%$). Given the fact that the so-called "similar" chimp DNA excluded large amounts of DNA that were kicked out by the alignment algorithm, the percent similarity is probably much lower. Nevertheless, 81 percent is certainly a much lower number than the 98 to 99 percent similarity touted by evolutionists and the popular press.

It is interesting that, despite the availability of genomic DNA sequences, no unbiased genome-wide similarity studies were actually performed until a study published in 2013 that will be mentioned at the end of this chapter. Its results will surprise you.

In evolutionary research, researchers only compare selected *similar* regions of the human and chimp genomes, as well as sets of genes that both organisms share. Keep in mind that these studies are biased because they use pre-selected data that already show high levels of similarity. There are large blocks of human and chimp DNA sequences that are not directly comparable because these regions of DNA are present in one organism and absent in the other. Furthermore, DNA comparison algorithms will exclude sequences from the analysis if the similarity drops below the threshold set by the algorithm. Many default settings of alignment algorithms will only keep sequences that are highly similar and discard everything else (e.g., >95 percent base identity).

Furthermore, scientists often only use the protein-coding parts of the genome for comparison. This effectively excludes more than 95 percent of the genome from the comparison. Most of the DNA sequence in the genome does not code for protein, but rather for gene and genome regulation, similar to the way instructions in a recipe specify what to do with the raw ingredients. This regulatory genetic information is stored in "non-coding regions" that are essential for the proper functioning of all cells, ensuring that the right genes are turned on or off at the right time in concert with other genes. When these non-coding regions of the genome, which are often much larger in size, are included in human and chimp similarity studies, the reported similarities can drop markedly and will vary widely according to the types of genomic areas being compared.

When comparing genes between different organisms, it is important to note that variants of the same protein can have different functions that can perform different tasks in different tissues. Evolutionary assumptions have driven the biased, over-simplified approach of protein-based sequence comparisons, providing few answers as to why humans and chimps are obviously so different.

In 2011, a research study was published describing a number of genome-wide DNA comparison experiments using chimp sequences known to be similar in humans.[4] The DNA similarities that were obtained for just the aligned regions varied between 86 to 89 percent. Remember that the computer algorithm excluded large amounts of DNA data when the alignment of the sequence became too non-similar and stopped, so these percentages would be even lower if the whole amount of chimp sequence being analyzed were accounted for. Surprisingly, the DNA similarity obtained for the similar aligned segments was a full 10 to 12 percent lower than the commonly claimed figure of 98 to 99 percent. Another important discovery from this study showed that on average, chimp DNA similarity to human DNA only occurs in stretches of DNA of fewer than about 700 bases.

In 2013, a comprehensive chromosome-by-chromosome comparison study was performed in which chimp DNA was compared to human using optimized sequence slices of fewer than 700 bases to overcome the limitations of the alignment algorithm.[5] This allowed for an unbiased, comprehensive, genome-wide alignment between chimps and humans to be obtained for the first time. In this study, the chimp chromosomes were digitally chopped into small pieces and then compared to their human chromosomal counterparts. This was done in multiple experiments for each chromosome until the optimal amount of chimp DNA was aligned. Excluding the Y-chromosome (which was very non-similar), the chimp chromosomes were on average between 66 and 76 percent similar to human, depending on the chromosome. Surprisingly, the chimp genome on average overall was only found to be 70 percent similar.

Current research in a field called functional genomics is confirming that much of what makes humans biologically unique (compared to chimps and other animals) is also explained by the way genes are controlled and regulated within the genome. Several studies within the past few years are demonstrating clear differences in individual gene and gene network expression patterns between humans and chimps in regard to a wide number of traits.[6,7] Of course, the largest differences are observed in regard to brain function, dexterity, speech, and other traits with strong cognitive components. To make the genetic landscape even more complicated, a number of recent studies are also confirming that most of the human genome is pervasively transcriptionally active and functional.[8] Keep in mind that not so long ago, scientists thought that only 3 to 5 percent of the genome that contained the protein coding regions was functional; the rest was considered "junk DNA."

So what is an appropriate response to the assertion that 98 to 99 percent similarity exists between human and chimp DNA, and thus proves human evolution? First, these numbers are way too high—the DNA similarity between just the regions that have similarity is 86 to 89 percent. Overall, the chimpanzee genome is only 70 percent similar to human. Second, we need to understand that what truly makes organisms unique is not just the small amount of protein coding sequence, but the huge amount of regulatory information in the genome. For the interested reader, a number of recent technical reviews have been published on this subject.[3, 9,10,11]

Notes

1. International Human Genome Sequencing Consortium. 2004. Finishing the euchromatic sequence of the

human genome. *Nature.* 431 (7011): 931-945.

2. The Chimpanzee Sequencing and Analysis Consortium. 2005. Initial sequence of the chimpanzee genome and comparison with the human genome. *Nature.* 437 (7055): 69-87.

3. Tomkins, J. 2011. How genomes are sequenced and why it matters: implications for studies in comparative genomics of humans and chimpanzees. *Answers Research Journal.* 4: 81-88.

4. Tomkins, J. 2011. Genome-Wide DNA Alignment Similarity (Identity) for 40,000 Chimpanzee DNA Sequences Queried against the Human Genome is 86 - 89%. *Answers Research Journal.* 4: 233-241;Calarco, J. et al. 2007. Global analysis of alternative splicing differences between humans and chimpanzees. *Genes & Development.* 21: 2963-2975.

5. Tomkins, J. 2013. Comprehensive Analysis of Chimpanzee and Human Chromosomes Reveals Average DNA Similarity of 70%. *Answers Research Journal.* 6: 63-69.

6. Nowick, K. et al. 2009. Differences in human and chimpanzee gene expression patterns define an evolving network of transcription factors in brain. *Proceedings of the National Academy of Sciences.* 106: 22358–22363.

7. Babbitt, C. C. et al. 2010. Both Noncoding and Protein-Coding RNAs Contribute to Gene Expression Evolution in the Primate Brain. *Genome Biology and Evolution.* 2010: 67-79.

8. The ENCODE Project Consortium. 2012. An Integrated Encyclopedia of DNA Elements in the Human Genome. *Nature.* 489 (7414): 57-74.

9. Tomkins, J. 2011. Response to Comments on "How Genomes are Sequenced and Why it Matters: Implications for Studies in Comparative Genomics of Humans and Chimpanzees." *Answers Research Journal.* 4: 161-162.

10. Bergman, J. and J. Tomkins. 2012. Is the Human Genome Nearly Identical to Chimpanzee? A Reassessment of the Literature. *Journal of Creation.* 26: 54-60.

11. Tomkins, J. and J. Bergman. 2012. Genomic monkey business—estimates of nearly identical human-chimp DNA similarity re-evaluated using omitted data. *Journal of Creation.* 26: 94-100.

25

CHROMOSOME 2: FUSION OR NOT?

Jeffrey Tomkins, Ph.D.

One of the leading arguments for humans supposedly having evolved from apes is the "chromosome 2 fusion model."[1] This hypothetical idea proposes that the end-to-end fusion of two small ape-like chromosomes produced human chromosome 2, which supposedly explains the difference in chromosome numbers between humans and great apes—humans have 46 chromosomes, while some types of apes (chimps, gorillas, and orangutans) have 48. See Figure 1 for a visual description of the fusion model.

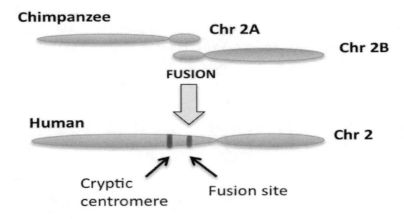

Figure 1. Depiction of a hypothetical scenario in which chimpanzee chromosomes 2A and 2B fuse to form human chromosome 2. The two sites showing where the fusion supposedly occurred and an inactivated cryptic centromere are depicted.

The purported site of proof for the fusion event is located on human chromosome 2. However, one of the primary problems with the so-called fusion site is that we now know that it is actually located in the middle of a functional gene called DDX11L2.[2,3] Functional genes cannot be created through inverted chromosomal fusions. Most importantly, the DDX11L2 gene and all the genes surrounding it in a 615,000-base window are not found on the end regions of the small arms of chimpanzee chromosomes 2A and 2B, the hypothesized sources of the fusion event.[2] Scientists call this a lack of synteny, meaning there is no genetic correspondence in this region between humans and chimps. All of this makes perfect sense, because the DNA sequence at the fusion site has a number of other serious problems that reduce its validity as a product of a real fusion event between two chromosomes. These issues will be discussed in turn below.

To understand the DNA sequence concepts surrounding the fusion model, it is important to understand what the ends of chromosomes look like. At the ends of all chromosomes are special DNA sequence end-caps called *telomeres*. In humans and other mammals, telomeres normally consist of thousands of repeats of the six-base sequence TTAGGG. Typical human telomeres contain 1,700 to 2,500 of these six-base repeats in perfect tandem.[4,5]

So the big question is, does the hypothetical fusion site on chromosome 2 have the expected characteristics of an end-to-end fusion of two chromosomes? First, it should be noted that documented chromosome fusions in living mammals do not involve telomere-telomere fusions, but instead are composed of a type of sequence called satellite DNA (satDNA) in one of two fusion scenarios: (1) satDNA-satDNA or (2) satDNA-telomere sequence.[6] Thus, the proposed evolutionary fusion of human chromosome 2 is not of the type that we actually observe happening in rare occurrences in nature.

One of the major issues surrounding the DNA sequence at the fusion site is that it does not clearly represent fused telomeres. Even if you assume an evolutionary timeline of up to six million years since the fusion occurred, the data do not match up with what is known about the rates of mutation in DNA. Secular evolutionary scientists have come to these conclusions in their research.[7]

Perhaps one of the most revealing reports was the first detailed DNA sequence analysis of the fusion region by evolutionary geneticists, in which they noted that the fusion DNA sequence was extremely "degenerate" (ambiguous or degraded) given its hypothetical recent evolutionary origin. Keep in mind that six million years is very little time on the evolutionary scale. The research paper emphasized this startling admission by stating the "head-to-head arrays of repeats at the fusion site have *degenerated significantly* from the near perfect arrays of (TTAGGG)$_n$ found at telomeres," and "if the fusion occurred within the telomeric repeat arrays less than ~6 Ma, *why are the arrays at the fusion site so degenerate?*" (emphasis added).[7]

In another DNA sequence analysis of the fusion site in 2011, researchers note that the hypothetical fusion site is located in an area of the human genome with low levels of recombination, because it is near a centromere.[8] This means that mutation rates in the area of the fusion site are extremely low, and that if a fusion did occur, very little degeneration should be apparent.

When we examine the fusion site in detail, it becomes apparent that the cluster of sequences that most closely resemble a fusion-like region is only about 798 bases in size.[7,8] This is an unexpectedly small segment of DNA compared to what should be present if a telomere-to-telomere fusion actually occurred in the ancient past. Even if two very small-size telomeres fused, a region of about 10,000 bases in size should be present. If two larger-size telomeres fused, the fusion site should be about 30,000 bases in size. Nevertheless, 798 bases is an extremely small signature for such an event.

In addition to being very small in size, it is very "degenerate" or ambiguous.[7,8] This means that very few intact telomere sequences actually exist in this small, 798-base chunk of DNA. The small number of randomly interspersed telomere sequences, both forward (TTAGGG) and reverse (CCCTAA), found on both sides of the purported fusion site is a serious problem for evolutionists. On the left side of the fusion site, there are only 10 intact telomere repeats and only one case where they are actually in tandem. On the right side of the fusion site, there are only 40 intact reverse complement telomeres and 12 in tandem. Overall DNA similarity of this degenerate fusion sequence compared to a hypothetical pristine telomere-telomere fusion of about 800 bases is only 72 percent.

Another very interesting fact about the 798-base core fusion sequence is that it is not unique to the purported fusion site. Portions of it contain significant levels of similarity to other areas throughout the human genome, including many internal regions that are not near telomeres.[8] Interestingly, researchers are now reporting that internally located telomere-like sequences in the middle of chromosomes are quite common in the human genome and may serve some functional purpose, including the regulation of gene expression.[9,10]

As mentioned earlier, the purported fusion site is located inside an important RNA helicase regulatory gene called DDX11L2 and appears to be highly functional, based on recent data shown at the UCSC Genome Browser website (genome.ucsc.edu). Specifically, the fusion site sequence has at least three different transcription factor proteins that bind to it, along with epigenetic profiles (DNA and histone modifications) showing that it is involved in active gene function.

The fusion-like sequence is actually located inside the first intron (non-coding section) of the gene and may interact with another set of DNA binding sites located in front of the gene's first exon (coding region). The DDX11L2 gene appears to be under complex control as it produces several different RNA transcript variants. These are classified as regulatory long non-coding RNAs (lncRNA) and appear to be part of a family of DDX11L genes in the human genome called RNA helicases.[11]

If a supposed fusion of two smaller chromosomes actually occurred, you would immediately also have two centromeres in the newly formed chimeric chromosome, one from each of the two parent chromosomes. (See Figure 1). A centromere is a specialized section of DNA located in the center part of a chromosome that serves as an attachment point for the cell machinery that moves the chromosomes around during cell replication (mitosis). You can only have one functional centromere per chromosome. In the case of a fusion, this would instantly create an unstable situation leading to the destruction of the cell. According to the evolutionary model, one of the two centromeres in the newly fused chromosome was somehow silenced and then degenerated over time.

To understand the centromere issue surrounding the fusion model, it is important to know that centromeres are composed of a type of DNA sequence called alphoid DNA, a clearly recognizable DNA sequence pattern about 171 bases in length.[12] Alphoid DNA is actually found all over the human genome, but it is important to understand that there are different types (variants) of alphoid DNA sequence, each with different functions in the genome.

Research has shown that the alphoid DNA at the fusion site is not the same type as that which is found at actual functional human centromeres.[8] The alphoid sequences at the putative cryptic centromere site are very diverse and form three separate sub-groups. In fact, the overall patterns of the alphoid sequence sub-members are not even similar to the patterns found in functional human centromeres.

Complicating matters further for the evolution fusion model is the fact that alphoid sequences differ markedly between humans and apes.[8,11] In fact, when the human alphoid DNA sequences at the supposed degenerate ancient centromere site are compared to the chimp genome, not a single similar positive match is obtained.[8] Thus, not only is the so-called fossil centromere sequence dissimilar to functional human centromeres, it has no sequence correspondence to the chimp genome either.

Conclusion: The Evidence Indicates a Lack of Fusion

Research has shown that the DNA sequence of the purported chromosome 2 fusion site is too ambiguous and small in size to determine a fusion event. In fact, recent genomic discoveries clearly show that the 798-base fusion-like region is a key regulatory feature inside the DDX11L2 gene. Complex genes like this do not form from random chromosome fusions. In addition, all of the genes within a 615,000-base region surrounding the purported fusion site have no chromosomal correspondence (synteny) with chimpanzee in the areas from which the fusion supposedly originated. All of these important facts strongly indicate that the so-called fusion site is not the result of a fusion at all.

Besides the discredited evidence for a fusion site, the DNA sequence signature for a purported fossil centromere is also highly questionable. The alphoid sequences in this region are not similar to known functional human centromere sequences and share no correspondence with alphoid sequences in chimpanzee.

In short, the chromosome 2 fusion model should no longer be used as support of an evolutionary relationship between humans and chimps. Evidence from modern genomics indicates that the landscape and function of the DNA sequence in these areas of the genome on chromosome 2 are unique to humans and not derived from an ancestral fusion of two ape chromosomes.

Notes

1. Yunis, J. J. and O. Prakash. 1982. The origin of man: A chromosomal pictorial legacy. *Science*. 215 (4539): 1525-1530.

2. Fan, Y. et al. 2002. Gene content and function of the ancestral chromosome fusion site in human chromosome 2q13-2q14.1 and paralogous regions. *Genome Research*. 12 (11): 1663-1672.

3. Kuhn, R. M. et al. 2013. The UCSC genome browser and associated tools. *Briefings in Bioinformatics*. 14 (2): 144-61.

4. Tomkins, J. P. and J. Bergman. 2011. Telomeres: implications for aging and evidence for intelligent design. *Journal of Creation*. 25 (1): 86-97.

5. Bergman, J. and J. Tomkins. 2011. The chromosome 2 fusion model of human evolution—part 1: re-evaluating the evidence. *Journal of Creation*. 25 (2): 106-110.

6. Adega, F. et al. 2009. Satellite DNA in the karyotype evolution of domestic animals—clinical considerations. *Cytogenetics and Genome Research*. 126 (1-2): 12-20.

7. Fan, Y. et al. 2002. Genomic structure and evolution of the ancestral chromosome fusion site in 2q13-2q14.1 and paralogous regions on other human chromosomes. *Genome Research*. 12 (11): 1651-1662.

8. Tomkins, J. and J. Bergman. 2011. The chromosome 2 fusion model of human evolution—part 2: re-analysis of the genomic data. *Journal of Creation*. 25 (2): 111-117.

9. Simonet, T. et al. 2011. The human TTAGGG repeat factors 1 and 2 bind to a subset of interstitial telomeric sequences and satellite repeats. *Cell Research*. 21 (7): 1028-1038.

10. Yang, D. 2011. Human telomeric proteins occupy selective interstitial sites. *Cell Research*. 21 (7): 1013-1027.

11. Costa, V. et al. 2009. DDX11L: a novel transcript family emerging from human subtelomeric regions. *BMC Genomics*. 10: 250.

12. Archidiacono, N. et al. 1995. Comparative mapping of human alphoid sequences in great apes using fluorescence in situ hybridization. *Genomics*. 25:477-484.

26

THE MYSTERY OF LIFE'S BEGINNING

Jeffrey Tomkins, Ph.D.

"The origin of life has not been seen in Earth's rock record and poor preservation of the earth's oldest rocks suggest that it will not be."[1]

The above statement made by evolutionary researchers deeply involved in the study of life's origins makes a key point: There is no fossil record of how life began. All evolutionary "origin of life" hypotheses are speculative stories that assume from the outset that naturalistic random processes were somehow responsible. As a result, one must keep in mind that this field of science is highly speculative and subjective.

The question of how life first arose on Earth is perhaps the greatest obstacle for the evolutionary paradigm. While the whole concept of biological evolution itself is full of serious problems, the origins of the first biomolecules and the first cell (not to mention the enormous amount of information contained within the cell) is a complete impossibility from a naturalistic perspective. In fact, without a plausible explanation as to the origin of the first cell, the whole evolutionary story collapses!

The hypothetical naturalistic formation of life out of the most basic molecules is called *abiogenesis* or *biogenesis*. This concept lies at the foundation of biological evolution, but it is often ignored by most evolutionists themselves. Because of its scientific impossibility, it represents the ultimate hurdle to evolution.

Early Earth Atmosphere Controversy

When judging the plausibility of abiogenesis models, one must consider the necessary conditions that could have allowed the formation of the first biomolecules needed for life: purines, pyrimidines, amino acids, sugars, and lipids. In living cells, these molecules are used to form large chains (polymers) and other important structures. These structures are protected within the confines of the cell from degradation by the atmosphere and solar radiation. Our current Earth atmosphere is about 21 percent oxygen by volume, and oxygen is destructive to biomolecules not safely enclosed inside a cell. The oxygen in the environment outside the cell rapidly degrades biomolecules through a process called oxidation (which is why our current atmosphere is called an *oxidizing* atmosphere).

Because oxidation rapidly degrades DNA, proteins, and membranes, some evolutionists have speculated that the early earth had an atmosphere with little or no oxygen (what is called a *reducing* atmosphere). They also believe that it must have been rich in nitrogen, hydrogen, and carbon monoxide in order to provide the basic molecules needed (amino acids, sugars, nucleotides). They believe this because our current atmosphere would have made life's origins impossible.

One big problem with this claim is that the geological data indicate that the earth's atmosphere has always been similar to what it is now (oxidizing), with significant levels of oxygen.[2,3] Geophysical research also shows that the biochemical precursors required by "origin of life" scenarios have never existed on Earth, or did so in levels that were far too low to allow abiogenesis to occur.[4,5,6]

To get around this problem, some have postulated that localized reducing environments may have been present around volcanic plumes.[7] However, the extreme temperatures and acidity in these environments would not be at all conducive to the formation of biomolecules. Evolutionists might take a little comfort in the fact that some "extremophile" microorganisms have recently been found to live in these environments, but these microorganisms contain highly specialized and unique cell systems that allow them to tolerate these extreme conditions. Therefore, they are not anything like the ancient simple cell prototypes that evolutionists believe existed.

Evolutionary researchers still have no plausible explanation for what sort of early Earth environment could have spawned the first hypothetical biomolecules. A highly prominent modern abiogenesis research leader, David Deamer, stated the current status of this highly significant, but largely unpublicized, problem in his 2011 book *First Life*.

> But someone from the outside world would be astonished by the lack of agreement among experts on plausible sites [for abiogen-

esis], which range all the way from vast sheets of ice occasionally melted by giant impacts, to "warm little ponds" first suggested by Charles Darwin, to hydrothermal vents in the deep ocean, and even to a kind of hot, mineral mud deep in Earth's crust.[8]

The First Biomolecules

Before the evolutionary process could even begin, a diverse array of basic molecules would have to be formed in some hypothetical primordial matrix or soup. These molecules would include various types of amino acids, purines, pyrimidines, sugars, and lipids. The spontaneous generation of these basic building blocks for life, in the correct forms and amounts needed, is itself a glaring impossibility. Arranging these basic molecules into larger polymer-based molecules containing coherent molecular information is also impossible! For the past 60 years, evolutionists have spent millions of dollars in research funding attempting to solve this problem, but the impossibility of evolutionary "origin of life" scenarios remains.

One of the first experiments claiming that naturalistic processes could synthesize the basic molecules of life was the famous 1953 experiment conducted by Stanley Miller and Harold Urey in which basic chemical gases (representative of those thought to be present in Earth's early atmosphere) were circulated through an elaborate device shown in Figure 1 and exposed to an electric discharge.[9] This early study is still held in high regard by the abiogenesis research community. In fact, archived samples of reactants from Miller's research project were rediscovered and analyzed, and the results were published in 2008 in the journal *Science*.[10]

In both Miller's original ex-

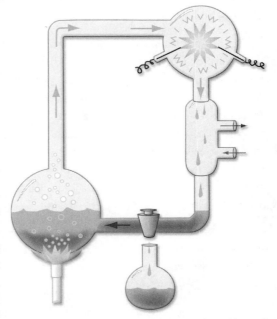

Figure 1. Apparatus used in Miller-Urey amino acid genesis experiments.

187

periment and subsequent similar experiments, methane, ammonia, hydrogen, and water vapor were circulated together in a device that exposed the gases to an electrical spark. In these experiments, the products of the reactions driven by the electrical discharge were filtered and collected in a trap before the products were cycled back through the system and destroyed by the same processes that created them (Figure 1).

The most recent results based on Miller's general design have done very little to help the abiogenesis model of origins. In what are considered to be the most successful versions of these experiments, scientists have been able to produce six of the 20 amino acids that are used in biological proteins. Nevertheless, there are a number of very serious problems with the results of these studies that completely negate their use as an argument for the naturalistic origins of life's first biomolecules.

First, the amino acids produced in these experiments are only the most simple of the amino acids. The more complex amino acids cannot be created using these techniques. But these more complex amino acids (which are central to all biological life) contain elaborate side chains or groups of molecules that can only be synthesized through the complex biochemical pathways found in *living* cells.

Second, the *chirality problem* prevents the few simple amino acids that *were* produced from being used in real-life proteins. Amino acids can exist in both right- and left-handed versions, just like your hands are similar in structure yet are unique because they are mirror images of each other. In Miller's system, both left- and right-handed amino acids were produced, but living cells only use left-handed amino acids to make proteins. Thus, living cells only synthesize left-handed amino acids. But in a hypothetical primordial soup, one would expect equal amounts of right- and left-handed amino acids to be produced. What "natural" process could separate the left- and right-handed amino acids from one another?

Third, the quantities of a number of the amino acids that were produced were far too dilute to be of any significant biological use, even if only left-handed ones were produced.

Besides failing to acknowledge that only a few simple amino acids were produced using these techniques, scientists generally fail to mention that the tar-like "goo" produced in the study also contained a variety of molecules that are actually harmful to cell life, such as hydrogen cyanide and formaldehyde.

Furthermore, Miller's system tended to destroy amino acids as fast as it could create them. This is why a trap was employed to filter off the products before they could be cycled back through the apparatus and destroyed.

The reason that Miller's work (and the similar work of other abiogenesis researchers) is often touted is because it represents one of the few instances where they can claim some minimal level of success—although in reality, the results have actually done very little to help the abiogenesis paradigm. In fact, these efforts do a better job of illustrating the futility of abiogenesis scenarios.

Unfortunately for evolutionists, the results of these experiments represent the *best* evidence to date. In fact, the evidence for the biogenesis of the other major basic molecules of cell life is essentially nonexistent. Evidence that the purines and pyrimidines needed for DNA and RNA could have spontaneously arisen apart from the cell's biochemistry is completely elusive. The same is true for the formation of sugar molecules like ribose or deoxyribose, which are also needed for DNA and RNA. The complex nature of cell membranes and the spontaneous origins of specific types of phospholipid molecules needed for their construction are also a complete mystery.

The Problem of Polymerization

Another key hurdle in biogenesis is the bonding together of long chains (polymerization) of base molecules according to specific information-based sequences. In living cells, amino acids and nucleotides are linked together via chemical bonds in a process using cell-based energy and complex enzyme (protein) complexes in specific ordered sequences in which the information is specified by genes in the cell's DNA.

In 1958, Sydney Fox published a set of experiments that attempted to provide a naturalistic explanation for the biological feature of polymerization. On the surface, the results appeared to add some credence to the notion that biopolymers could form spontaneously. Using starting solutions of pure left-handed biological amino acids, Fox was able to get amino acids to bind together in short, unordered globs by heating them to high temperatures.[11] The starting solutions of pure biologically active (left-handed) amino acids bore no resemblance whatsoever to anything produced by abiogenesis experiments like Miller's. Fox essentially baked the mixtures, driving out the water molecules and linking the amino acids together in crude aggregates. He also observed the coalescing of these structures into crude spheres when they were placed in certain solutions. Fox claimed, not just a primitive form of polymerization, but the beginning of early cells! Abiogenesis researchers now widely agree that this line of study was completely fruitless. However, Fox's ideas are still promoted in many educational circles as evidence for abiogenesis.

In 2004, a group of researchers investigated how carbonyl sulfide oxide, a simple chemical compound found in volcanic gases, can activate amino acids to form peptide bonds.[12] However, no more than a few molecules could be linked together, and polymers of any appreciable size could not be formed. At present, evolutionists still have no plausible explanation for how biomolecule polymerization for proteins or nucleic acids could have occurred under primitive naturalistic conditions.

An RNA World?

Given the enormous difficulties associated with claims that amino acids could have formed themselves into the primitive functional proteins that would have served as the first enzymes, some scientists have proposed that the first biomolecules were composed of RNA. This is because some RNA molecules have exhibited catalytic properties. Because RNA can contain both genetic information and, in some cases, simple enzymatic-like properties, evolutionists have proposed that RNAs may have been the first key biomolecules in biogenesis. However, this proposition actually has even more problems than the amino acid-based origins model.

RNA and DNA molecules are composed of five nucleobases, two sugars, and a phosphate. The nucleobases contain two different purines (adenine and guanine) and three different pyrimidines (cytosine, thymine, and uracil). Therefore, before an evolutionist even considers the possibility that RNA was the first major biomolecule, he must first explain the origin of these necessary nucleobases. Second, he must explain the origin of ribose and deoxyribose, the sugars that help link nucleobases. Third, he must explain the origin of phosphate biochemistry in biological systems, a relatively uncommon molecule that plays a variety of key roles in biomolecule chemistry. Fourth, he must answer the "recurring polymerization problem": How did the complex bonds involving sugars and phosphate form a connective backbone for the polymerization of purines and pyrimidines to take place? In fact, the random generation of these molecules, along with the immensely complicated problem of their polymerization, is an even larger hurdle than that which existed for proteins.

Even if RNA molecules somehow miraculously appeared, they are inherently very unstable molecules that are quickly degraded outside the cell or outside sterile, highly controlled lab conditions. Needless to say, such conditions would not have been present on the early earth in an evolutionary scenario! In the cases where RNA has exhibited enzymatic-like catalysis, they are isolated subprocesses of much larger complex cell systems. Furthermore, their activity is based on the complex two-dimensional folding patterns that they achieve based on highly specific predetermined genetic information transferred from DNA molecules. These catalytic RNAs and the system in which they are found to function are irreducibly complex and hardly represent vestiges of evolution. And as we shall describe later, this whole scenario presents a Catch-22 for the evolutionist. If the DNA molecule encodes the information for RNA and proteins, but RNA and proteins are required for the replication and usage of information stored in DNA, which came first?

Lipids and Cell Membranes

Because complex molecules are quickly degraded or destroyed outside the protective confines of a cell, evolutionists have argued that the biochemical reactions that supposedly led to life's origins must have taken place within some sort of protected and enclosed space. Therefore, many evolutionist researchers believe that primitive lipids self-assembled themselves into little semi-permeable, sphere-like structures that were able to capture and house the first biomolecules. This supposedly led to some sort of primitive replicating proto-cell that eventually evolved into the different forms of life that we see today.

The lipids that form real biological cells, however, are actually fairly complex structures containing different lipid chains combined with a phosphate to form unique polar structures called phospholipids. They are very different structures compared to the simple single-lipid chains supposedly involved in the first proto-cell. Cell membranes are also very complex assemblages that contain a wide variety of imbedded proteins and carbohydrate molecules for signaling and the import and export of a wide variety of compounds needed for cell function and metabolism. Thus, biogenesis researchers encounter many problems of required complexity for even the most primitive of cell membranes.

Summary

Instead of focusing on the impossibility of life's most basic molecules arising by chance random processes, most biogenesis research has instead focused on other "downstream" aspects of the problem, although these avenues of research are fraught with insurmountable problems as well.

Neither models of amino acid synthesis nor the ideas surrounding an RNA world have produced any convincing scientific scenarios for how life began. Of course, random naturalistic DNA or RNA synthesis in a primordial soup or matrix is even more problematic. Specifically, protein, DNA, and RNA present a complex three-way version of the ancient "chicken or the egg" conundrum. DNA encodes RNA transcripts, but both RNA transcript production and DNA replication are dependent on specific proteins. And proteins are themselves encoded in genes (DNA) and produced from RNA transcripts that are copied from genes in DNA. All three of these major biomolecules need each other in the cell system, so which biomolecule evolved first? This is an irreducibly complex situation that could not have evolved by random naturalistic processes.

One evolutionary solution to this scenario is that the precursor molecules required for cell life came from extraterrestrial sources, such as some sort of planetary meteoritic bombardment, or even the intentional "seeding" of Earth by space aliens! However, even these scenarios only "push back" the problem and do not really explain the ultimate origin of these complex biomolecules. Outside of special creation as recorded in the Bible, life doesn't stand a chance.

Notes

1. Zahnle, K., L. Schaefer, and B. Fegley. 2010. Earth's Earliest Atmospheres. *Cold Spring Harbor Perspectives in Biology*. 2 (10): a004895.

2. Davidson, C. F. 1965. Geochemical Aspects of Atmospheric Evolution. *Proceedings of the National Academy of Sciences*. 53: 1194.

3. Austin, S. 1982. Did the Early Earth Have a Reducing Atmosphere? *Acts & Facts*. 11 (7).

4. Abelson, P. H. 1966. Chemical Events on the Primitive Earth. *Proceedings of the National Academy of Sciences*. 55: 1365-1372.

5. Ferris, J. P. and D. E. Nicodem. 1972. Ammonia Photolysis and the Role of Ammonia in Chemical Evolution. *Nature*. 238:268-269.

6. Bada, J. L. and S. L. Miller. 1968. Ammonium Ion Concentration in the Primitive Ocean. *Science*. 159: 423-425.

7. Bada, J. L. and A. Lazcano. 2003. Prebiotic soup – revisiting the Miller experiment. *Science*. 300: 745-756.

8. Deamer, D. 2011. *First Life: Discovering the Connections between Stars, Cells, and How Life Began*. London: University of California Press, Ltd., 25.

9. Miller, S. L. 1953. A production of amino acids under possible primitive earth conditions. *Science*. 117: 528-29.

10. Johnson, A. P. et al. 2008. The Miller volcanic spark discharge experiment. *Science*. 322: 404-405.

11. Fox, S. W. and K. 1958. Harada Thermal Copolymerization of Amino Acids to a Product Resembling Protein. *Science*. 128: 1214.

12. Leman, L., L. Orgel, and M. R. Ghadiri. 2004. Carbonyl Sulfide-Mediated Prebiotic Formation of Peptides. *Science*. 306: 283-286.

GEOLOGY

RECENT FLOOD OR
MILLIONS OF YEARS?

27

THE FLOOD IS THE KEY

John D. Morris, Ph.D.

According to Scripture, there have been three great worldwide events that impacted planet Earth. Every system on Earth was either formed or altered by these events. First, the Bible declares that God created the earth, "and without Him nothing was made that was made" (John 1:3). Nothing in the organic or inorganic realms arrived through purely natural causes. Everything observed would either have descended from the original entities created by God in distinct kinds, or have been reshaped by subsequent events.

Second, we learn that after creation, God placed Adam in charge of creation as His steward. When Adam rebelled against God's authority, his entire domain came under the penalty of sin, and "the wages of sin is death" (Romans 6:23). Now all things "die" or wear down. Living things die biologically, but physically, so do inanimate objects. The sun is burning out. The moon's orbit is decaying. Friction burns up available energy. Mankind, God's very image, also undergoes spiritual death. Only man can sin, but Adam's sin disrupted all of creation. And today, everything is in this inward spiral of death and decay as a result of Adam's sin.

Third, the results of sin soon dominated the planet to such an extent that God had to wash it clean. He sent the Flood of Noah's day to rid the planet of its sinful and violent inhabitants, "by which the world that then existed perished, being flooded with water" (2 Peter 3:6). He used processes familiar to those we recognize (such as moving water and volcanic eruptions) to judge the earth, but in their wake everything was changed. Every location and every system was impacted. Where could you go on planet Earth and not encounter a flooded terrain?

These three great worldwide events form the basics of a biblical worldview of Earth history. All things were created in a "very good" form (Genesis 1:31)

197

by God, and maintained by His action. But then all things were cursed by God, and thus they inexorably decay or die. This was followed by a worldwide flood that restructured the entire earth. Thankfully, the story does not stop there, for Scripture also tells us that the Creator stepped back into His completed, cursed, and flooded creation to pay its sin penalty and redeem fallen men. Furthermore, this earth will itself someday pass away and be replaced by the "new heavens and a new earth in which righteousness dwells" (2 Peter 3:13). The Creator's eternal intent for creation will then be realized. It has been delayed, but not thwarted.

Both historically and currently, the great Flood of Noah's day has been the key to unlocking the creation/evolution question. Throughout the early 1900s, evolution and great age were taught with hardly a contrary voice in the schools, and even within the church. Christians were fully intimidated by the claims of secular scientists, and accommodated great ages and evolutionary changes within the Bible. It was thought that science had disproved a plain-sense reading of Scripture. In particular, rocks and fossils were held to maintain the truth of evolution. They appeared to be so old and seemingly took so long to be deposited. Hardly anyone believed Genesis could be taken literally.

It wasn't until the groundbreaking book *The Genesis Flood*, co-authored by a scientist and a theologian, was published in 1961 that a serious scientific case for creation could be made. For the first time, rocks and fossils could be accounted for in Scripture. The book pointed out that almost all fossils are found within sedimentary rock, by definition deposited as sediments by moving water. Furthermore, almost all fossils are of marine creatures, like clams, coral, trilobites and fish—things that live in water.

Secular thought is shackled by the concept of uniformitarianism, whose slogan is "The present is the key to the past." In this view, all past processes—geologic, biologic, etc.—that have ever occurred are possible today and have shaped our planet, life, and the entire universe. But this directly contradicts the teachings of Scripture, which claim that God created using creation processes from which He has rested. All forms of life were directly created without ancestry at a point in time. His completed creation was subsequently restructured by a dynamic flood in the days of Noah—a global flood the like of which He promised would never happen again. Such a flood would necessarily have deposited vast amounts of sediments that have now hardened into sedimentary rock, full of dead things which have become fossils. The processes involved required rates, scales, and intensities not normally seen today. Much higher energy levels are implicated.

Uniformitarianism cannot adequately explain the past as it relates to rocks and fossils. Major one-time events of the past were responsible. But if you ask an evolutionist "Where is the evidence for great ages?," the answer will inevitably be "In the rocks." If you ask "Where is the evidence for evolution?," the answer has traditionally been "In the fossils." But if Scripture is correct, the Flood laid down both rocks and fossils. Almost all rocks and fossils are the result of and the evidence confirming the great Flood of Noah's day. Both sides have the same evidence, but we interpret it differently. One relies on the assumption of uniformitarianism for an understanding of the unseen past. The other view relies on the eyewitness of One who observed the past deposition of rocks and fossils, and He tells us of unimaginably dynamic processes involved.

Both views can handle the data to varying degrees. Each side can even use the other's data set. Recognizing that both sides are attempting to reconstruct history, the unseen past, what can be done? The two "models" can only be compared to see which better interprets the data, with fewer internal contradictions and fewer *ad hoc* explanations. Without a doubt, one is more faithful to God's revelation about the past than the other. Scientifically, we can evaluate which historical reconstruction is more faithful to the data. Both views are entirely dependent on the assumptions held at the start. The issue becomes: Which view is more credible?

The contention of this book is that the creation/Flood reconstruction will better handle the data than the secular reconstruction of history, and will do so in a God-honoring fashion. Any attempt to reconstruct history is plagued by access only to partial information, by limited understanding and interpreter bias. Neither effort can be a strictly scientific one, dealing as it does with the unobserved past. Science and the scientific method necessarily deal with observation, and neither creation nor evolution has ever been observed in a scientific sense. We can only make predictions of the data. Each side can predict that "if my view is correct, I would expect to see certain things when I gather the data." The other side can do the same, and the one that more successfully predicts the data will be recognized as more likely correct.

As it relates to the Flood, we acknowledge that Scripture teaches that while it utilized modern processes, they were operating at rates, scales, and intensities far more dynamic than modern processes. If the Flood account of Scripture is correct, we would expect to observe rocks and fossils requiring energy levels never seen operating. Conversely, the uniformitarian would expect the majority of rocks and fossils to have been deposited at energy levels comparable to those possible today. What do the rocks say? What do the fossils tell us?

We would further expect Flood-deposited rocks to be on a grand scale. The Flood was worldwide according to Scripture, and thus we expect its products to be laterally extensive. Each episode of the Flood was not necessarily doing the same thing at all locations around the world, but we would expect that, in general, the sedimentary and tectonic evidence to at least be regional or even continental in area. The uniformitarian, relying on processes similar to today's processes, would expect to find strata of local geometry, like ocean fronts, lake beds, stream channels, deltas, etc.

Deposition due to the uniform processes of today acting on a local scale—that's what uniformitarianism predicts. Conversely, catastrophic deposition on a regional scale—that's the expected signature of the great Flood of Noah's day. These expectations of the evidence could hardly be more different. Which of these multiple working hypotheses do the data favor?

28

THE FLOOD WAS GLOBAL ACCORDING TO SCRIPTURE

John D. Morris, Ph.D.

Does Scripture necessarily demand that the Flood was global in extent? The biblicist must always glean the scriptural information before attempting a historical reconstruction of unobserved events. The Bible doesn't give us all the scientific data, but it does provide the basic framework within which we must interpret scientific observations. The Author of Scripture was present when the events occurred, is capable of accurately describing what He saw and did, and cannot lie. His record is trustworthy.

On many occasions and in many ways, the Bible reveals the global nature of the Flood. To begin with, the Flood was said to cover the mountains (Genesis 7:19-20). Obviously, that implies a deep flood, but it also covered "all the high hills under the whole heaven." The term "all" can possibly be used in a limited sense, but here the all refers to everything under the whole heavens, the word for the entire atmosphere. Certainly the atmosphere is worldwide, thus the Flood was worldwide. Using military terms for the "conquering" of the land, the Flood was said to have "prevailed exceedingly." Use of the double superlative in Hebrew can only imply everything. The writer of Genesis understood the Flood as global.

The duration of the Flood also instructs us. Comparing the Flood's starting date (Genesis 7:11) with its ending date (8:13), we see that the Flood was about one year long. It rose for the first five months, prevailed over the land, and then abated. No local flood could do this, for the mountains are too high, and over time, water flows downhill. There can be no such thing as a year-long, mountain-covering local flood; it must have been global. The waters are also described as coming and going (8:3), and moving water accomplishes much more work than standing water. The scriptural account can only be implying a global flood.

The listed causes for the Flood were all worldwide in scope, implying their effect was also global. At the Flood's start, it was mentioned that suddenly "all the fountains of the great deep were broken up, and the windows of heaven were opened" (Genesis 7:11). The "deep" is the oceans and the "heavens" is the atmosphere. A global cause implies a global effect.

Next, consider the fact that God instructed Noah to build the huge Ark so his family and the animals could escape drowning. It appears Noah had 120 years' warning the Flood was coming (Genesis 6:3). In this amount of time, he, his family, and the animals could have walked or flown around the world several times. There was no need for the Ark if the Flood was only local. Yet it was needed, and those not on board perished (7:23).

The Flood's primary goal was to judge sinful man (6:5-7), and secondarily the animals (6:11-13). But animals live all around the earth, as does man. No local, "uniform" flood could accomplish its main goal. It had to be global and energetic.

When the Flood ended, Noah made sacrifice to God, after which God promised there would never again be such a flood sent to judge the earth (9:11). But there have been many local floods since then, even regional floods that did much damage. If the great Flood was local and failed in its main mission—i.e., if it was not a global, world-restructuring cataclysm—then God lied to us. But God doesn't lie. His word is sure.

Perhaps most important lesson comes from the testimony of Jesus Christ Himself when He was teaching His disciples about the end times and the final judgment of sinful mankind. He compared the days immediately preceding the Flood to the days right before He returns:

> As it was in the days of Noah, so it will be also in the days of the Son of Man: They ate, they drank, they married wives, they were given in marriage, until the day that Noah entered the ark, and the flood came and destroyed them all. (Luke 17:26-17)

Note that the Flood destroyed them "all." Whether or not people lived all around the globe before the Flood, they do so today. The coming judgment will apply to all men, thus will not be local or normal. Only if the Flood of Noah's day was global and world-destroying does Christ's instruction make sense.

In a very similar fashion, Peter reminds his readers of the past time when "the world that then existed perished, being flooded with water" (2 Peter 3: 6), and bases his doctrine of the coming time of judgment when the entire "heavens and the earth which are now" will "pass away with a great noise, and the elements will melt with fervent heat; [and] the earth…will be burned up" (vv. 7, 10). The coming destruction and renovation of the entire planet—indeed the entire universe—producing a "new heavens and a new earth" (v. 13) is likened to the past destruction and renovation of the entire earth.

To those who advocate a lesser flood theory, we might ask: "Will the coming re-creation of the new earth be just a local re-creation? Will it only concern the portions of Earth in which man sins? How does the uniformitarian flood concept not imply that only part of the earth is "reserved for fire" (v. 7)? Will some sinners escape God's coming wrath? What hope does this give the sinner?" Obviously, the local flood proposal leads to doctrinal nonsense.

Problems Arising from a Global Flood

If the Flood was really global and tectonically destructive, several problems seem to arise. These are not new questions. They have bothered Christians for centuries. Where did all the water come from for the Flood? Where did it go? How did all the animals get on board? What about the dinosaurs? How could the animals be gathered and cared for? Do other cultures mention the Flood? These questions all have good answers based on the Bible and sound science. Questions regarding the geology of the Flood likewise have good answers, as we'll see in subsequent chapters.

The Water. An impressive volume of water still resides on Earth's surface today, contained primarily in the deep oceans. Actually, the oceans cover about 70 percent of the globe and they are, on average, much deeper than the continents are high. If the earth's surface were completely smoothed, with no deep oceans and no high continents, the oceans would cover the entire globe to a depth of about a mile and a half. There's plenty of water for the Flood.

Today's mountains didn't need to be covered, for they didn't even exist before the Flood. Made up primarily of Flood-deposited sediments, they were laid down at the bottom of the ocean during the Flood, then uplifted into continents and mountain chains as the Flood ended, where they hardened into rock. With the present topography, it would be hard to have a worldwide Flood, but not with the previous topography. The waters drained into the modern oceans as the Flood ended and as the ocean basins sank.

The Animals on the Ark. To get a picture of the animals on the Ark, we must first know how many animals are involved, their average size, and the volume of the Ark. Scripture gives the size of the Ark as about 450 feet long, 75 feet wide, and 45 feet high—or about 1.5 million cubic feet of space. The animal "kinds" were commanded to come in as pairs. The definition of kind probably relates to the potential to mate. For instance, domestic dogs readily mate with coyotes and wolves, thus they would be within the same kind, even though they are categorized as different species today. Only two representatives of the dog "kind" or the cat "kind" were on the Ark. Post-Flood adaptations have produced our modern varieties.

The same would apply for many other animal types. Generous estimates place the total number of animals on the Ark as less than 25,000 pairs, and probably much fewer. The average size of all animals is surprisingly small. There are only a few large animals, but many small ones, with the average size on the Ark estimated as being approximately that of a rat.[1] There was plenty of room on board the Ark for 50,000 rats.

The dinosaurs present a different problem, but one that has a good answer. All things, including dinosaurs, were created during creation week, and there is abundant evidence that humans and dinosaurs lived at the same time after the Flood. This means they also lived in Noah's day before the Flood. Traditionally, they have been classed as reptiles, but an argument rages today. If they were a special category of reptiles, perhaps we can look to other large reptiles for guidance, and most of the larger ones live for many years and grow throughout their lives. In Scripture, we read that some humans of that time lived for almost 1,000 years. If dinosaurs were like modern reptiles, then the older ones might have been huge. It's hard to know for sure, because dinosaurs are extinct and there is a lot scientists don't really know. God selected the animals to come to the Ark for safety. Its purpose was survival and reproduction after the Flood, and He would not have chosen the oldest, largest specimens. More likely, He would have selected young, strong ones, able to reproduce each kind. The Ark was immense, certainly big enough for the job, especially if the dinosaurs were represented by young adults.

Nearly all animals have an innate instinctive ability to migrate when faced with danger and go into a hibernation-like state until the danger passes. Maybe God, the Creator of animals, instilled these abilities into the chosen pairs of animals, and all of their descendants retain them.

Flood Legends. Human cultures also retain a "memory" of the great Flood. All people alive today descended from those eight people on the Ark. Shortly following the Flood, humans gathered at Babel in disobedience of God's command to fill the earth. God separated their languages, thus forcing migration, and as they journeyed they remembered their history of the great Flood and passed it down to later generations. Today, almost every civilization around the world has a flood legend in its body of folklore. Each account may differ from the others in detail, but the essence of the story remains. Together, they all tell of a prior "golden age" that was destroyed by God due to man's sin. They tell of a faithful, favored family who was warned of the coming Flood and who built a large boat and saved themselves and the animals.

Even the difficult questions have satisfying answers.

Note

1. Woodmorappe, J. 1996. *Noah's Ark: A Feasibility Study.* Dallas, TX: Institute for Creation Research, 13.

29

THE FLOOD WAS GLOBAL
AND CATASTROPHIC
ACCORDING TO GEOLOGY

John D. Morris, Ph.D.

As we contemplate the great Flood of Noah's day and its geologic results, we need to recognize two things about it. First, it was global in extent, and second, it was catastrophic in character. Thus, geological evidence for the Flood would include strata deposited by that Flood revealing a catastrophic origin and widespread nature. The Flood, while global, was not necessarily acting the same at all points on the globe at every moment. There would be local differences, but the same overall cause. For instance, no Flood-caused tsunami could hit all portions of the globe simultaneously, nor would we expect it to. The strata would nonetheless be dominantly catastrophic and at least regional in extent. And this is what we see.

There are many examples of regional, even continental, strata. Consider the well-known Grand Canyon. The lowest layer of horizontally bedded strata is known as the Tapeats Sandstone. It is the first layer laid down in the Cambrian system, and the first to contain abundant multicellular fossils. There are hardly any fossils in the layers below the Cambrian, but the "Cambrian explosion of life" contains fossils of every basic body type, even vertebrate fish. Evolutionists claim this happened 550 million years ago, but creationists insist that this layer was deposited near the beginning of the Flood. Right below the Tapeats is an erosion surface so extensive it is called the Great Unconformity. It seems the first burst of the Flood accomplished unthinkable erosion and then began to deposit large sand grains, then smaller sand grains. This sandstone can be traced throughout Grand Canyon and into Utah, to the north. Using drill cores to spot it, geologists have also found it at the same stratigraphic interval across the United States and into Canada. A nearly identical layer rests in Europe and across the northern hemisphere.

The Tapeats Sandstone

Evolutionists have traditionally taught this layer was deposited by normal waves as a shoreline migrated across the continent. In recent years, many geologists have noticed evidence that the depositional agent must have been a series of massive underwater flows of sandy mud. Perhaps the time has come to consider the Flood explanation.

Another layer of great significance is the St. Peter Sandstone. Properly called a "blanket sand," it too covers much of America, thousands of miles wide, but only 50 to 300 feet thick. Comparing its width to its thickness, it becomes the equivalent of a sheet of onion-skin paper. For this thin deposit to collect on a shoreline implies an underlying extensive, extremely flat surface scoured by erosion, with no mountains or hills anywhere higher than 300 feet.

No equivalent surface or depositional scenario exists today. Surely an environment quite different from those existing in the present dominated in the past. Something like a worldwide flood, perhaps?

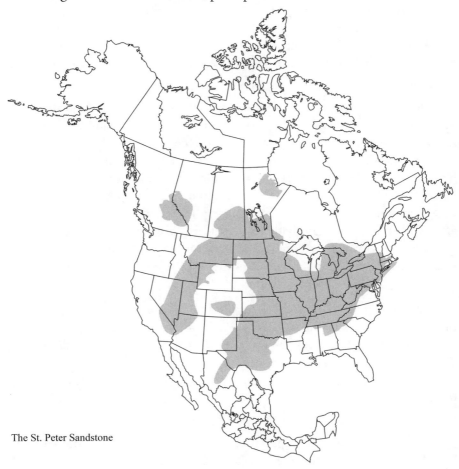

The St. Peter Sandstone

Similar descriptions could be given of extensive limestone deposits. The majority of sedimentary deposits are extremely fine-grain, like shale, originally deposited as mud. But the tiny grains of mud only collect today on the ocean bottom in still water. The grains filter down through the water at a very slow rate, sometimes taking months to reach bottom. No such long-term calm water location can be comprehended in our world, for there are always currents and water disturbances that would keep the grains suspended. Yet the world abounds with mudrocks. Can there be another solution?

Indeed, there is. Something must cause the grains to adhere to one another in a clump. This can happen in laboratory experiments only when the water is treated with unusual chemicals. As larger agglomerations, they fall easily through the water and can flow down a gradual slope. Such a fortuitous combination of circumstances can hardly happen in nature today, and could never occur on a wide scale. But during such a flood as the great Flood, they would happen and could account for the vast deposits of shale and other mudrocks we see all around us.

Other types of rocks come into play here. Consider salt deposits, made mostly of common table salt. Of course, salt is in seawater and remains when the water boils away. Students are normally taught that when seawater gets trapped in a lagoon, the salt collects as the water evaporates. Obviously this happens on a small scale, but is it reasonable to account for the semi-continental salt beds? It must be proposed that a lagoon filled over and over again, each time evaporating and refilling. The salt left behind in a dried lagoon today is always "dirty" and contaminated. But salt beds are amazingly pure. Consider the fact that salt beds are often thousands of feet thick and cover extensive areas. Only by proposing a scenario quite unlike modern ones can large salt deposits be accounted for.

Creationists have proposed that when the "fountains of the great deep" broke open, they spewed super-saturated, hot brines into the much cooler ocean, where the chemicals crystalized and collected on the ocean bottom. There are certain places (such as local salt "volcanoes" in the Red Sea) where similar things happen today, where deep vents are active, but not nearly on the same scale as happened in the past. The "fountains" idea is reasonable and sufficient to account for the deposits of salt we see.

But there's more. Oil exploration efforts have discovered the strata are bundled in sequences. These are due to oceanic "transgressions" onto the continents depositing strata, and "regressions" back off the continents eroding the strata. In general, the packages of strata begin (at the bottom) with sandstone consisting of coarse sand at the base. (Lower layers came first, geologically speaking. The layers on top came later.) The successive layers are of ever-fining particles, and finishing with a chemical precipitate on top (such as limestone).

Each grouping of sedimentary layers (called a megasequence) contains features best understood in the sense of a transgression of the ocean onto the continents, followed by a regression of the waters back into the sea and the resulting erosion, followed by a second sequence, and then another. Uniformitarians interpret each sequence as having taken many millions of years.

During transgression, the waters brought and deposited sediment (usually marine) onto the continent. During regression, the waters eroded much newly deposited and older sediments as they ran off the continents, producing a recognizable erosional boundary called an unconformity. The six (or more) megasequences comprise the entire fossil-bearing part of the geologic column, and have been correlated with beds right across North America and even onto other continents. Since rapidly moving water can accomplish much geologic work, while stationary water does little, this concept bears promise as the primary character of the great Flood of Noah's day.

The lowest megasequence is the Sauk Megasequence, with the previously mentioned Tapeats Sandstone at its base and other layers of finer-grain shale and tiny-grain limestone above, which are capped by an erosional unconformity. The overlying megasequence is called the Tippecanoe Megasequence. The pure quartz sandstone at its base is called the St. Peter Sandstone, and above that lie shale and limestone beds, also followed by erosion.

The erosion unconformity that ended the Sauk Megasequence was totally unlike anything we have ever witnessed. This erosional episode planed off the recent Sauk deposits to a nearly flat, featureless plain. On the entire continent, no mountain remained, for the St. Peter Sandstone covers essentially the entire continental area with a thin sheet of sand! Evidently, even though subsequent erosion removed the sandstone in some areas, it was essentially continuous at first, implying there were no high places on the continent that received no sediment. This could not have been accomplished by river erosion. The only adequate mechanism known is by "sheet erosion"— rapidly flowing water of equal depth that covered a wide area. That's catastrophism with a vengeance!

The standard view considers both sandstone beds mentioned to have been deposited by a transgressing shoreline, with sand accumulating on the beach and offshore over about five million years, all the while migrating across the continent.

The Genesis account of the global Flood succinctly describes stage after stage of that unique catastrophe. It even intimates successive episodes of transgression and regression. Genesis 8:3 summarizes the stage in which the floodwaters began to drain enough to allow Noah's Ark to come to rest. But while the waters were moving, they followed a remarkable rhythmic pattern of ocean-water movement—specifically, a repetitious action described in Genesis as a "to and fro" (or "back and forth") motion.

> And the waters receded continually from the earth. At the end of the hundred and fifty days the waters decreased. (Genesis 8:3)

The Hebrew words justify special scrutiny. The recession of the floodwaters is denoted by the verse's first verb, which means "and they returned" to where they had originated. The next two Hebrew words provide a verbal picture of the draining waters swaying in a rhythmic mega-wave movement. Although the New King James Version translates this two-word phrase with the one word "continually," the Hebrew phrase connotes the water motion as being continually "to and fro" or "back and forth" —the waters were *continually* going and returning.[1]

A repetitive back-and-forth movement of floodwaters is the rock-solid evidence we observe as megasequences in the geological record of the Flood. The sedimentary rocks and fossils left in the floodwaters' wake contain abundant evidence of the ocean-waters transgressing over the continents and then regressing back into the ocean.

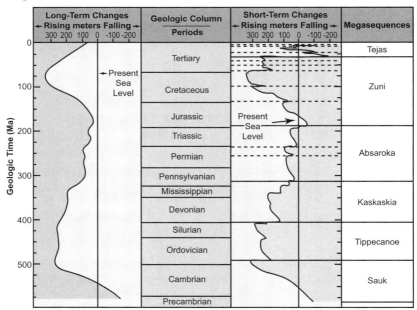

Sea level changes over geologic "time," with transgressions swinging to the left and regressions back to the right. Note that the sea level changes ignore geologic periods but define the megasequences. Modified after Sloss and Vail.[2]

The accompanying chart references the standard concept of geologic "time," with the long-ago past at the bottom and the present at the top, with the megasequences "coming and going" throughout all periods.

Of course, recognizing that old-earth scenarios are hopelessly flawed,[3,4] we would certainly disagree with the chart's long time span of 600 million years, preferring instead to interpret the whole as the record of the great Flood of Noah's day. Moving upward, we see the bottom as the early Flood period, then the mid-Flood, the waning stages of the Flood, and the post-Flood time at the top. The Genesis 8:4 grounding of the Ark occurred during the later Zuni, when floodwaters were at their maximum and then began to wane. Within the rising and maintaining Flood portions of the chart is where geologists have seen these six (maybe subdivided into more) megasequences. During the final drainage, the waters came and went with greater frequency.

Each of these sequences begins with a record of violent incursion of the ocean over the land, first depositing a basal coarse sand, then smaller grains, and then chemical precipitation as the energy levels lessened, ending with the water rushing back seaward with a mighty erosion episode. Each transgression landward followed each regression seaward in a continuous cycle of floods, until all was totally destroyed. These were not separate floods, but one un-imaginable super-flood, with repeated pulses of terror.

Scripture doesn't give us all the details of the Flood events, but geology can "fill in the blanks." Remember, God's primary purpose for the great Flood was total annihilation of the continents and the life they held (Genesis 6:7).

The Flood involved much more than water flooding the land, standing above the mountains for a while, and then draining. Moving water contains much energy, while standing water does little work. God promised He was going to destroy the wicked, violent inhabitants of Earth along with the earth, and super-powered cleansing floodwaters—washing "back and forth" across the land—appear to be the tool God chose to accomplish it.

Notes

1. Young, R. 1980. *Young's Analytical Concordance to the Bible*. Peabody, MA: Hendrickson Publishers, 17, 47.

2. Sloss, L. L. 1963. Sequences in the cratonic interior of North America. *Geologic Society of America Bulletin*. 74: 93-114; Vail, P. R. and R. M. Mitchum, Jr. 1979. Global cycles of relative changes of sea level from seismic stratigraphy. *American Association of Petroleum Geologists Memoir 29*, 469-472.

3. Morris, H. M. and J. C. Whitcomb. 1961. *The Genesis Flood: The Biblical Record and Its Scientific Implications*. Phillipsburg, NJ: Presbyterian and Reformed Publishing Company; Morris, J. 2007. *The Young Earth*,

revised ed. Green Forest, AR: Master Books.

4. Johnson, J. J. S. 2008. How Young Is the Earth? Applying Simple Math to Data Provided in Genesis. *Acts & Facts*. 37 (10): 4-5.

30

THE YOUNG EARTH IN SCRIPTURE

John D. Morris, Ph.D.

Genesis 1 references the events of creation occurring during six "days." How long were the days of Genesis? Old-earth advocates point out that the English word "day" is a translation of the Hebrew word *yom*, which can have a variety of meanings, including an indefinite period of time, just as it can in English. The word is a common one in the Old Testament, used hundreds of times. In both languages, the term most often refers to a solar day, defined by one revolution of the earth on its axis. If I say "today," you know what I mean. Or when I say "the day of your birth," it's clear. Perhaps I could modify the word by a numerical adjective, like "first day" or "three days," and you would know what I meant. But I could say "in the day of George Washington" and you would know I was referring to a period of time around the Revolutionary War. It all depends on context. How the word is used specifies its meaning in any particular usage.

In Genesis 1, God apparently went out of His way to make sure we didn't misunderstand, for He defined *yom* the first time He used it. On Day One, after creating the heavens and the earth, God created light (v. 3), and "God divided the light from the darkness" (v. 4). This light/dark cycle was further identified when "God called the light Day [*yom*], and the darkness He called Night" (v. 5). Throughout the rest of the passage, He uses the term for the first day through the seventh day.

Evening and Morning

The meaning of the term "day" is further limited by the use of the modifying terms "evening" and "morning." Do these terms have figurative meanings? The Old Testament uses this combination of words 38 times. Each time it occurs, the meaning clearly must be a normal day. Obviously, when the words "morning" and "evening" are used in the same verse with *yom*, they refer to a normal day.

The door to misinterpretation is closed in Exodus 20:11, where God wrote in stone some things He really didn't want us to misinterpret. The fourth of the Ten Commandments concerns our work week, where we are commanded to work six days and rest on the seventh: "For in six days the LORD made the heavens and the earth, the sea, and all that is in them, and rested the seventh day." Same word, *yom*, same context, same modifiers, same tablet of stone, same Author, same finger that wrote it. If words have meaning, then God created in six days just like our days. His work of creation becomes the pattern for our work week.

"Day" can mean a period of time when the context demands, but in the creation account "day" means a real day. Christians need to allow the unchangeable Scripture to define its own terms and not rely on the temporal musings of men.

What can we conclude concerning the length of the days of creation? On the surface, the text is that of a straightforward narrative, conveying sober history. The usage of the word "day" with a number means a 24-hour period as it is used here. Further, the use of "evening" and "morning" indicates that normal time is meant in Genesis 1. God, Himself, revealed in the Ten Commandments that the creation took only six days. We also must ask, did Moses and God deceive us by using the word "day" to communicate an indefinite, but lengthy, period of time? If so, how can we trust it in any other area?

The Time Since Creation

Creationists often agree the age of the earth in Scripture may not be given in precise terms, but it is on the order of 6,000 to 10,000 years. Where does this figure come from?

The Bible gives much chronological and historical data, referencing its teachings to real historical events. For our purposes, let us admit that Abraham lived around 2000 B.C. (4,000 years ago), a date accepted by historians and archaeologists, as well as biblical students. Before Abraham's day, we can only rely on Scripture, with dates given for the ages of the patriarchs given in Genesis 5 and 11. From Genesis 11, we see that from Abraham back to Noah and the Flood was only 300 or so years. Here we must admit the genealogies are somewhat loose, but with no possibility of inserting much time. Marching back from Noah to Adam, we find a very "tight" listing of patriarchs and their lifespans, with a total time span of 1,656 years. Of course, before Adam, only six days lapsed, since he was created on Day Six of the creation week. (See chapter 6 for an event-to-event calculation of the time from Adam's creation to Abraham's birth.)

Adding this all together, we find that the total age of planet Earth is on the order of 4,000 years + 300 years + 1,656 years + 6 days. This gives a total age of about 6,000 years or so. When other ancient manuscripts of Scripture are considered, and taking the most extreme case, we arrive at about 10,000 years. The authors of this book lean to the lower age.

Other Scriptures

One will search in vain for any hint of "millions and millions of years" in the pages of Scripture. There are several that speak of long ago, but these are better understood as long ago in a human sense and not of the deep time of geology. For instance, we read that "before the mountains were brought forth, or ever You had formed the earth and the world, even from everlasting to everlasting, You are God" (Psalm 90:2). Old-earth advocates use this to buttress their claim of great ages, but the passage simply refers to the creation week, which in a biblical framework was long ago.

One clear passage regarding instantaneous creation is in Psalm 33:6, 9: "By the word of the LORD the heavens were made, and all the host of them by the breath of His mouth....For He spoke, and it was done; He commanded, and it stood fast." No implication of deep time here, nor the use of any lengthy process. Scripture doesn't give us all the details on every subject, but the information it does relate can only imply a recent creation. The biblical texts contain clear indications that creation occurred in six literal days, not very long ago.

Of course, the real lens through which we must view all physical evidence regarding creation and the time of creation is the great Flood of Noah's day. As we have seen, Scripture will allow no other interpretation than that of the global Flood. All old-earth arguments, either from science or Scripture, must start with downgrading the Flood from global to local, and from catastrophic to uniformitarian.

31

THE YOUNG EARTH IN GEOLOGY

John D. Morris, Ph.D.

As we have discussed, both good science and the Bible point to the catastrophic past of planet Earth. Geological data demand dynamic solutions to origins questions and do not allow uniformitarian ones. Both science and the Bible also teach the companion doctrine, that of the young age of the earth. Numerous examples could be considered, but a few may suffice. They will not only point to recent creation, but demonstrate the bankruptcy of uniformitarian thinking. Space does not allow full discussion of all of them.

Salt in the ocean. The oceans are salty and growing more salty each year as rivers bring in more dissolved salts. Knowing the ocean's volume and average salt concentration, we can calculate how much salt is there. We can measure how fast it arrives by rivers, and how fast it is removed. Evolution teaches that life evolved in a salty sea about three billion years ago. But at present (uniform) in and out rates, even in "only" one billion years the ocean would be so choked with salt that life would be impossible. Uniformitarianism is incompatible with the ocean's salt makeup.

Erosion of the continents. The volume of the continents above sea level is known. The sedimentary rock on the continents is made up primarily of sediments containing marine fossils. Uniformitarianism considers them to have risen from the sea hundreds of millions of years ago. We can measure how fast the continents are eroding. At present rates, all the continents would be gone in just a few million years, yet they are still here. If uniformitarianism is true, they should all be gone. In some places the land is rising, but at far slower rates than it is eroding elsewhere. There shouldn't be any sedimentary rock left, no fossils, no granitic core—it should all be gone. Uniformitarian thinking doesn't explain the facts, yet it dominates our universities.

Helium in the atmosphere. Each time an atom of uranium-238 (or thorium) undergoes alpha decay into a lead atom through a series of decay steps, it ejects eight alpha particles, which are essentially helium atoms (two protons and two neutrons = a helium nucleus, to which electrons attach). Of course, helium's light weight causes it to rise through the pores in the rocks and eventually enter the atmosphere. Through sensitive sensors, we can measure how much helium enters the atmosphere. We can also measure how much helium is in the atmosphere. If present rates have continued for the supposed previous millions of years, there should be lots more helium than is currently there. Actually, all of the current helium can be accounted for (at present rates) in only about two million years.

Helium in the rocks. A similar calculation can be made regarding helium content in the rocks. Select a rock of "known" uniformitarian age and measure the amount of radioactive uranium in the rock. By knowing the rate of decay, we can calculate how much helium should be present. Helium atoms are quite tiny and slippery, and some will leak out through rock's pores over time, faster than it is generated. If the rocks are as old as the standard view supposes, the helium should have mostly leaked out. Instead, way too much helium is still present. Helium is still building up! It looks like the rocks are not so old after all.

Soft-sediment deformation. Sedimentary rocks were once saturated sediments, deposited (almost always) by moving water. Sediments harden into rock rather quickly in the presence of an adequate cement binding the particles together. Later, the layers of sediments can be deformed, either by folding or faulting. Often, the sediments give evidence of still being soft and pliable when deformed. It appears there was not enough time between deposition and deformation to harden the sediments, even though uniformitarianism often assigns dates to the two processes many millions of years apart.

Sediments in the ocean. As the continents erode and the sediments are carried downstream, they build up on the ocean floor. If the continents have been eroding for hundreds of millions of years at their present rate, there should be a predictable large amount there. With submarines and drill cores, we have been able to observe how much is down there, but it's not nearly as much as uniformitarianism requires. All of the sediment down there would accumulate in a time far shorter than uniformitarianism predicts.

Human history. Real history is human history, during which reliable eyewitnesses observed an event and recorded it for those who follow. True history began with the invention of writing, agriculture, and human society, and historians tell us that began around 5,000 years ago. Bible-believers recognize this time as about the time of the Flood. Before then, nothing survived except traditions. Any thoughts of times before 5,000 years ago are based on either biblical revelation or the concept of uniformitarianism, and that concept has proved inaccurate and based on false assumptions about the unseen past.

Sedimentary Structure Shows a Young Earth

Consider also the nature of the rocks underfoot. They were not only deposited catastrophically, but recently as well—or so it seems. Sedimentary rock, which makes up most of the surface cover of the continents, is by definition deposited by moving fluids. Normally, the sediments contain evidence of their waterborne history in what is called *sedimentary structures*. These features may be in the form of cross-bedding, paleo-current markers, graded bedding, laminations, ripple marks, etc. If the hardening conditions are met (i.e., the presence of a cementing agent and pressure to drive water from the matrix), the sediments soon harden into sedimentary rock, making the "structure" permanent. Erosion will eventually destroy even hard rock features, but rocks abound with such markings, virtually frozen in place.

Geologists have traditionally surmised that most deposits are the results of the calm and gradual uniformitarian processes currently in operation. Conversely, more recent geologic models recognize that processes of the past may have acted at rates and intensities exceeding those of today, while catastrophists look to processes far exceeding those. They may have been the same basic processes, but were acting at catastrophic levels, accomplishing much depositional work in a short time. Continuing catastrophic action would quickly deposit a second layer, and then more. The question remains: How long ago did this rapid depositional sequence of events take place?

While the muddy sediments are still fresh and soft, the ephemeral sedimentary structures within the deposits are in jeopardy of being obliterated by the action of plant and animal life. We know that life proliferates in every near-surface layer of soft sediment. This is true on land, and especially true underwater. Plant roots penetrate the soil. Animals such as worms, moles, clams, etc., burrow through the sediment, churning it up and turning it over through a process called *bioturbation*. This obviously destroys the sedimentary structure. But how long does it take?

A recent study undertook to determine just how much time was required to destroy all such structures.[1] Numerous recent storm deposits dominated by sedimentary structure were investigated in their natural setting. It was observed that within months, all sedimentary structure was destroyed, so intense is the bioturbation in soft sediments. As long as the sediments are still soft, they will be bioturbated until all structure is lost. Yet the geologic record of Earth history abounds with such features. This comprises a good geological age indicator, and in fact points to a young earth. The total picture must be considered when considering sedimentary rocks.

Virtually all sediments require only a short time to accumulate in various high-energy events. Hardening of sediments into sedimentary rock itself normally takes little time, if the conditions are met. Soft at the start, the sediment's internal character would necessarily be subjected to the rapid, destructive action of plant and animal life. Within a relatively short time (months or years), all sedimentary structure would disappear through their action alone. The surface of each layer would be exposed to bioturbation until the next layer covered it and until hardening was complete

The evidence suggests that each layer was laid down in a short period of time. Each soft deposit could not have been exposed for long before the next deposit covered it; they appear to have been isolated from destructive bioturbation. Thus, the length of time between the layers could not have been great. The total time involved for the entire sequence must therefore have been short.

The Lessons from Mount St. Helens

When Mount St. Helens erupted in 1980, it was not only a major but local tectonic incident with predictable volcanic results, it spawned numerous water-related processes and products as well. Before the eruption, the mountain had been capped by a thick glacier. Sudden heating melted the glacier, and water avalanched down the mountain's northern slope. Water flowing with tsunami-like intensity savaged the forest and hillsides below, combining with ash fall and pyroclastic flows from the eruption itself. Some rock strata were quickly eroded, and sediments were instantly deposited on other areas in layers looking much the same as those to which geologists normally attach great age.

Layers of sediment up to 600 feet thick were deposited at the mountain's base, which in a few years hardened into rather solid rock. Canyons soon were gouged into these layers, producing a scale model of Grand Canyon in one afternoon. Elsewhere, wood is petrifying, coal is forming, etc.—all in the few years since the 1980 eruption. The igneous rock (dacite) that should date "too young to measure" by radioisotope dating instead gives an anomalous date of 2.4 million years old when the proper isotopic dating method (potassium-argon) is used.[2] Modern local catastrophes such as the eruption of Mount St. Helens can give us a glimpse into Earth's past and geological power, even on the worldwide scale of Noah's Flood.

Thus, the Mount St. Helens catastrophe becomes a model for the great Flood. It teaches us about volcanism, erosion, deposition, solidification, fossilization, etc., all acting in a short time. A catchy slogan helps illustrate this. To form geological features, *it either takes a little bit of water and a long time, or a lot of water and a short time.* Even though we didn't witness the great Flood, we do see modern catastrophes, and they rapidly accomplish things the Flood did on an even grander scale. In a short, biblically compatible timescale, such a flood can account for all the features we see on Earth's surface, features that many geologists normally misinterpret as evidence for great age. Earth doesn't really look old, but it does look flooded.

ICR has found that there is no better "first dose" of creation information than the lessons learned at Mount St. Helens. It has often been an individual's introduction to creation thinking and research, made all the more powerful because the eruption was so well-observed and studied. Earth features that had been considered to have taken long ages to form were seen to have happened rapidly, almost instantaneously.

Lessons learned at Mount St. Helens include:

- Up to 600 feet of rapidly deposited sediments, virtually identical to those found worldwide in the greater geologic record;

- A deep, eroded canyon through those sediments that has been dubbed the Little Grand Canyon, carved in one afternoon;

- Fresh volcanic rocks called dacites are dated by radiometric means to be over a million years old, yet are only decades old;

- A log mat of about four million trees, remains of a forest that was catastrophically ripped from the ground, now floating in a nearby lake;

- A thick peat layer accumulating under the mat that is poised to become a coal deposit if certain events take place;

- Upright floating logs that look like they grew in place have the signature appearance of the petrified "forest" at Yellowstone National Park.

Scripture specifies that the time elapsed for all of creation and Earth history has not been very long. Geology confirms it.

Notes

1. Gingras, M. K. et al. 2008. How fast do marine invertebrates burrow? *Palaeogeography, Palaeoclimatology, Palaeoecology*. 270 (3-4): 280-286.

2. Morris, J. and S. A. Austin. 2003. *Footprints in the Ash*. Green Forest, AR: Master Books, 67; Austin, S. A. 1996. Excess Argon within Mineral Concentrates from the New Dacite Lava Dome at Mount St. Helens Volcano. *Creation Ex Nihilo Technical Journal*. 10 (3): 335-343.

32

THE REAL NATURE
OF THE FOSSIL RECORD

John D. Morris, Ph.D.

The fossil record leaves an inescapable impression on the honest observer. It certainly doesn't communicate the macroevolutionary picture. The record of the past written in stone contains no evidence that any particular animal ever morphed into a fundamentally different type of animal. No trend can be found of gradual, Darwinian alteration through mutation and natural selection. These processes may occur, but they are not mechanisms for true evolution of basic body styles.

Nor do we see punctuated equilibrium transforming them rapidly. Without a doubt, we see sudden changes in dominant fossil shapes as we ascend the geologic column, but this is not macroevolution. The species changes touted by punctuated equilibrium that we do see are either common variation of individual offspring or adaptation of a population to differing conditions. Punctuated equilibrium doesn't even address the larger changes needed for meaningful evolution.

The array of fossils usually constitutes the main evidence for evolution. The standard geologic column presents a column of fossils with the oldest near the bottom, less ancient ones toward the middle, and recent fossils near the top—supposedly showing the progress of evolution over time, from bottom to top, from simple life to more complex life. Note that while the chart appears to be a presentation of the way fossils are found, it is really a time chart. The stack of individual periods can be considered analogous to the various geologic layers, with older ones on the bottom and newer ones on the top.

While creationists rightly reject the time component and implications of the column, it does contain good information, compiled from thousands of valid observations. The rock layers at the bottom are better understood as having been deposited at the start of the Flood, with the ones nearer the top laid down later in the Flood. The first layers document the early bursts of the "fountains of the deep" and accompanying tsunamis, which would primarily impact ocean-bottom dwellers. Episodes to follow would bury upper marine life, then coastal life, then the life on land. But rather than "demonstrating" evolution, does it tell us something else? We can consider it almost an ecological chart, preserving the stages of the great Flood. Once reinterpreted, it actually supports the creation/Flood concept.

In general, the animals portrayed near the chart's bottom all lived in the ocean's depths, while those in the middle lived higher in the water and on the coastlines, and those even higher on the chart lived on land. While evolutionists use the column as a statement of evolutionary dogma as documented by the fossils, we have seen that the fossils really tell a much different story.

Sudden Appearance of Basic Types

The fossil record communicates sudden appearance of basic types, complete with all the features that characterize them. Lots of variety is on display, even at times enough to lead to a new species.

But variety is not evolution. Cats are cats and dogs are dogs and always have been so. There are similarities between them, but no hint of relatedness. Both appear to have been suddenly created to live in similar environments, breathe the same air, eat the same foods, drink the same water, and survive through circulation of similar blood. We should expect similarities. But cats when they reproduce yield kittens, and reproducing dogs have puppies. They did not originate by mutations in a different type of common ancestor, nor did one come from the other. And this is what the fossils show.

Basic Types Show Stasis

Once a basic type appeared, it demonstrated stasis. Individuals varied in appearance and whole populations varied over the generations to accommodate changing conditions as they "multiplied and filled" Earth's varied environments, but always they were fundamentally the same as the parent group.

The fossil record features stasis as a dominant trend. It does not speak of major changes. Evolution, or the descent from a common ancestor model, demands that major changes visited every population. But this is the evolu-

226

tionary "story," not the conclusion drawn from the fossils.

Complexity at the Start

Each plant or animal alive today exhibits amazing complexity. Each of its body parts is precisely designed to perform its function, and all work together for the good of the whole. Indeed, there often is no use for a particular part without the others. Some may only be used at a limited period of life or in an unusual circumstance, at which time they must be present for survival. All must be present for any to accomplish any useful purpose.

From the very first time a fossil type appears (i.e., the lowest stratigraphic interval in which it's found), it shows all the design features that make it special. Evolution necessitates the gradual accumulation of body parts through random mutation and amalgamation of previous parts with different functions into a new whole. The elegance of design, however, argues *against* a patchwork origin and *for* an intelligent cause. Mutations only mar, but do not erase, evidence of exquisite design.

Extinction, Not Evolution

Extinction is well-documented in the fossil record, and while extinction is a necessary part of the evolutionary scenario, it is not evolution. It might better be considered as the opposite of evolution. Losing a type is not what is in question, but the gaining of new types—now, that would be interesting.

A case can be made by fossil "splitters" that new species can be found as one ascends the strata. However, speciation within basic kinds is different from the introduction of new kinds, and evolution requires a dizzying array of basic new kinds. The origination of a new form has never been documented in the modern world of scientific observation, while perhaps several species every day go extinct. The opposite of evolution occurs today, and fossils show that the opposite of evolution also occurred in the past.

No Ancestor/Descendant Relationships

Evolution necessarily implies the concept of "descent from a common ancestor or ancestors." Yet no ancestor/descendant relationship can be advocated with certainty based on the fossils. Indeed, the differences are obvious and make classification of types possible.

The similarities between distinct types is not a sure footing on which to base an ancestral relationship, as proved by the many mutually competing cladograms advanced by evolutionists. Whose opinion, if any, is correct? The separateness of each type is witness to their separate creations.

Fossil Record Is Complete

The fossil record can be deemed essentially complete. Darwin was concerned about its lack of transitional forms, hypothetical creatures that demonstrate one type changing into another over time. He was hopeful they would be found one day.

But extensive exploration and fossil discovery in following years have not brought such in-between forms to light. The vast majority of taxonomic orders and families that live today are also found as fossils, yet without fossil transitions. We can be certain the record is substantially complete.

All Phyla Present at the Start

The "Cambrian explosion" constitutes a major episode in the history of life. If evolution were true, one would expect the record to start with one type of animal life, then increase to two, and so on. Yet fossil studies have shown that essentially all phyla were present at the start, each distinct from the others and each fully equipped to function and survive. Even vertebrate fish were present in the lower Cambrian.

Some phyla have gone extinct over subsequent years, but most have continued into the present. There is no evolutionary tree found in the fossils, as Darwin and his disciples have claimed. Rather, it is more like a lawn than a tree.

Many Fossils Found Throughout the Column

Stasis can be seen in the large, vertical, stratigraphic ranges of many fossil types. Index fossils are thought to exist only for a brief time span. True enough, some fossils are only found in a relatively few layers. But many other fossils, such as the brachiopod *Lingula*, can be found throughout the geologic column and into the present. This animal would seemingly make a good potential ancestor for others, but it never changed into anything or arose from anything.

Various fossil types are found in many layers, with more fossil ranges being continually extended by new discoveries. Statistical treatments give reason to believe that essentially all types lived throughout a large portion of history.

Most Fossils Are Marine Invertebrates

At least 95 percent of all animal fossils are marine invertebrates. They are found in great variety, but all are well-designed for life in the sea. Some lived in high-energy, near-shore environments, but others lived in deeper waters, away from the pounding action of the waves.

Among the vertebrates, most fossils are fish, again mostly marine creatures. Of the terrestrial fossils, by far most are plants. Land-dwelling animals, such as mammals and dinosaurs, are poorly represented in the fossil record. The majority of animals depicted on evolutionary fossil charts in textbooks, however, are land vertebrates. It is claimed that a possible case for evolution can be made from them, but exceptions do not accurately portray the real fossil record. Where good evidence exists, no evolution can be seen.

Fossils Found in Catastrophic Deposits

These fossilized marine creatures are typically found in catastrophic deposits. Even marine creatures that live in high-energy zones cannot live in catastrophic conditions. Many died where they were fossilized. They were either buried alive, or their remains were transported by dynamic processes to their present resting places before they decayed or were scavenged.

The processes involved must have been highly destructive, yet rapidly acting. The major forces that sculpted Earth's surface were not like the processes of today.

Indications of Violent Death

Often the fossil remains are found in a death pose. The famous *Archaeopteryx* fossil lies with its neck and tail arched back as if it were dying a horrible, drowning death. Clams are found with both halves tightly shut, "clammed up" as a living clam does for protection from danger.

Dinosaur fossils, also in death poses, are found ripped apart but often not scavenged. Fossilized animals give every indication they were violently killed and/or transported to the places we now find them.

No Complete Ecosystems

The fossils are usually entombed in deposits with no complete ecosystems present that could have supported them in life. Often evolutionists portray a fossil's tomb as a snapshot of life and tell stories about the creature's habits.

But these plants and animals are not necessarily found where they lived, or where they died. They are found where they were buried. It is not honest to presume patterns of life from transported remains of once-living things.

Animals from Mixed Habitats

Fossil graveyards often contain numerous animals from mixed habitats. Saltwater fish are sometimes found with upland dwellers. Crocodile fossils are found with deep-sea denizens and desert and arctic mammals.

They could scarcely be lumped together in this way by the uniform processes of today. Some great cataclysm is needed.

Fossils Found Mostly on Continents

The catastrophic deposits in which the (mostly marine) fossils are found are almost all on the continents. A series of marine cataclysms inundated the land, destroying nearly everything there and laying down a record plain enough for all to see. Those terrestrial fossils that were deposited primarily date from the Ice Age that followed the great Flood of Noah's day.

Summary

Combining all these major concepts, we see that the fossil record is a record quite different from that presented in support of evolution. Each basic plant and animal type appeared abruptly and fully functional and then experienced stasis throughout its tenure. Each type was complex and distinct at the start, without having descended from some other ancestral type, particularly from a less complex type.

All basic types that have ever lived were present at the start, and while some have subsequently gone extinct, no new basic types have appeared since the beginning. We have reason to believe substantially all basic forms that ever lived have been found as fossils.

A general rule is that the fossils extend through a lengthy stratigraphic range with little or no change. Most of the fossils are remains of marine invertebrates, found in catastrophic deposits, often in death poses with an incomplete ecosystem present. These predominately marine fossils are almost all found on the continents, not in the ocean.

The fossil record is thus quite incompatible with evolution and uniformitarianism, but remarkably consistent with the biblical record—creation of all things in perfect form and function, the Curse on all things due to man's rebellion, and the great Flood of Noah's day that first destroyed and then renovated the entire planet.

Creation thinking predicts the evidence, while evolution must distort and flex the evidence and its position to accommodate it.

33

DO RADIOISOTOPE DATING METHODS PROVE AN OLD EARTH?

Jake Hebert, Ph.D.

Without a doubt, radioisotope (or radiometric) dating methods are one of *the* main arguments for an old earth. Volcanic and metamorphic rocks are "dated" by these methods to be millions or even billions of years old. Likewise, the carbon-14 dating method sometimes yields ages of multiple tens of thousands of years for carbon-containing materials (generally from formerly living organic matter). Do these methods present an unanswerable challenge to the Bible's 6,000 year timescale?

No, they do not. But before explaining why, it is necessary to briefly describe the theory behind the method. Some atoms are unstable, which means that they spontaneously change into other atoms through a *decay* process. For instance, uranium-238 (^{238}U) changes into lead-206 (^{206}Pb)[1] through a multi-step process that involves the emission of, among other things, *alpha particles* (helium nuclei consisting of two protons and two neutrons) from the nucleus. The rate at which ^{238}U decays into ^{206}Pb has been accurately measured, and this decay rate may be expressed in terms of a *half-life*, the amount of time required for half a sample of ^{238}U to be converted into ^{206}Pb.[2] Uranium-238 is called the *parent* element, while lead-206 is the *daughter* element. Since the rate of decay is known, it is thought that measuring the amount of daughter material compared to the amount of parent material can reveal the age of a sample. But scientists cannot directly measure the age of rocks or organic remains. In order to "convert" these element quantities into an age, some assumptions must be made.

An analogy illustrates these assumptions.[3] Suppose we enter a lecture hall. At the front of the hall is a table on which sits a basket of potatoes, some of which have been peeled and some of which have not. We notice that once every minute, a man standing by the table grabs a potato, peels it, and then places it back into the basket. After ten minutes of observation, we wonder how long the man has been peeling potatoes.

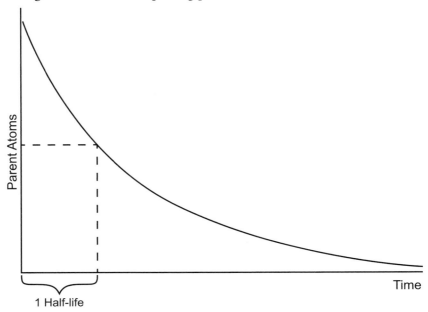

Figure 1. One half-life is the time needed for half an arbitrary number of parent atoms to undergo radioactive decay.

If the basket contains 35 peeled potatoes, we might conclude that the man has been peeling potatoes for 35 minutes. This seems reasonable, but we implicitly made some assumptions in order to reach this conclusion, and our · conclusion will *only* be correct if those assumptions are accurate. What are the assumptions?

First, we assumed that none of the potatoes had already been peeled beforehand. But it's possible that some of them *had* already been peeled at the time the man began the peeling process.

Second, we assumed that no peeled potatoes were added to or removed from the basket before we began observing. What if the man got hungry and ate some of the peeled potatoes before we arrived?

Third, we assumed that the man has been peeling potatoes at a constant rate, even for the time we did not observe him. Perhaps he was peeling faster in the past, but simply tired and slowed down to our observed rate of one potato per minute. Although it may seem *reasonable* to assume that his rate of peeling was constant in the unobserved past, we simply *don't know* that this is really the case.

Despite the sometimes complicated math involved, radioisotope dating uses very similar assumptions to estimate the age of a given rock. As noted earlier, a scientist can't measure the age of a rock directly—rather, he measures the number of *daughter* atoms within a rock compared to the number of *parent* atoms. In the analogy, the peeled potatoes are analogous to the daughter atoms, while the unpeeled potatoes are analogous to the parent atoms.

Fundamental Assumptions of Radioactive Dating Techniques

1. Known initial conditions of the sample
2. The amount of parent or daughter elements altered only by radioactive decay
3. Constant decay rate (or half-life)

Figure 2. Radioisotope dating is based on certain assumptions.

So, are radiometric dating assumptions correct? There is a simple way to find out. If radiometric techniques yield nonsensical or inconsistent results, this is a clear indication that one or more of these assumptions is wrong. There are indeed many examples of nonsensical radiometric dating results:

- **Incorrect estimated "dates" for rocks of known age.** Theoretically, a rock's radioisotope "clocks" should be reset whenever it melts. This implies that newly formed volcanic rocks should have radiometric ages of essentially zero. Yet radioisotope ages for "young" rocks of known age are often very old. For instance, volcanic rocks from New Zealand's Mount Ngauruhoe were radiodated by a respected laboratory. Despite the fact that the rocks were *known* to have been formed during eruptions less than 50 years earlier, potassium-argon dating yielded "ages" for the rocks ranging from less than 270,000 years to 3.5 million years.[4] Of course, one could claim that the lower value is the correct one—a 50-year-old rock *is* less than 270,000 years old— but this is only because the true ages of the rocks are *known*. Without that knowledge, one easily could have reached the erroneous conclusion that the rocks were millions of years old. Many similar examples could be cited.[5, 6]

- **"Dates" that contradict each other.** Different radioisotope "clocks," and even the *same* clock applied to *different* parts of the *same* geological formation, often yield dramatically different ages.[7, 8]

- **Detectable amounts of carbon-14 (^{14}C) in specimens that are supposedly hundreds of millions of years old or more.** Because ^{14}C decays quickly into nitrogen-14 (^{14}N), it has a relatively short half-life of 5,730 years. Therefore, you would not expect ^{14}C to be present in specimens that are millions of years old.[9, 10] Yet measurable amounts of ^{14}C have *consistently* been found in carbon-containing specimens that are supposedly tens and even hundreds of millions of years old, at levels far above the detection limits of the measuring apparatus.[11] Measurable ^{14}C has even been found in diamonds, which are supposedly more than a *billion* years old![12] Because diamond is extremely hard, and because laboratories take great pains to avoid contaminating samples, it is very difficult for uniformitarians to blame these results on "contamination."

- **Helium in zircon crystals found within hot "Precambrian" granitic rock.** These zircon crystals contain uranium that has partially decayed into lead. The amount of decayed uranium suggests an apparent radioisotope age of 1.5 billion years for the zircons. The helium atoms that are formed as a result of alpha emission during the decay process "leak" (or diffuse) out of the zircons so quickly that very little helium should still remain in the zircons if they are really that old, yet the zircons still contain *large* amounts of helium.[13]

These results indicate problems with all three radiometric dating assumptions. If we are not present when lava cools to form a volcanic rock and are unable to observe it throughout its entire history, we simply cannot confirm the validity of the first and second assumptions. Uniformitarians have devised techniques such as the isochron method in an attempt to overcome some of the uncertainties in radioisotope dating, but even the isochron method makes assumptions and often yields contradictory results.[14,15,16]

Most important, these results show the error of the third assumption. The high amounts of helium in zircon crystals within "old" granitic rock can be explained if nuclear decay rates have *not* been constant throughout time: 1.5 billion years of nuclear decay—based on today's rates—*did* occur (along with the accompanying alpha emission), but did so quite rapidly during an episode or episodes of "accelerated" decay within the last 6,000 years. This is why the helium has not yet had time to leak out of the zircon crystals. Likewise, the presence of detectable ^{14}C in supposedly very ancient specimens is another indication that nuclear decay rates have changed in the past. These specimens are said to be hundreds of millions of years old in large part because of radiometric dating's assumption of constant decay rates, yet this very assumption leads to a contradiction: Detectable ^{14}C, with its relatively short half-life, simply *should not be present* in such specimens if they are really that old—and yet it is!

In short, although this is an area of ongoing research, no Bible-believing Christian should be intimidated by the claims of radiometric dating.

Notes

1. The 238 in ^{238}U refers to the *mass number* of uranium, the sum of the number of protons and the number of neutrons within the nucleus of this variety (isotope) of uranium. Likewise, the 206 in ^{206}Pb means that this particular variety of lead has a combined total of 206 protons and neutrons within its nucleus.

2. Today's measured half-life for ^{238}U is about 4.5 billion years.

3. Morris, J. D. 1994. *The Young Earth*. Colorado Springs, CO: Master Books, 45-47.

4. Snelling, A. 1999. Radioactive 'dating' failure. *Journal of Creation*. 22 (1): 18-21.

5. Swenson, K. 2001. Radio-dating in Rubble, *Journal of Creation*. 23 (3): 23-25.

6. Morris, *The Young Earth*, 54-56.

7. Snelling, A. 2000. Conflicting "Ages" of Tertiary Basalt and Contained Fossilized Wood, Crinum, Central Queensland, Australia. *Journal of Creation*. 14 (2): 99-122.

8. Snelling, A. 2005. Radioisotope dating of rocks in the Grand Canyon. *Journal of Creation*. 27 (3): 44-49.

9. Many are surprised to learn that even if one started with a "lump" of ^{14}C with the same mass as the earth itself, the decay of ^{14}C occurs so quickly that *all* the ^{14}C would be gone in less than a million years! See footnote 3 in reference 12 for the details of this calculation.

10. Baumgardner, J. R. et al. 2003. Measurable ^{14}C in Fossilized Organic Materials: Confirming the Young Earth Creation-Flood Model. In *Proceedings of the Fifth International Conference on Creationism*. Pittsburgh, PA: Creation Science Fellowship, 127-142.

11. Baumgardner, Measurable ^{14}C in Fossilized Organic Materials.

12. Sarfati, J. 2006. Diamonds: a creationist's best friend. *Journal of Creation*. 28 (4): 26-27.

13. Humphreys, D. R. 2008. Helium evidence for a young world continues to confound critics. Creation Ministries International. Posted on creation.com November 29, 2008.

14. Austin, S. A. 1994. *Are Grand Canyon Rocks One Billion Years Old? Grand Canyon: Monument to Catastrophe*. Santee, CA: Institute for Creation Research, 119.

15. Snelling, A. 1994. U-Th-Pb "Dating": An Example of False "Isochrons." In *Proceedings of the Third International Conference on Creationism*. Pittsburgh, PA: Creation Science Fellowship, 497-504.

16. Austin, S. A. 1998. Discordant Potassium-Argon Model and Isochron "Ages" for Cardenas Basalt (Middle Proterozoic) and Associated Diabase of Eastern Grand Canyon, Arizona. In *Proceedings of Fourth International Conference on Creationism*. Pittsburgh, PA: Creation Science Fellowship, 35-51.

34

WAS THERE AN ICE AGE?

Jake Hebert, Ph.D.

There is abundant geological evidence that northern hemisphere glaciers (large bodies of ice resulting from the accumulation of snow) once extended to lower latitudes than they do today. For instance, unconsolidated dirt and rock debris (moraines) similar to those associated with modern-day glaciers are found at these lower latitudes and elevations. Likewise, scratches or grooves on surface rocks are believed to have been formed by rocks embedded within these large, slow-moving bodies of ice.[1]

A period characterized by the expansion and advance of high-latitude ice sheets and mountain glaciers is called an "ice age."[2] Evolutionists currently believe more than 50 ice ages have occurred within the last few million years.[3] Eight ice ages have supposedly occurred within roughly the last 800,000 years, each one lasting about 100,000 years. The glacial phase of each one is thought to have lasted about 90,000 years, with an interglacial phase lasting about 10,000 years.[4]

Although evolutionists routinely mention these supposed multiple ice ages, they have great difficulty explaining even a single ice age. In fact, a popular magazine listed this as one of the great remaining mysteries in science.[5]

One might think that colder winters are the key to producing an ice age, but there's more to it than that. Extremely cold temperatures generally result in less, not more, snowfall due to the lower moisture content of extremely cold air.[6] Also, some places on Earth today are very cold in the winter, but warm summers melt the winter snow before glaciers can form.[7]

An ice age requires cold summers and much more snowfall, and the conditions must persist over many years. In that way, snow and ice can build up year after year.

It is difficult to meet both of these conditions for any extended period of time in today's world. For instance, realistic computer simulations have shown that even a dramatic 12°C summer temperature decrease in northeastern Canada would result in only a modest advance in permanent snow cover. The snow cover would not even extend past the southern tip of Canada's Hudson Bay.[8] Yet geological evidence indicates that glaciers once extended well into the northern United States. Conditions in the past must have been radically different in order to produce an ice age.

The Genesis Flood provides these conditions. Extensive, dramatic volcanism would have occurred during the Flood, as a consequence of the breaking up of the "fountains of the great deep" (Genesis 7:11) and the resulting tectonic activity. Abundant evidence for such catastrophic volcanism on a continental scale appears in the geological record, although evolutionary scientists incorrectly assign ages of millions of years to these formations.

Basaltic lava flows during the Flood were hundreds—and even thousands—of cubic kilometers in volume.[9, 10] Large amounts of lava and hot water would have entered the ocean, causing the water during and after the Flood to have been considerably warmer than today, perhaps by tens of degrees Celsius.[11, 12] Flood currents and Earth movements would have mixed the water so that, after the Flood, the oceans would have been very uniform in temperature, which is unlike today's varied ocean temperatures. More evaporation would have occurred, particularly at the mid and high latitudes, as a result of a higher average ocean surface temperature. This would have provided the additional atmospheric moisture needed for greater snowfall.

The Flood would also have made possible the cooler summers needed to keep the winter snow from melting due to the extensive volcanism that occurred more frequently during the Flood and less frequently afterward. Explosive volcanic eruptions would have ejected large amounts of aerosols (tiny particles) into the stratosphere. Even today, aerosols from explosive volcanic eruptions remain suspended in the atmosphere for a number of years, so the same would have been true after the Flood. These aerosols would have reflected a great deal of sunlight back to space, resulting in the cooler summers needed for snow to accumulate.

Modern-day volcanic events have shown that volcanic aerosols can cause such cooling, as they did in the 1783 Laki basaltic eruption in Iceland and the 1991 eruption of Pinatubo in the Philippines.[13] Yet these eruptions were miniscule in comparison with the volcanic activity that occurred during the Flood.

As the earth slowly returned to equilibrium after the Flood, residual volcanism would have continued to sporadically eject aerosols into the stratosphere for many years, ensuring that summers remained cool enough to prevent the ice from melting. Also, because water has a high heat capacity, it relinquishes heat slowly. It would therefore have taken a significant amount of time for the oceans to cool to their present average surface temperature. As the oceans gradually cooled, evaporation would have decreased, resulting in less snowfall. Decreasing volcanic activity would have meant a gradual reduction in the amount of stratospheric aerosols, enabling more sunlight to reach Earth's surface. That would have enabled the glaciers to begin melting.

Meteorologist Michael Oard used "heat budget" equations to estimate the amount of time for the oceans to cool to their present average temperature. Although there are considerable uncertainties in the calculation, he estimated that the post-Flood Ice Age lasted for about 700 years—500 years for the glaciers to reach their maximum extent, and another 200 years for the glaciers to recede.[14] Since the Flood occurred around 2300 B.C.,[15] this would mean that the post-Flood Ice Age could have possibly lasted until about 1600 B.C.

It may not be a coincidence that the book of Job, believed by conservative scholars to have been written around 2000 B.C., has more references to snow and ice than any other book of the Bible. And harsher conditions as the Ice Age ended likely resulted in the extinction of many animals, including the wooly mammoths.[16, 17]

As noted earlier, evolutionists claim many ice ages have occurred throughout history, even in the (supposed) distant past. For instance, they claim that nearly the entire earth was frozen at least twice between 750 and 580 million years ago (the "Snowball Earth" hypothesis).[18] However, the argument for these ancient ice ages is based largely upon the existence of diamictite, or lithified rubble, in sedimentary layers that is interpreted to be glacial in origin. However, almost all the diamictite properties cited in support of this view can be duplicated by other mass-flow processes,[19] especially underwater debris flows and "turbidity currents."[20] Moreover, many of their properties are more consistent with underwater debris flows.[21, 22] Within the creation model, one would expect many catastrophic underwater mass flows to have occurred during the Genesis Flood.

So, not only is the Ice Age not a problem for the creation model, the creation model does a far better job of explaining the data than the evolution model does.

Notes

1. Oard, M. 2006. Where Does the Ice Age Fit? In *The New Answers Book 1*. K. Ham, ed. Green Forest, AR: Master Books, 207-219.

2. Ibid, 208.

3. Walker, M. and J. Lowe. 2007. Quaternary science 2007: a 50-year retrospective. *Journal of the Geological Society*. 164 (6):1073-1092.

4. Oard, Where Does the Ice Age Fit?, 210-211.

5. Watson, T. 1997. What causes ice ages? *U.S. News & World Report*. 123 (7): 58-60.

6. Lutgens, F. K. and E. J. Tarbuck. 2010. *The Atmosphere: An Introduction to Meteorology,* 11th ed. New York: Prentice Hall, 145-146.

7. Warm summers in Siberia prevent glaciation despite very cold winter temperatures.

8. Williams, L. D. 1979. An Energy Balance Model of Potential Glacierization of Northern Canada. *Arctic and Alpine Research*. 11 (4): 443-456.

9. Woodmorappe, J. and M. Oard. 2002. Field studies in the Columbia River basalt, Northwest USA. *Journal of Creation*. 16 (1): 103-110.

10. Silvestru, E. 2001. The Permian extinction: *National Geographic* comes close to the truth. *Journal of Creation*. 15 (1): 6-8.

11. Vardiman, L. 2001. *Climates Before and After the Genesis Flood*. San Diego, CA: Institute for Creation Research, 60.

12. Vardiman, L. 1998. Numerical Simulation of Precipitation Induced by Hot Mid-Ocean Ridges. In *Proceedings of the Fourth International Conference on Creationism*. Pittsburgh, PA: Creation Science Fellowship, 595-605.

13. de Castella, T. 2010. The eruption that changed Iceland forever. *BBC News Magazine*. Posted on news.bbc.co.uk April 16, 2010.

14. Oard, M. 1990. *An Ice Age Caused by the Genesis Flood*. San Diego, CA: Institute for Creation Research, 93-117.

15. Osgood, J. 1981. The Date of Noah's Flood. *Journal of Creation*. 4 (1): 10-13.

16. Oard, M. 2000. The extinction of the woolly mammoth: was it a quick freeze? *Journal of Creation*. 14 (3): 24-34.

17. Oard, M. 2004. *Frozen in Time*. Green Forest, AR: Master Books.

18. Cronin, T. M. 2010. *Paleoclimates: Understanding Climate Change Past and Present*. New York: Columbia University Press, 59-64.

19. Oard, M. 1994. Submarine Mass Flow Deposition of Pre-Pleistocene "Ice Age" Deposits. In *Proceedings of the Third International Conference on Creationism*. Pittsburgh, PA: Creation Science Fellowship, 407-418.

20. A turbidity current is a sediment-laden, rapidly moving current of water that flows through a larger body of water.

21. Molén, M. 1990. Diamictites: Ice-Ages or Gravity Flows? In *Proceedings of the Second International Conference on Creationism*. Pittsburgh, PA: Creation Science Fellowship, 177-190.

22. Oard, M. 1997. *Ancient Ice Ages or Gigantic Submarine Landslides?* Chino Valley, AZ: Creation Research Society Books.

35

DO SEAFLOOR SEDIMENT AND ICE CORE DATA PROVE LONG AGES?

Jake Hebert, Ph.D.

Sediments today are being deposited very slowly on the seafloors. At current rates, it can take a thousand years to lay down just a few centimeters of sediment.[1, 2] Scientists have drilled and extracted cylindrical cores from these sedimentary layers that can have combined lengths of hundreds of meters. Given these slow deposition rates, uniformitarians argue that these sedimentary layers were deposited over many millions of years.

Likewise, very old "ages" are assigned to layers within the high-latitude ice sheets. For instance, ice in the Greenland GISP2 ice core from a depth of 2,800 meters was supposedly deposited about 110,000 years ago.[3]

Clearly, these old ages are incompatible with the Bible's timescale of about 6,000 years. Do ice core and seafloor sediment data really require long ages?

The fact that sedimentation and precipitation rates would have been much higher shortly after the Genesis Flood (not to mention during the Flood itself) enables the seafloor sediment layers and high-latitude ice sheets to easily form within the biblical timeframe. However, uniformitarians might counter that their denial of recent creation and the Flood is justified. They would claim that ice core and seafloor sediment data both tell consistent "stories" about how climate has varied in the distant past. If completely independent data sets really tell similar and consistent stories of climate variation over hundreds of thousands of years, this would indeed be a strong argument for an old earth.

But is this really the case? In order to answer this question, it is necessary to briefly explain a quantity called $\delta^{18}O$ and what is known as the "astronomical theory."

$\delta^{18}O$ Variations within Seafloor Sediment Cores

The $\delta^{18}O$ ratio is a comparison of the amount of a "heavy" variety (or isotope) of oxygen (oxygen-18, or ^{18}O) compared to a "lighter" variety (oxygen-16, or ^{16}O). Values of $\delta^{18}O$ in the calcium carbonate ($CaCO_3$) shells of marine organisms called Foraminifera can be measured.

Past researchers used a relationship between the $\delta^{18}O$ ratio in the calcium carbonate and that of the seawater associated with the $CaCO_3$'s formation to estimate the $^{18}O/^{16}O$ ratio of seawater at the time the $CaCO_3$ was deposited. Because the $^{18}O/^{16}O$ ratio of seawater is temperature-dependent, it was used as a means of inferring seawater temperatures.[4]

Researchers now believe that the $\delta^{18}O$ ratio is strongly dependent upon the volume of the high-latitude ice sheets, so they now interpret it more as an indicator of the amount of glaciation than of temperature per se.[5] Since these values are thought to be indicators of the amount of ice cover on Earth, $\delta^{18}O$ within a seafloor sediment core can be used, in theory, to construct a chronology of climate variations in Earth's past.

The Astronomical (Milankovitch) Theory

The amount of sunlight reaching Earth varies with latitude and season. Moreover, Earth undergoes slow changes in its orbit over time. These orbital changes cause variations in the latitudinal and seasonal distribution of the sunlight reaching Earth. Because uniformitarians believe the solar system is very old, they extrapolate these slow changes back into the distant past. They think that the variations in $\delta^{18}O$ found in the seafloor sediments indicate changes in climate that were caused by these orbital variations. The "match" between $\delta^{18}O$ variations and supposed past changes in climate expected from these orbital variations is said to be an argument for an old earth.

However, this "astronomical theory" has serious problems. One such problem is that glacial-interglacial climate cycles supposedly occurred at 100,000-year intervals for about the last 800,000 years. This is thought to match a 100,000-year period of variation in the "eccentricity" (elongation) of Earth's orbit around the sun, but variations in eccentricity would result in only *tiny* changes in the sunlight reaching Earth. Many other serious difficulties with the theory could be cited.[6, 7]

If the astronomical theory has such serious difficulties, why then is there apparently good agreement between its predictions and the variations in $\delta^{18}O$ found in seafloor sediments? Despite its difficulties, uniformitarians are so certain the astronomical theory is correct that they use it to "tune" their seafloor sediment age-depth models.[8] In some cases, dates based upon radioactive dating have been adjusted based on "orbital tuning" considerations.[9] Not surprisingly, such tuning results in good agreement between predictions of the theory and what is found in the sedimentary record. Even some uniformitarians have acknowledged that this approach could be criticized as circular reasoning.[10]

Determining Annual Layers in Ice Cores

Because snow and ice generally do not melt in the polar latitudes, they accumulate over time. Thus, a previous layer of snow is covered by a succeeding layer, and that layer is covered by another layer, and so on. As layers of snow accumulate and the vertical thickness of the ice increases over time, the snow is transformed into ice as the air is squeezed out.

This accumulated ice contains "layers" that can theoretically be used to construct a chronology. Summer and winter snow layers are distinct from one another. For instance, winter snow tends to be more homogeneous than summer snow.[11] Likewise, because nitric acid (HNO_3) production in the stratosphere is higher in the spring/summer, variations in the acidity of the ice (determined by measurements of the ice's electrical conductivity) could also conceivably be used in the construction of a chronology.[12]

As in the case of seafloor sediments, scientists drill and extract cores from the ice in the hopes of using layers within the cores to date events in Earth's past.

Difficulties in Determining Annual Layers

Earth scientists would like to be able to determine the elapsed time since a layer within an ice core was deposited by visually inspecting and counting the annual layers within the ice. In actual practice, however, there are complicating factors.

Layering becomes more indistinct at greater depths within the core. This means that one cannot simply visually inspect and count these deeper layers if one wants to extend the chronology into the more distant past. Nor can one simply "guess" the locations of these "deeper" layers based on corresponding layer thicknesses higher in the core. The weight of the overlying snow and ice causes the layers to be forced downward, with a corresponding "thinning" of the layers that increases at greater core depths (see Figure 1). Hence, a theoretical flow model is needed to convert a measured distance down the length of the core into a time. These flow models implicitly assume that the ice sheets have been in existence for vast amounts of time.[13] Not surprisingly, they yield enormous ages for the ice sheets. Based on the target age from flow models and particular events recorded in the ice sheets, annual layer counting is matched to these flow models.[14, 15] Moreover, the dates from the seafloor sediment cores are used to determine the timescales for the glacier flow models![16]

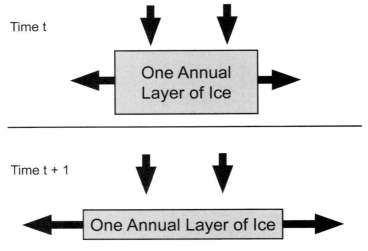

Figure 1. Annual layers of ice are compressed vertically due to pressure from the ice above. Horizontal lengthening compensates for the vertical shortening.[17]

The "reinforcement syndrome" is another factor contributing to the supposed match between the seafloor sediment and ice core data and the predictions of the astronomical theory. Researchers have a tendency to "see" in the data what they expect. This is not necessarily intentional dishonesty, but a subtle, usually unconscious form of bias.

Examples of the reinforcement syndrome abound in the historical sciences. Geologists used to believe that four ice ages had occurred within the last few million years, and this model was supposedly confirmed by virtually all the data for about 60 years.[18] Even within the last decade, some museum displays still taught this older model of Earth history.[19] Yet this older model has now been abandoned in favor of the modern astronomical theory, with its much higher number of ice ages. Why, then, did so many evolutionists "see" evidence for a view of Earth history that even they now admit is wrong? [20]

So, the "matches" between the predictions of the astronomical theory and what is found in ice and seafloor sediment cores are not independent arguments for an old earth.

Creation Models

Creation scientists Michael Oard and Larry Vardiman have constructed separate age models for seafloor sediments and glacial ice.[21, 22] These models quite reasonably assume higher deposition rates shortly after the Flood. For instance, during the latter stages of the Flood, one would expect sediments to be deposited into the oceans at much higher rates than those of today. Likewise, shortly after the Flood, high-latitude precipitation rates would have been much higher than they are today. This, combined with cooler summers in the years after the Flood, would have enabled the high-latitude ice sheets to be formed in just hundreds of years (see chapter 34).

These creation models result in greatly reduced ages for the ice sheets and seafloor sediments, ages that are compatible with the biblical timescale. Moreover, these models can explain aspects of the data that puzzle evolutionists.[23, 24] As is often the case in the creation-evolution controversy, the "facts" are not neutral. The conclusions one draws from the data are dramatically affected by one's starting assumptions.

Notes

1. Cronin, T. M. 2010. *Paleoclimates: Understanding Climate Change Past and Present*. New York: Columbia University Press, 28.

2. Vardiman, L. 1996. *Sea-Floor Sediment and the Age of the Earth*. El Cajon, CA: Institute for Creation Research, 10.

3. Meese, D. A. et al. 1997. The Greenland Ice Sheet Project 2 depth-age scale: Methods and results. *Journal of Geophysical Research*. 102 (C12): 26,411–26,423.

4. Vardiman, *Sea-Floor Sediment and the Age of the Earth*, 49.

5. Walker, M. and J. Lowe. 2007. Quaternary science 2007: a 50-year retrospective. *Journal of the Geological Society*. 164 (6): 1073-1092.

6. Cronin, *Paleoclimates*, 130-139.

7. Oard, M. 2007. Astronomical troubles for the astronomical hypothesis of ice ages. *Journal of Creation*. 21 (3).

8. Herbert, T. D. 2009. Paleoceanography: Orbitally Tuned Timescales. In *Climates and Oceans*. J. H. Steele, ed. Amsterdam, NL: Academic Press, 370-377.

9. Ibid, 374.

10. Ibid.

11. Alley, R. B. et al. 1997. Visual-stratigraphic dating of the GISP2 ice core: Basis, reproducibility, and application. *Journal of Geophysical Research.* 102 (C12): 26,367–26,381.

12. Meese, 26,412.

13. Dansgaard, W, and S. J. Johnsen. 1969. A flow model and a time scale for the ice core from Camp Century, Greenland. *Journal of Glaciology.* 8 (53):215-223.

14. Oard, M. 2005. *The Frozen Record.* Santee, CA: Institute for Creation Research, 74-75.

15. Meese, The Greenland Ice Sheet Project, 26,417–26,419.

16. Waelbroeck, C. et al. 1995. A comparison of the Vostok ice deuterium record and series from Southern Ocean core MD 88-770 over the last two glacial-interglacial cycles. *Climate Dynamics.* 12: 113-123.

17. Oard, *The Frozen Record,* Figure 3.13, 45.

18. Ibid, 122.

19. Ham, K (ed.). 2006. *The New Answers Book.* Green Forest, AR: Master Books, 211.

20. Other examples of the reinforcement syndrome in the creation-evolution controversy could be cited. See Lubenow, M. 1995. The pigs took it all. *Creation.* 17 (3): 36-38.

21. Vardiman, L. 2001. *Climates Before and After the Genesis Flood.* El Cajon, CA: Institute for Creation Research, 41-80.

22. Oard, *The Frozen Record,* 35-50.

23. Ibid, 133-140.

24. Patrick, K. 2010. Manganese nodules and the age of the ocean floor. *Journal of Creation.* 24 (3): 82-86.

36

CATASTROPHIC PLATE TECTONICS

John D. Morris, Ph.D.

Plate tectonics dominates geologic thinking today. First proposed by creationists in 1860, and adopted by secularists in the 1960s to explain a host of geological and tectonic observations, it has become the unifying concept in Earth history. Today there are virtually no advocates of the stable continent idea, either among creationists or uniformitarian geologists.

The secular version of the theory proposes that today's continents drifted into their present locations as subsurface fluid movements dragged the continents along at nearly imperceptibly slow speeds. Evidence cited in support of this includes the fit of plate boundaries now separated by oceans (for example, eastern South America fits the west coast of Africa quite nicely), and the fact that certain faults and linear mountain chains line up when the continents are placed together. Unique fossil content of now-separated areas sometimes matches when reassembled. Utilizing sensitive GPS-like systems, tiny continental movements can be observed today in the general direction of theorized past movements and directions.

The biggest question is: How can you move a continent? They are much too large to pull—they would break. They are also too weak to push—they would crumple. Perhaps they could be moved by the slow underground fluid currents advocates propose, but these have not been observed and involve an exotic state of rock. There simply is no way to move continents using forces we recognize.

To most students of Earth history, it does appear that the continents were once together and have separated. The questions remain—did these movements occur at present velocities, and were they caused by today's forces?

Earth's surface is divided into tectonic plates observed to move relative to one another. The rate of movement is slow today, only discernible by sensitive satellite-based measuring equipment. The boundaries of these plates are active earthquake zones, allowing us to discern the relative direction of movement. Some plates are sporadically moving horizontally past the adjacent plate, such as along the famous San Andreas Fault in California. Some plates, such as along the mid-Atlantic Ridge, are moving away from each other, leaving a low-lying rift valley behind. Others are moving toward each other, and the collisions either crumple up mountains (e.g., the Himalayas) or cause the more dense oceanic plate to plunge beneath the less dense continental plate, resulting in volcanoes, earthquakes, and occasional tsunamis.

Creation/Flood advocates generally accept plate tectonics, but consider the spreading speed to have been much greater in the past, and the forces more dynamic and quite different from those acting today. In general, a planet-wide cataclysm like the great Flood of Noah's day, which restructured the globe, must have been involved, a situation that implies much different conditions than those observed today.

It may be that on the original created Earth, all continents were connected into one great stationary super-continent, but we can't be sure. Reconstructing the former world is difficult if not impossible, for the forces in action during the Flood destroyed much of the evidence. Whether or not they were together at creation, it does appear that at least all the land masses were together sometime during the Flood. From matching rock strata traits and boundaries, creationist geophysicists consider it likely that they were indeed together at the height of the Flood and then separated.

Consider the implications of what the Bible reveals. Forces powerful enough to rend a plate asunder and then to move huge continents away from their original locations were evidently not acting when creation was initially completed, nor were they activated by the Curse. A more likely scenario, and one implied by Scripture, is that the plates were set in motion by the same causes that initiated and facilitated the great Flood.

One of the most important research successes in creation thinking was the development of the concept of Catastrophic Plate Tectonics by six of the leading creationist theorists, experts from several fields of science. They recognized the evidence for plate tectonics was quite strong, but that it was interpreted wrongly by uniformitarians. The data fit better into the short chronology of Scripture. Rightly considered, Scripture describes the breaking up of the "fountains of the great deep" (Genesis 7:11) as the primary mechanism for not only causing the great Flood and subsequent plate movements, but also for ending the Flood and redistributing Earth's land mass to its present configuration.[1]

Evidence has been found that the oceanic plates subducted under adjacent continents quite rapidly. This possibility has been understood as more has been learned concerning the properties of rock under intense heat, temperature, and stress. Basaltic ocean plates are denser than the granitic continents, and would thus normally tend to come to rest at lower elevations. Remnants of the pre-separation continents have actually been discovered deep underground, near the interface of Earth's core and mantle. Therefore, some vast cataclysm (i.e., the great Flood) is required to have broken them loose and caused them to rapidly sink.

At the height of the Flood, water stood above the mountains, but at its end the waters rushed off into deep ocean basins, where they are now. Scripture poetically tells us concerning the Flood that "You [God] covered it [the earth] with the deep as with a garment; the waters stood above the mountains. At Your rebuke they fled; at the voice of Your thunder they hasted away. They went up over the mountains; they went down into the valleys, to the place which You founded for them" (Psalm 104:6-8).

Some global tectonic mechanism must have been involved to deepen the oceans (the "valleys") and raise the continents. Plate tectonics no doubt played the major role, for as the continents rifted apart, they would have gouged out a low place. This must have involved rapid movements, not the modern miniscule rates. The continents "sprinted" rather than "drifted" to their new locations, leaving behind low-lying trenches into which the Flood waters drained, thereby exposing the land. The Flood's waters didn't need to be annihilated; they needed only to be redistributed to reveal the land. Concurrently, new oceanic plates formed as basaltic magma rose along the mid-ocean rifts.

Today, we see the evidence of past movement at much greater rates. The plate tectonic model and reconstruction of continents using catastrophic considerations resembles that of the standard view, except for the rate of plate movements. There are several unexplained enigmas in uniformitarian plate tectonics that Catastrophic Plate Tectonics explains quite plausibly.[1]

Note

1. Baumgardner, J. 1986. Numerical Simulation of the Large-Scale Tectonic Changes Accompanying the

Flood. In *Proceedings of the First International Conference on Creationism*. R. E. Walsh, C. L. Brooks and R. S. Crowell, eds. Pittsburgh, PA: Creation Science Fellowship, Inc., 17-28; Austin, S. A. et al. 1994. Catastrophic Plate Tectonics: A Global Flood Model of Earth History. In *Proceedings of the Third International Conference on Creationism*, R. E. Walsh, ed. Pittsburgh, PA: Creation Science Fellowship, Inc., 609-621; Baumgardner, J. 2003. Catastrophic Plate Tectonics: The Physics Behind the Genesis Flood. In *Proceedings of the Fifth International Conference on Creationism*. R. L. Ivey, Jr., ed. Pittsburgh, PA: Creation Science Fellowship, 113-126; Baumgardner, J. Runaway Subduction as the Driving Mechanism for the Genesis Flood. In *Proceedings of the Third International Conference on Creationism*, 63-86.

37

DEVELOPING A SENSIBLE APPROACH TO HUMAN ORIGINS RESEARCH, PART 1: FOSSILS AND BIAS

Randy J. Guliuzza, P.E., M.D.

Why not accept the evolutionary explanation for human origins? This is a fair question that is sure to come up. There is no need to jump right into a list of the many scientific problems regarding the supposed evolution of humans. It might be better to frame a discussion with a few comments on biblical authority and a reminder of how real science is performed.

Biblical history and evolutionary stories of human origins cannot be reconciled. If you are discussing human origins with a Christian, all believers should know that the Bible clearly teaches that humans are all descended from one human couple, Adam and Eve (Genesis 1:28; 3:20; 5:1-3; Mathew 19:4-6; Mark 10:6-9; Acts 17:26). Adam was a direct creation by God (Genesis 2:7; Luke 3:38); Eve was formed from tissue from Adam's side (Genesis 2:21-23; 1 Corinthians 11:8-9; 1 Timothy 2:13); and both were specially created in the image of God (Genesis 1:26-27; 5:2; Colossians 3:10). A real Adam disbelieved God's word, disobeyed, and brought the whole human race under God's condemnation in need of the Lord's salvation brought to mankind by the Second Adam, Jesus Christ (Romans 5:6-21; 1 Corinthians 15:45-47). Those truths should settle the issue for Christians.

Evolutionists claim that humans evolved over several million years from an ape-like ancestor. Theistic evolutionists hold to an evolutionary origin of man. A current popular teaching among some self-described "evangelical" Christians is that there was not a literal Adam and Eve, there was not a genuine "fall of man," and the starting population of humans was about 10,000.[1]

This position clearly clashes with biblical history and is, therefore, in error.

But excellent scientific genetic studies have been published confirming biblical history.[2, 3, 4]

Human origins research cannot be verified by observation and experiment-based science. Evolutionary paleontological "science" is *different* from sciences that use natural, repeatable, and verifiable methods to explain phenomena. The phenomena in this case are bone fragments unearthed around the world. Evolution is fundamentally a historical narrative—a story—attempting to reconstruct unseen events.[5] Because human origins research is so subjective, one student of the researchers voices a caution applicable to all: "We have only to recall the Piltdown adventure to see how easily susceptible researchers can be manipulated into believing that they have actually found just what they had been looking for."[6]

Therefore, explanations for the history, and especially origins, of bone fragments are based on personal interpretation, which is the weakest form of evidence since it factors in a multitude of biases.

- Know that paleontology is based on historical narratives; it is not the same type of experimental science as physics or chemistry.
- Be aware that at times in human origins research, fast fame trumps facts.

Interpretations of fossil fragments lack independent oversight. Generally, the same researcher(s) discovers the bones, maintains initial access to the bones, publishes the first headline-grabbing description, and interprets where these fossils fit into the line of human origins—if at all—and their significance.[7] There is clearly an unavoidable bias and a predisposition to hype a discovery's significance, especially when paleontological politics and scientific credibility are big factors.[7, 8] If other researchers can get access to the originals—a big "if"—their published critiques come much later with less fanfare. Thus, lacking verifiable experimental data, consensus is rare[9] and often results in personal conclusions of the fossil remains far in excess of what the data will support.[10]

- Be cautious of fossil examinations carried out in secret.
- Realize critical analysis is limited, since only a few get to study the fossils.
- Remember, history shows that nearly all fossil finds are initially over-hyped and under-investigated.[11, 12]

Preconceived ideas can blind a person to alternative interpretations of data.

Similarities are poor evidence for an ape-like ancestor to the human family tree. Every claim about humans and apes sharing a common ancestor hangs on one type of evidence—similarities. These similarities are anatomical, physiological, social, and genetic. The huge problem is that this argument is nothing but one huge exercise in circular thinking, namely, that the evidence for common ancestry is common features, and any common features found are explained by common ancestry.

Darwin disregarded the circularity of this argument just like his followers do today. For them, this is an axiom—an obvious truth—not needing outside experimental validation. In 1859, Darwin's explanation was more like dogma: "The similar framework of bones in the hand of a man, wing of a bat, fin of the porpoise, and leg of the horse…and innumerable other such facts, at once *explain themselves* on the theory of descent with slow and slight successive modification."[13]

"Inconsistent" is the best word to describe how evolutionists compare similar features amongst organisms. This is because similar features are just that—similar—and the myriads of combinations organisms possess do not necessarily fit branching evolutionary trees. If evolutionists believe a similar feature is from a common ancestor, they say it is due to "divergent evolution," whereas if organisms share a similar feature not due to common ancestry, it is conveniently called "convergent evolution." Scientific-sounding lingo is substituted for data to explain why organisms with essentially no common ancestry have extraordinarily similar features, such as the camera-like eye shared by squids and humans.[14]

- Circular arguments are naturally self-certifying.

- Explanations for the presence or absence of similar features are totally arbitrary.

- Evolutionists pick and choose which similar traits, especially human-chimp genetic comparisons,[15] to showcase…or to make excuses for inconsistencies (anatomical, molecular, or anatomical-to-molecular) of the data.

Bias, and More Bias

So what do the fossilized bones say for themselves? Nothing. They must always be interpreted. Interpretations of fossil fragments are constrained by personal bias; often, these interpretations are eventually determined to be in error. Nevertheless, one source of evolutionary bias is unalterable: The fossils will *always* be interpreted within the total evolutionary context. Though this is just another example of circular thinking, for evolutionists it would be inconceivable not to interpret these fossils as evidence for evolution.

Donald Johanson, co-discoverer of the famous fossil Lucy, summed up this self-evident fact: "Unique Lucy may be, but she is incomprehensible outside the context of other fossils. She becomes meaningless unless she is fitted into a scheme of hominid evolution." This interpretation is fitted into a bigger context of descent from a common ancestor: "That story could not even begin to be told, of course, until Charles Darwin suggested in 1857 [*sic*] that we were descended from apes and not divinely created in 4004 B.C. as the Church insisted."[16]

- Ask "what is the evidence" and "does it make sense" regardless of what "the experts" say.

- Recognize that human evolutionary theory is "plastic"…easily absorbing any observation or finding.

Developing a Sensible Approach to Human Origins Research,
Part 1: Fossils and Bias

Notes

1. Hagerty, B. B. Evangelicals Question the Existence Of Adam And Eve. NPR *Morning Edition*. Posted on npr.org August 9, 2011.

2. Carter, R. W. The Non-Mythical Adam and Eve!: Refuting errors by Francis Collins and BioLogos. Creation Ministries International. Posted on creation.com August 20, 2011.

3. Carter, R. W. Does Genetics Point to a Single Primal Couple?: A response to claims to the contrary from BioLogos. Creation Ministries International. Posted on creation.com April 30, 2011.

4. Thomas, B. Christian Professor Claims Genetics Disproves Historical Adam. *Creation Science Update*. Posted on icr.org August 26, 2011.

5. Mayr, E. Darwin's Influence on Modern Thought. *Scientific American*, July 2000, 80. Later, Ernst Mayr (Harvard University's leading evolutionary theorist) reiterated the role of historical narrative in paleontological sciences when he said, "The earliest fossils of *Homo*, *Homo rudolfensis* and *Homo erectus*, are separated from *Australopithicus* by a large, unbridged gap. How can we explain this seeming saltation? Not having any fossils that can serve as missing links, we have to fall back on the time-honored method of historical science, the construction of a historical narrative." Mayr, E. 2004. *What Makes Biology Unique?* New York: Cambridge University Press, 198.

6. Maienschein, J. 1997. The One and the Many: Epistemological Reflections on the Modern Human Origins Debates. In *Conceptual Issues in Modern Human Origins Research*. Clark, G. and C. Willermet, eds. Hawthorne, NY: Aldine de Gruyter, 413.

7. Johanson, D. and B. Edgar. 1996. *From Lucy to Language*. New York: Simon & Schuster, 32.

8. Holden, C. 1981. The Politics of Paleoanthropology. *Science* 213 (4509): 737-740.

9. Keim, B. Bone Crunching Debunks 'First Monkey' Ida Fossil Hype. *Wired Science*. Posted on wired.com October 21, 2009.

10. Gee, H. 2001. Return to the planet of the apes. *Nature*. 412 (6843): 131

11. Thomas, B. and F. Sherwin. Ida: Separating the Science from the Media Campaign *Creation Science Update*. Posted on icr.org May 22, 2009. See also Thomas, B. 2009. The Ida Fossil: A Clever Campaign for a Lackluster "Link." *Acts & Facts*. 38 (7): 17.

12. Thomas, B. New Fossil Hype Fits Old Pattern. *Creation Science Update*. Posted on icr.org May 27, 2009

13. Darwin, C. 1872. *The Origin of Species By Means of Natural Selection*, 6th ed. London: John Murray, 420 (emphasis added).

14. Guliuzza, R. 2009. *Clearly Seen: Constructing Solid Arguments for Design*. Dallas, TX: Institute for Creation Research.

15. Tomkins, J. and J. Bergman. 2012. Genomic monkey business—estimates of nearly identical human-chimp DNA similarity re-evaluated using omitted data. *Journal of Creation*. 26 (1): 94-100.

16. Johanson, D. and M. Edey. 1981. *Lucy: The Beginnings of Humankind*. New York: Touchstone, 24.

38

DEVELOPING A SENSIBLE APPROACH TO HUMAN ORIGINS RESEARCH, PART 2: UNDERSTANDING THE FOSSILS

Randy J. Guliuzza, P.E., M.D.

Artistic License Fills Great Gaps in Fossil Evidence

Researchers use a great deal of artistic license in interpreting what fossils look like. The problem is that there is rarely enough bony material to provide reliable information to put flesh on the bones.

Thus, when it comes to reconstructing a fossil considered to be "hominid" (the category into which evolutionists lump both apes and humans), the researcher's and artist's preconceived bias will determine facial and other anatomical features as expressed in type of skin, amount and color of hair, posture, and if it will have distinctively unique human features such as the white portions of the eyes, and, in females, a wide pelvis and permanently enlarged breasts. Conversely, fossils with distinctly human features such as *Homo erectus* often have artistic renditions emphasizing ape-like characteristics.

Though these artistic features may have nothing to do with reality—since no one can verify if they are right or wrong—they can greatly skew any conclusions about the fossil evidence, which is more akin to propaganda. A famous evolutionary artist reverently commented on his reconstruction of the fossil called Lucy, "I wanted to get a human soul into this ape-like face, to indicate something about where she was headed."[1]

- Be cautious of "scientific conclusions" with signs of strong emotional or spiritual bias.

- Note that evolutionary artists regularly "ape-ify" humans and humanize apes.

- Never underestimate the power of reconstruction.

"Hominid" Fossils Fall into Basically Two Discontinuous Categories: Apes and Humans

Though interpretations of such fossils are confined by bias, there are several telling facts about these bones that make evolutionary interpretations difficult. First, they are generally fragments. One leading evolutionist said these "fragments of jaws" and "scraps of skulls" serve as the "basis for endless speculation."[2] Second, there are not very many of them...especially to build a strong case for human evolution.[3]

Third, major fossils for supposed human ancestry fall into distinct types that are "seemingly separated by discontinuities from their nearest ancestors and descendents. This is particularly true for the break between *Australopithecus* and *Homo*."[4] (In general, the fossils called australopithecines show predominantly ape-like traits and those labeled *Homo* show human-like traits.) Fourth, human-like fossils demonstrate a sudden increase in brain capacity and essentially appear suddenly in the fossil record.[5]

Distinct types of fossils fall into ape-like fossil or human-like fossil categories—they are not transitional. One fossil called Ardi (*Ardipithecus ramidus*) received much media attention in 2009 as possibly leading to an ancestor of the australopithecines. The significance of Ardi in that regard may have been overblown,[6] but by all accounts Ardi is clearly ape-like.[7] The australopithecines, which include Lucy, are also plainly ape-like,[8] with questionable evidence that they were upright bipedal walkers,[9] and, as noted earlier, are discontinuous with *Homo*. The 2011 report of *A. sediba*, the supposed youngest australopithecine, describes a creature with principally ape-like features.[10]

Fossils of the group called *Homo*, principally *H. erectus*, *H. neanderthalensis*, and *H. sapiens*, demonstrate features most similar to living humans. (Notable exceptions are *H. habilis* and *H. rudolfensis*, which are now in the Rudolfensis group due to more ape-like features.) Fossil skeletons of both *H. erectus* and *H. neanderthalensis* are within the range of living humans, and all evidence suggests that both of these are so similar, they probably could have reproduced with *H. sapiens* (humans living today).[11,12]

Not surprisingly, therefore, four general depictions of fossils of these creatures are the same as for fossils in general: 1) They appear abruptly in the fossil record; 2) they remain essentially unchanged throughout their history; 3) a fossil and its living counterpart show no or only minor differences; and 4) there are discontinuities between kinds.

The "Neandertals" and *H. erectus* were not "sub-humans" who lived before Adam, but were people who lived after the Flood.[13] They were not dimwitted, clumsy brutes, as characterized in much of evolutionary literature or rendered as "cavemen" by evolutionary artists. At least for Neandertals, they could be characterized as culturally similar to other humans living contemporaneously.[14]

Many post-Flood humans certainly did live in caves after dispersal at the Tower of Babel. The patriarch Job, who lived only a few centuries after the Flood, describes this condition: "They were driven out from among men, they shouted at them as at a thief. They had to live in the clefts of the valleys, in caves of the earth and the rocks" (Job 30:5-6). In absolute contrast to evolutionary stories, the Bible teaches that humans were created fully functional, fully human, and fully in the image of God (Genesis 1:26-28).[15]

- Fossils of both ape-like and human-like creatures are scarce.

- Be ready for the usual overblown fanfare trumpeting all new "ancestors to humans."

- Know that both ape-like fossil and human-like fossils appear suddenly in the record.

- Be aware that major discontinuities exist between ape-like fossil and human-like fossils.

- Focusing on fossils or similar features sidetracks discussion from the main question evolutionists have failed to answer, which is: How did the complex information and molecular construction machinery needed to make any feature on any creature originate?

Notes

1. Johanson, D. 1996. The Dawn of Humans: Face-to-Face with Lucy's Family. *National Geographic.* 189 (3): 96-117.

2. Gould, S. 1980. *The Panda's Thumb: More Reflections in Natural History.* New York: Simon & Schuster, 22.

3. Holden, C. 1981. The Politics of Paleoanthropology. *Science* 213 (4509): 737-740.

4. Mayr, E. 2001. *What Evolution Is.* New York: Basic Books, 238. In a later publication, Mayr wrote on the same topic and said, "The earliest fossils of *Homo, Homo rudolfensis* and *Homo erectus*, are separated from *Australopithicus* by a large, unbridged gap. How can we explain this seeming saltation? Not having any fossils that can serve as missing links, we have to fall back on the time-honored method of historical science, the construction of a historical narrative." Mayr, E. 2004. *What Makes Biology Unique?* New York:

Cambridge University Press, 198.

5. Mayr, *What Evolution Is,* 246.

6. Thomas, B. Scientists Back Off of Ardi Claims. *Creation Science Update.* Posted on icr.org December 4, 2009.

7. Wood, B. and T. Harrison. 2011. The evolutionary context of the first hominins. *Nature.* 470 (7334): 347-352. Thomas, B. 2009. Did Humans Evolve from "Ardi"? *Acts & Facts.* 38 (11): 8-9. Thomas, B. 2010. Evolutionist Tosses out 'Ardi' as Human Ancestor. *Creation Science Update.* Posted on icr.org June 8, 2010, accessed July 31, 2012.

8. Morris, J. 2010. *The Fossil Record: Unearthing Nature's History of Life.* Dallas, TX: Institute for Creation Research, 107.

9. Spoor, F., B. Wood, and F. Zonneveld. 1994. Implications of early hominid labyrinthine morphology for evolution of human bipedal locomotion. *Nature.* 369 (6482): 645-648. Lubenow, M. Lucy's child, "Selam," from Ethiopia. Answers in Genesis. Posted on answersingenesis.org November 1, 2006.

10. Dewitt, D. It's an Ape...It's a Human...It's...It's...a Missing Link! Answers in Genesis. Posted on answersingenesis.org September 13, 2011.

11. Johanson, D. and M. Edey. 1981. *Lucy: The Beginnings of Humankind.* New York: Touchstone, 144.

12. Dalton, R. Neanderthals may have interbred with humans. *Nature News.* Posted on nature.com April 20, 2010.

13. Cuozzo, J. 1998. *Buried Alive.* Green Forest, AR: Master Books.

14. Ibid, 103. Thomas, B. Humans Used Fire Earlier than Believed. *Creation Science Update.* Posted on icr.org May 21, 2012. Sherwin, F. Humans Are Humans, After All. *Creation Science Update.* Posted on icr.org April 5, 2008.

15. Guliuzza, R. 2009. *Made in His Image: Examining the complexities of the human body.* Dallas, TX: Institute for Creation Research.

DINOSAURS AND MAN

WALKED TOGETHER OR
RULED APART?

39

DINOSAURS AND THE BIBLE

Frank Sherwin, M.A.

In the war of the worldviews, creationists and evolutionists have very different understandings regarding the origin and demise of dinosaurs. Christians have the written record of One who was there "in the beginning," while the evolutionist has no such record and must speculate within a naturalistic framework.

Dinosaur Origin

When discussing dinosaurs, one must know where true scientific research (experimental or empirical) leaves off and where non-scientific interpretation begins. For example, a biologist conducts research on plants and animals in the laboratory or in the field by observing, testing, and repeating a biological process. Conversely, a historian collects reliable past material and eyewitness accounts in order to verify a certain historical event, be it a war, election, or assassination. The historian does not test or repeat, as the scientist does.

This should be remembered when discussing the *origin* of plants, animals, people, or planets. Simply put, the origin of dinosaurs (or any other creature) cannot be "proved" by laboratory science techniques. It is a past event that cannot be presently tested. We must consult eyewitness accounts instead. A judge will tell you that when reconstructing the past—either ancient or recent—the testimony of reliable eyewitnesses routinely takes precedence over other forms of evidence.

Whatever their zoological classification (see below), God tells us clearly that He created dinosaurs on Day Six of the creation week just 6,000 years ago. Evolutionists maintain dinosaurs evolved from non-dinosaur ancestors around 235 million years ago. However, it is interesting that when dinosaurs are unearthed, they are 100 percent dinosaurs—as predicted by creationists.

In Genesis 1:24, we read of the formation of "cattle" (referring to domestic animals), "creeping things" (small creatures), and "beasts of the earth" (the large, non-domestic animals). There were perhaps about 50 different basic "kinds" of dinosaurs, and their fossils show that they had well-proportioned bodies that were well-designed for the life each led. Some dinosaurs, like *Compsognathus* or *Mussaurus*, were small "creeping things." But others, like *Tyrannosaurus* or *Ultrasaurus*, were large "beasts of the earth" made alongside man on Day Six, according to the testimony of the only One who was actually there.

So we see the first and most important eyewitness when it comes to dinosaur origin was the Creator Himself. He wrote in Genesis 1:25:

> And God made the beast of the earth according to its kind, cattle according to its kind, and everything that creeps on the earth according to its kind.

Evolutionists claim that dinosaurs were wiped off the earth millions of years before the arrival of humans. But Genesis makes clear that dinosaurs did not become extinct (if indeed they are) before man because he was given dominion over all types of animals (Genesis 1:28).

Evolutionists, of course, routinely dismiss the eyewitness biblical record. In 2001, a husband/wife team wrote, "Likewise, humans did not directly observe the evolution of the dinosaurs, but their evolution is nonetheless considered to be scientific fact."[1] But the authors simply *assume* that real or vertical evolution occurred—in a book dedicated to defending vertical evolution.

Meanwhile, a 2011 *Science* magazine article stated:

> The demise of *T. rex* and most other dinosaurs some 65 million years ago may grab all the headlines. But paleontologists are equally concerned with puzzling out how these mighty beasts got their start. Who were their ancestors?[2]

Dinosaurs called titanosaurs "were one of the most widespread and successful species of sauropod dinosaurs, [but] their origin and dispersion are not completely understood."[3]

Dragons and Dinosaurs

Ancient cultures worldwide, as well as having flood legends, also have dragon legends. One of the more fascinating recent discoveries is a fossil called

Dracorex hogwartsia unearthed in North America. It had spiky horns and a long muzzle that surprised paleontologists. In a press release from Stanford University, an evolutionist stated, "The skull looks strangely familiar to anyone who has studied dragons! *Dracorex* has a remarkable resemblance to the dragons of ancient China and medieval Europe."[4] Creationists maintain that many different cultures in the past (e.g., ancient Welsh, Babylonian, Chinese, Australian aboriginal, and Egyptian) have similar dragon legends that they could not have gotten from just viewing dinosaur fossils. It is probable that ancestors of various people groups actually saw these dragons (dinosaurs) and passed the sightings on to the next generation.

Many are familiar with England's St. George and the dragon with which he had to contend. Alexander the Great's army encountered a dragon, as did Marco Polo. Flavius Philostratus provided this account in the third century A.D.:

> The whole of India is girt with dragons of enormous size; for not only the marshes are full of them, but the mountains as well, and there is not a single ridge without one. Now the marsh kind are sluggish in their habits and are thirty cubits long, and they have no crest standing up on their heads.[5]

Pliny the Elder also referenced large dragons in India in his *Natural History.*

What exactly is a dinosaur? Answering this question is not as easy as it first seems. Until the advent of dinosaur soft tissue discovery, paleontologists only had mineralized remains—fossils—of these creatures. Because we have just the fossils, it is difficult, though not impossible, to say how many different kinds of dinosaurs there were.

Additionally, were dinosaurs warm-blooded or cold-blooded? How do zoologists classify them—as mammals, reptiles, or just uniquely dinosaurs? Answers to these scientific questions require more research.

Dinosaurs in Scripture

One cannot find "dinosaur" in the King James Bible (1611) because the word did not exist when it was translated. Dinosaurs were rediscovered as fossils in 1822 (remember, Adam and his progeny saw living dinosaurs first!), and the word "dinosaur" was coined in 1841 by creationist Sir Richard Owen, first superintendent of the prestigious British Museum.

The book of Job offers eyewitness testimony, providing the reader with a good answer to the question regarding dinosaurs and the Bible. In addition, James, Ezekiel, and Paul refer to the book of Job, authenticating its historical reliably.

In chapter 40 beginning at verse 15, God compares Job to the power of a large creature called behemoth, a term that may be defined as a "huge beast." We read, "Look now at the behemoth, which I made along with you…he moves his tail like a cedar." Unfortunately, many Bible commentators inexplicably think the creature Job describes is a hippopotamus or elephant, despite their both having a tail that is nothing like a cedar. It would seem that these modern commentators are influenced by corrupt evolutionary thinking, supposing that dinosaurs were long-extinct by Job's day.

Further in Job 40, we read the phrase "first of the ways of God." This phrase indicates this was the largest land animal God created, and the elephant and hippo were certainly not the largest land animals.

Jeremiah 9:11 and 10:22 (KJV) speak of "den of dragons," using the Hebrew word *tannim* meaning "monsters." There's no reason to think Jeremiah was not referring to dinosaurs that survived for centuries in isolated areas after the Flood.

Dinosaurs, the Flood, and the Ark

At least two of each land-dwelling, air-breathing kind, including dinosaurs, went aboard the Ark. Genesis 7:8-9 states, "Of clean animals, of animals that are unclean, of birds, and of everything that creeps on the earth, two by two they went into the ark to Noah, male and female, as God had commanded Noah." The three sons of Noah were firsthand eyewitnesses to these events and co-authored this section of Scripture, which ends with their "signatures" in Genesis 10:1.

Those who claim that dinosaurs could not have fit on the Ark might recall that the average dinosaur size was on the order of a large dog. Even the massive dinosaurs started out from football-size eggs, and juveniles of these groups could have easily been selected to board the life-saving vessel. All air-breathing, land-dwelling animals—including the dinosaurs—found outside the Ark perished in the worldwide deluge described in Genesis 6–9. The massive sedimentary (water-deposited) rock units containing billions of fossils of dinosaurs (and other animals and plants) on the continents are testimony to the Deluge. Most dinosaur fossil deposits are composed of solid-rock fossils formed during and soon after the Flood. But dinosaur soft tissue has been discovered (and discoveries continue to be made) that is described as "still squishy" and containing recognizable blood cells. Science continues to demonstrate that dinosaurs did not predate humans and that dinosaur kinds did not go extinct (*if* they all have) until after the Flood. Indeed, a mummified (*not* fossilized) hadrosaur (dubbed "Leonardo") was studied in a *Discovery Channel* special in September 2008. The whole body was still intact, making it "unquestionably one of the most unexpected and important dinosaur discoveries of all time."[6]

Post-Flood Dinosaurs

After the Flood 4,300 years ago, dinosaurs migrated throughout Europe, China, and the rest of the post-Flood world. Even evolutionists maintain at one period (of evolutionary time!) dinosaurs "radiated dramatically."[7] Certainly after the Flood, when the Ark rested on Mount Ararat, there was a period of dramatic radiation of all animals—including the dinosaurs.

Despite evolutionary stories of dinosaurs living and dying countless millions of years ago, the evidence of archaeology, history, and geology all point to the accuracy of the Bible's depiction of the unique creation of dinosaurs at the same time as man just 6,000 years ago.

Notes

1. Alters, B. J. and S. M. Alters. 2001. *Defending Evolution in the Classroom: A Guide to the Creation/Evolution Controversy*. Sudbury, MA: Jones and Bartlett Publishers, Inc., 119.

2. Balter, M. 2011. Pint-Sized Predator Rattles the Dinosaur Family Tree. *Science*. 331 (6014): 134.

3. Plant-eating dinosaur discovered in Antarctica. Posted on phys.org December 19, 2011.

4. Dinosaurs and Dragons, Oh My! Stanford Fossil Historian Links Dinosaur Bones to Mythological Creatures. Stanford University Humanities press release, October 2008.

5. Flavius Philostratus (c170-c247 A.D.). 1912. *The Life of Apollonius of Tyana*, volume I, book III. F. C. Conybeare, trans. New York: Macmillan Co., 243-247.

6. Unveil the "Holy Grail" of Paleontology in Secrets of the Dinosaur Mummy. Discovery Channel. Posted on discovery.com.

7. Benton, M. 2005. *Vertebrate Paleontology*, 3rd ed. Malden, MA: Blackwell Science, 153.

40

ORIGINAL TISSUE FOSSILS CANNOT BE MILLIONS OF YEARS OLD

Brian Thomas, M.S.

Many paleontologists assume that Earth's rock layers represent millions or billions of years. They haven't looked for fresh tissue inside dinosaurs and other fossils because such tissue would have completely mineralized or decayed long ago if the evolutionary timeline is true. But fresh biological material is continually being discovered, despite the biochemistry of molecular decay that clearly shows it should not exist after "all this time."

Researchers have detected molecules such as proteins, sugars, pigments, and DNA—as well as intact cells and, in some cases, skin, ligaments, retinas, bones, and blood vessels—in fossils that are supposedly many millions of years old. Below are just a few of the dozens of original tissue fossil discoveries published in the secular scientific literature.

Animal	Supposed Age (millions of yrs)	Biochemical	Date	Reference
T. rex	68	Collagen	Jun. 2007	Schweitzer, M. *Science*
Psittacosaurus	125	Collagen	Apr. 2008	Linghan-Soliar, T. *Proc. RSB*
Hadrosaur	80	Elastin	Jul. 2009	Schweitzer, M. *Science*
Mosasaur	65-68	Hemoglobin	Aug. 2010	Lindgren, J. *PLoS ONE*
Lizard	40	Keratin	Mar. 2011	Edwards, N. P. *Proc. RSB*
Mosasaur	70	Collagen	Apr. 2011	San Antonio, J. D. *PloS ONE*
Squid	160	Eumelanin	May 2012	Glass, K. *PNAS*
Scorpion	310	Chitin + protein	Feb. 2011	Cody, G.D. *Geology*

A much longer list is available online at www.icr.org/soft-tissue-list. The fossils in this chart likely formed during the year-long Flood of Noah's day. Local catastrophes during the post-Flood Ice Age deposited other soft tissue fossils. Paleontologists and others who insist on millions of years of Earth history have no credible explanation for these soft tissue discoveries.

Those who are skeptical of the original tissue discoveries often allege that the tissues are really contaminants, or foreign substances, that were added to the fossilized remains after they were unearthed. For example, after scientists published the specific amino acid sequence of a dinosaur's collagen protein, other scientists suggested that the sequence was accidentally taken from a nearby substance and not from the dinosaur itself. One evolutionary paleontologist even said that he believed the protein was taken from a field worker's lunch! It stretches credulity to assert that carefully repeated scientific research procedures were unable to filter out such contaminants—but it is simply irresponsible to declare that dozens of carefully repeated scientific research procedures conducted by scores of scientists working with fossil material from all over the world have all got it wrong.

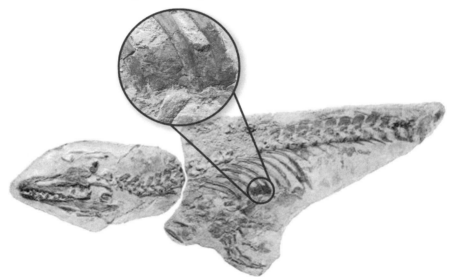

Scientists confirmed partially decayed hemoglobin in the expected positions of this mosasaur's heart and liver. Hemoglobin is a blood protein with a shelf life of thousands of years. If the fossil really is millions of years old, it would have no hemoglobin left at all. Credit: Public Library of Science (PLoS)

Other skeptics have alleged that the proteins found in fossils were manufactured by bacteria. But the kinds of materials produced by bacteria last an even shorter time than proteins that make up vertebrates' bodies. Since the supposed source of food for the bacteria would have rotted millions of years ago, any remaining substances couldn't possibly be the result of bacterial activity. Plus, bacteria do not produce collagen protein, which scientists actually sequenced using multiple, separate labs. It is proper for scientists to be skeptical. But when the data pass all of the skeptic's tests, like original tissue fossils have, then it is time for skepticism to cease and for scientists to deal with the implications of these finds.

Weak excuses like lost lunch and bacteria do not account for the original soft tissue in fossilized remains found in so many places and in such high quality. One British researcher said that the naturally mummified skin of a hadrosaur fossil that his team excavated in North Dakota was "absolutely gob-smacking."[1] The skin still has the original dinosaur reptile scales. How could skin scales be mistaken for somebody's lunch? In any case, this scientist would not have been so surprised if he understood that the dinosaur fossil was deposited by Noah's Flood only thousands of years ago.

Many scientific reports of "soft tissue" actually describe tissue that has been partly or totally mineralized. Mineralization occurs when mineral-rich water replaces the fragile original tissue, resulting in a rock in the shape of the tissue—whether it is bone, skin, or other organs. However, other scientific reports describe, using an array of different techniques, the chemistry of what

This hadrosaur (called *Trachodon* by Henry F. Osborn in 1912) was discovered by Charles Sternberg in 1908. It is the world's best-preserved dinosaur, just as other fossils from the Hell Creek Formation in Montana are well-preseved. It was given a 68 million-year age assignment, but carbon dates (the first for a Hell Creek dinosaur) for other hadrosaur bones in the same area implied an age of 28,790 and 20,850 carbon years.

Right: Close-up of mummified skin from hadrosaur fossil below.

looks like still-fresh, original, unmineralized tissue. One study used six different techniques to verify original lizard leg protein chemistry in a fossil from Wyoming.[2] So, although some "soft tissues" are actually mineralized, original tissue fossils also exist.

Secular scientists have described original tissue fossils, or at least biochemistry original to the fossils, from several of the United States, Brazil, England, Germany, Belgium, Spain, Madagascar, Canada, and two Chinese provinces. Many more will probably be described in future years, perhaps from even more places. Some may sit in museum warehouses even now. This happened to a fossil mosasaur taken from a chalk formation in Kansas. Mosasaurs were marine reptiles whose fossils are found on every continent, including Antarctica. This particular one sat for over 40 years in the Natural History Museum of Los Angeles County before researchers finally tested its chemistry, finding original but partly decayed hemoglobin and still-purple retina cells.[3]

These tissues should not exist if they are millions of years old. When shown this evidence, many people ask how original tissues could possibly have lasted even as long as the thousands of years since the Flood. The answer is that laboratory measurements of protein decay rates demonstrate that they can last for thousands of years. One particular protein that can survive a very long time is collagen inside bone. Collagen is not soluble in water, a property that guards against decay and transport. Some soft tissue fossils consist of only collagen. In these cases, water removed the other rapidly decaying biomaterials. Collagen locked inside bone still spontaneously decays according to the second law of thermodynamics, which describes how overall randomness always increases. The collagen decay rate depends on the temperature. The warmer it is, the more atoms bump into one another to perform more chemistry, thereby accelerating decay.

Rigorous and repeated experiments provide the decay rate of bone collagen at a given temperature. A well-known formula called the Arrhenius equation transforms the experimental data to express the decay rates and thus the maximum time-to-dust estimates at different temperatures. For example, according to one recent study of collagen decay rates, "extrapolation from high temperature experimental decomposition rates using this activation energy suggest [*sic*] that at a constant 10°C (the approximate mean annual air temperature in present-day Britain) it will take between 0.2 and 0.7 Ma [million] years at 10°C for levels of collagen to fall to 1% in an optimal burial environment."[4,5]

This means that bone collagen can last no longer than 700,000 years at 50°F. So, any sample of original bone collagen tissue that is assumed to have been no warmer than 50°F since it was deposited must be younger than that. It could last as long as one million years if kept at 40°F, but some of the original tissue fossil discoveries are given an age of 70 to over 100 million years, and all of them are assigned ages of multiple millions. Clearly, the age assignments for these fossils conflict with their collagen age inferences.

On one hand, the rocks contain original cells and biochemicals from dinosaurs and other creatures. Except for having decayed somewhat, these biochemicals are real—not mineralized, and not transformed into different, more resistant molecules.

On the other hand, repeatable laboratory experiments have proved that the same biochemicals discovered in fossil tissues spontaneously decay at measurable rates that limit fossil biochemistry to tens or perhaps hundreds of thousands of years maximum. They certainly could not last for a million or more years if sustained at the usual average annual temperatures of the areas where such fossils are found.

Something has to budge. Some paleontologists simply deny the measured decay rates, pretending that tissue decays much more slowly than laboratory tests show. Other researchers continue to deny that soft tissue fossils are original, ignoring the dozens of rigorous reports from the field. Both tactics struggle to accommodate millions of years. A third approach is to jettison the millions-of-years timeline, which does not come from scientific observations but from a strongly held belief system into which scientific data is force-fitted. One can accept both the measured decay rates and the well-characterized original tissue fossils—that is, the actual sciences of biochemistry and paleontology—by removing the millions-of-years age assignments.

Original tissue fossils of dinosaurs and other creatures provide very strong scientific evidence that the world is as young as the Bible plainly describes.

Notes

1. Mummified dinosaur skin yields up new secrets. The University of Manchester press release, July 1, 2009.

2. Edwards, N. P. et al. 2011. Infrared mapping resolves soft tissue preservation in 50 million year-old reptile skin. *Proceedings of the Royal Society B*. 278 (1722): 3209-3218.

3. Lindgren J. et al. 2010. Convergent Evolution in Aquatic Tetrapods: Insights from an Exceptional Fossil Mosasaur. *PloS ONE*. 5 (8): e11998.

4. Buckley, M. and M. J. Collins. 2011. Collagen survival and its use for species identification in Holocene-lowever Pleistocene bone fragments from British archaeological and paleontological sites. *Antiqua*. 1: e1.

5. The phrase "optimal burial environment" is important. Some old-world apologists claim that bone collagen can last much longer than what the measured decay rate implies because certain regions of the proteins adhere to the nearby bone mineral. They ignore the fact that the experiments used to measure the decay rate already take those effects into account. Plus, this "explanation" ignores skin, blood, and other cells and proteins found in fossils that have not been mineralized.

41

WERE THERE REALLY
FEATHERED DINOSAURS?

Brian Thomas, M.S.

The concept of "feathered dinosaurs" is now very prevalent. Most museums and textbooks that have dinosaur displays or pictures also include artistic renderings of dinosaurs sporting colorful feathers. If some dinosaurs really did have feathers, they would seem to support the recently popular doctrine that an as-yet-unidentified theropod dinosaur evolved into the first bird, which then evolved into all other bird kinds.[1]

For example, one placard at the Rocky Mountain Dinosaur Resource Center in Colorado Springs states, "Fossil feather impressions are far more rare, but have been found at several localities in Asia. These wonderful fossils prove that some dinosaurs, particularly the small theropods, had an integument [skin] closer to a bird."

Unfortunately for this story, evolutionary researchers do not all agree that fossil dinosaurs had feathers. Plus, dinosaur skin was covered in scales—closer to reptiles than birds. Overall, there are far more reasons to doubt the feathered dinosaur idea than there are reasons to affirm it. Just like the well-illustrated but totally faked feathered dinosaur *Archaeoraptor* that adorned the November 1999 issue of *National Geographic*, the entire feathered dinosaur enterprise may soon be viewed as one of paleontology's big mistakes.

The idea of feathered dinosaurs became popular after researchers found uniquely well-preserved dinosaur remains in fossil assemblages in China. Published descriptions of dark filaments associated with dinosaur remains began in the 1990s. Evolutionary proselytizers soon attributed the mysterious filaments to not-yet-evolved feathers they called "protofeathers." But the veneer of feathered-dinosaur factuality presented in textbooks and museums hides hotly debated arguments in the scientific literature over the identity of these filaments.

Thus, the author of the *Archaeoraptor* article in *National Geographic* stretched far beyond scientific reality when he said, "We can now say that birds are theropods just as confidently as we say that humans are mammals."[2] But as argued below, we can now say that birds are actually *not* theropods (unless we completely change the definition of "theropod") just as confidently as we can say that *Archaeoraptor* is a known fake.

Just like *Archaeoraptor*, a concept does not necessarily correspond to reality just because it has a name. Since 1999, evidence has accumulated to show that scientists may have designated the fossil fibers as evolutionary feather precursors merely because they so desperately needed fossil support for the concept of dinosaurs evolving into birds. But this evolutionary idea relies far more on fiction than fossils. One authoritative book on the subject, *The Feathered Dinosaurs: The Origin of Birds*, contains artists' illustrations of how certain feathered dinosaurs may have looked, but no images of any real fossils.[3]

Similarly, in 2011 Frank Sherwin, a contributing author of this book, and I scrutinized the displays at the temporary "Chinasaurs" exhibit at the Museum of Nature and Science in Dallas, looking for real fossil evidence of feathers. Both of us were mystified by the lack of such evidence. Again, there were plenty of artistic depictions of feathered dinosaurs, but the fossil evidence was just not there. We posted one of my photographs of that display on the ICR website so that readers can see and judge for themselves.[4]

Nevertheless, feathered dinosaur claims continue to emerge. And in every case so far where photos of the original fossils can be examined, the darkly colored "fibers" are simple and straight, without branches. In other words, they never have looked like real feathers.

A very recent example is a dinosaur fossil discovered in China that was named *Yutyrannus huali*, which means "beautiful feathered tyrant," even though it was most likely not covered with beautiful feathers. It made headlines as by far the largest yet found of the now famous Chinese "feathered dinosaurs." The authors describing it titled their article "A gigantic feathered dinosaur from the Lower Cretaceous of China." But the detailed description below the title does not support that claim, since it admits that the fibers are merely "filamentous integumentary [skin] structures."[5] It also ignores any alternate explanation for them.

Facsimile fossil of *Caudipteryx* at the "Chinasaurs" museum exhibit. Dark smudges along its spine were not very feather-like. Credit: Brian Thomas

Real bird feathers are complicated, with semi-hollow cores and branching barbs and barbules, but the fossil's filaments had none of these features. If the word "feather" just means "filament," then should any filament—like a hair or plant fiber—also be called a "feather"?

Answering this correctly is important. Why would God have placed feathers on dinosaurs when, today at least, only birds have feathers? God could have done so, but it is hard to imagine why. What purpose would bird feathers serve on those tough dino hides? On the other hand, "the idea of protofeathers has strengthened the resolve of many palaeontologists that birds are direct descendents of theropod dinosaurs."[6] This resolve did not waver even after these same kinds of simple fiber "feathers" were discovered on non-theropod dinosaurs, too.

Three other observations fail to fit the dinosaur feather hypothesis. First, neither dinosaur skin impressions nor original dinosaur skin have large follicles like those that produce feathers in bird skin.[7] Second, actual bird fossils are found mixed among dinosaur remains. Museums do not show birds and dinosaurs side by side, as they should. However, scientific literature lists fossils from ducks, loons, albatross, parrot, other water birds, as well as extinct bird kinds that had clawed wings—all found in conjunction with dinosaurs or in dinosaur-bearing layers. How could dinosaurs be evolving pre-feathers destined to adorn birds if real feathered birds were already on the scene? In fact, those who insist that dinosaurs evolved into birds have to willfully ignore the fossil bird footprints found in rock layers containing some of the "earliest" dinosaurs![8] Feathered dinosaurs just don't fit the fossil evidence. So what were these fibers?

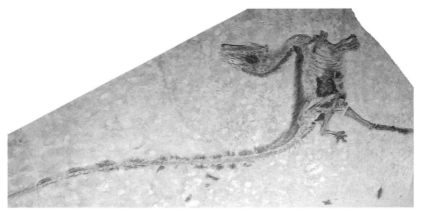

None of the supposed "feathered dinosaur" fossils have actual feathers, except fossil birds that researchers conveniently call "dinosaurs." Instead, the dark "protofeathers" along the spine of such dinosaurs are probably just partly decayed skin, just like the dark smudges inside its body cavity are partly decayed or carbonized tissues. Credit: Sam / Olai Ose / Skjaervoy from Zhangjiagang, China

They are more straightforwardly interpreted as the fossilized fragments of partly decayed skin. Skin contains collagen protein fibers that decay more slowly than the soluble biomaterials that surround them. The famous Chinese dinosaur fossils probably began rotting as they were transported by the waters of Noah's Flood only 4,500 or so years ago, even as modern carcasses rot. The soluble flesh would have rotted first. The thickly woven collagen fibers would have soon rotted, too, but the mud or wet sand encompassing the carcass quickly turned to dry rock that inhibited the growth of collagen-eating microbes.

Evolutionary paleontologists performed a very important series of experiments on the subject, publishing their results in 2005.[9] They found an excellent match between partially decayed skin from a variety of animal carcasses and "feathered dinosaur" fibers. The authors even contended that calling dinosaur fibers "feathers" was "misleading" people into believing that theropods evolved into birds. It turns out that "protofeathers" are just protein fibers that once supported dinosaur skin.

These study authors also admitted that theropods have "exactly the wrong anatomy for flight." A bird's center of gravity is balanced between its wings in the front of its body, and a dinosaur's center of gravity was balanced over its thighs near the back of its body.[9] The authors instead choose to believe that some reptile other than the theropod dinosaur evolved into birds—though it is not yet discovered.

Even if science will someday discover genuine feathers on a dinosaur fossil, we can be confident that dinosaurs never evolved into birds because of their either-or anatomies. Transmutating a dinosaur skeleton into a bird skeleton would have rendered key transitional creatures unfit, unable to fly or walk properly. One study demonstrated that if a bird's legs or ribs were removed or significantly altered, the resulting creature would suffocate.[10] This clearly implies that an imaginary dino-to-bird transition would have suffocated, too.

Here's why. Bird breathing depends on a rigid connection between their hip and thigh bones. This structure supports air sacs that connect to their one-way, flow-through lungs. As a result, birds run by bending their legs at the knees. In contrast, theropod and other dinosaurs walked or ran by bending their legs primarily at their thighs, the same as modern reptiles and mammals. Imagine a creature that had evolved rigid bird-like thighs but did not yet have the musculature or other bone length and strength adjustments for it to walk either like its theropod parents or like birds. How well would it survive if it couldn't even walk? No matter how the bird feather question is resolved, we can rest assured that anatomy nullifies the notion of bird evolution.

Confuciusornis, a fossil bird from China. It had fully formed feathers and came from rock layers below some "feathered dinosaur" fossils. Credit: Brian Thomas

A famed fossil called *Archaeopteryx* has long served as the poster child of Darwinian change, an alleged link via theropod dinosaurs between reptiles and birds. Upon closer inspection, this fossil was fully bird, and not a transition at all. Unlike dinosaurs, *Archaeopteryx* had a large braincase for the increased motor control and sensory input that were required for flight. It had a robust furcula (wishbone), a trait characteristic of strong fliers that keeps flight muscles from crushing the bird's delicate internal air sacs. No evidence supports the story that such fully formed wings with fused clavicles "evolved from" the tiny, clavicle-free theropod forelimbs. Even claw measurements of *Archaeopteryx* fall within the range of true perching birds. It was a bird without a single transitional feature.

Scientists recently applied a new technique that detects element ratios without destroying the material to an *Archaeopteryx* bird fossil from Solnhofen, Germany. The results indirectly, but certainly, identified original feather and bone proteins. It had the same biochemistry that comprises today's feathers.[11] Fossils don't just fail to show whole creature evolution, they also fail to show evolution within feather chemistry and construction.

The original *Archaeopteryx* tissue also showed how young the fossil must be. Its evolutionary age assignment is about 150 times older than its protein decay age estimate. So, not only does it look purposefully created, but it also appears to be recently fossilized. A separate study found that the supposed "feather" filaments in another Chinese dinosaur were comprised of original biochemicals.[12] These could persist in this state for perhaps hundreds of thousands of years, but there is no good reason to suggest that they could have lasted even a million. So, instead of "protofeathers" that show bird evolution, these dino-filaments actually appear to be original protein fibers that showcase recent creation!

Were there really feathered dinosaurs? Evolutionists have not yet found fossil fibers that they all agree were feathers. Sometimes, they call fossil birds "dinosaurs," but that's not a feathered dinosaur either. One may someday be discovered, but even then, feathers on a dinosaur would not solve evolution's biophysical impasse of converting a reptile skeleton into that of a bird. And so far, the evidence for feathered dinosaurs is much better interpreted as decayed skin fibers.

Overall, fossils show that dinosaurs and birds have always been separate creatures.[13] And this is exactly what one would expect if dinosaurs and birds were created separately, each to reproduce "after their kind," as Genesis 1 describes.

Notes

1. Theropod dinosaurs had three toes, had lizard-like hip bone structure, and include *T. rex*.

2. C. P. Sloan. 1999. Feathers for T. rex? New birdlike fossils are missing links in dinosaur evolution. *National Geographic*. 196: 98-107; Spotts, P. Dressed to kill: A feathered tyrannosaur is discovered in China. *Christian Science Monitor*. Posted on csmonitor.com April 4, 2012

3. Long, J. and P. Schouten. 2008. *The Feathered Dinosaurs: The Origin of Birds*. New York: Oxford University Press.

4. Thomas, B. Feathers Missing from 'Feathered Dinosaur' Display. *Creation Science Update*. Posted on icr.org August 25, 2011.

5. Xu, X. et al. 2012. A gigantic feathered dinosaur from the Lower Cretaceous of China. *Nature*. 484 (7392): 92-95.

6. Lingham-Soliar, T., A. Feduccia and X. Wang. 2007. A new Chinese specimen indicates that 'protofeathers' in the Early Cretaceous theropod dinosaur Sinosauropteryx are degraded collagen fibres. *Proceedings of the Royal Society B*. 274 (1620): 1823-1829.

7. Thomas, B. Mummified Dinosaur Skin Looks Young. *Creation Science Update*. Posted on icr.org July 30, 2009.

8. Melchor, R. N., S. de Valais, and J. F Genise. 2002. Bird-like fossil footprints from the Late Triassic. *Nature*. 417 (6892): 936.

9. Feduccia, A., T. Lingham-Soliar, and J. R. Hinchliffe. 2005. Do Feathered Dinosaurs Exist? Testing the Hypothesis on Neontological and Paleontological Evidence. *Journal of Morphology*. 266: 134.

10. Quick, D. E. and J. A. Ruben. 2009. Cardio-pulmonary anatomy in theropod dinosaurs: Implications from extant archosaurs. *Journal of Morphology*. 270 (10): 1232-1246.

11. Bergmann, U. et al. 2010. Archaeopteryx feathers and bone chemistry fully revealed via synchrotron imaging. *Proceedings of the National Academy of Sciences*. 107 (20): 9060-9065.

12. Zhang, F. et al. 2010. Fossilized melanosomes and the colour of Cretaceous dinosaurs and birds. *Nature*. 463 (7284): 1075-1078; Lingham-Soliar, T. 2011. The evolution of the feather: Sinosauropteryx, a colorful tail. *Journal of Ornithology*. 152 (3): 567-577.

13. Oard, M. 2012. Did Birds Evolve from Dinosaurs? In *Dinosaur Challenges and Mysteries*. Atlanta, GA: Creation Book Publishers, 144-155.

42

HOW DO THEY DATE
A FOSSIL ANYWAY?

Brian Thomas, M.S.

Nothing in recent times has been more effective in robbing people of their confidence in God's Word than the supposedly scientific claim of an old earth. If the world is millions of years old, then evolution seems plausible, and God's Word—which has no hint of it—is placed in doubt. However, if Earth and its fossils are only thousands of years old, then evolution is impossible and the history and authorship are affirmed.

Few habits better serve the agenda of building strong belief in millions of years than the constant reiteration in popular news, media programs, and secular science reports that such-and-such fossil is so-and-so millions of years old. This univocal affirmation holds powerful sway over even Christian thinkers, but there are good reasons why it's wrong. We will see that the process of deciding a fossil's age leans more critically on assumptions than on observations.

Because a fossil's date is not written on it like it is on an ancient coin, tablet, or reliably copied document, age-dating a fossil is not straightforward. The first step is the most critical, and yet it goes largely unrecognized by those who use it. In order to date a fossil or rock layer, any researcher must bring an interpretive framework to what is observed. This is because any age-informative clues that a rock or fossil might contain are circumstantial, not absolute. In other words, one can choose to interpret any clue in any number of ways. Like the blind man who touches the elephant's side and declares it a wrinkly wall, one cannot correctly interpret evidence without the correct big picture in mind.

The Basic Steps in Age-Dating

Standard secular belief holds that rock layers are millions of years old. This is the filter through which "facts" must pass before they are deemed acceptable. At least one secular scientist recognized a similar self-serving circle that characterized evolutionists in the early 20th century who were having difficulty matching fossil data to Darwinian evolution.

> In other words, when the assumed evolutionary processes did not match the pattern of fossils that they were supposed to have generated, the pattern was judged to be 'wrong.' A circular argument arises. Interpret the fossil record in terms of a particular theory of evolution, inspect the interpretation, and note that it confirms the theory. Well, it would, wouldn't it?[1]

In much the same way, secularists approach all data with evolutionary time already well-ensconced in their thinking. They interpret the fossil record in those terms, then note that their interpretation confirms millions of years. This self-serving system should be severed from science.

In the next steps to age-dating a fossil or its rock layer, a paleontologist records the color, size, and chemistry of the rock, as well as any species of common, abundant, small fossils like those of clams, brachiopods, or even pollen. She then may search for other rock layers in the surrounding area that share these characteristics but also dovetail or interfinger with another geological feature—such as a volcanic rock layer—that contains minerals with radioactive elements that might be used in radiodating.

Then she matches her field observations with technical charts that were worked out usually by a prior generation of paleontologists. These charts assign period names and date numbers to each characteristic rock layer. Or she may simply cite an age that was already published by other paleontologists, trusting that they did their age determinations accurately.

At this point, the researcher invokes a second major, but rarely questioned, assumption—that each characteristic layer represents a time or era that is separated from adjacent time periods by huge numbers of years.[2] Having inherited this doctrine from respected authorities, the mere idea that perhaps all the layers could have formed from successive tsunami-like pulses during a short-lived gargantuan cataclysm rarely crosses researchers' minds.

The secular researcher is confident in the geologic chart because others in her field often refer to it. Long ago, Flood geologists made the first of these charts, believing the rock layers to represent catastrophes that perhaps occurred during the Flood year or resulted indirectly from the Flood's after-effects. But secular thinkers from Enlightenment Europe hijacked the charts and affixed ancient ages to them. It has been very difficult for people to think of the layers correlated by field observation as something separate from their assigned ages.

If the paleontologist is able to find associated material such as igneous rock that can be radiodated, she sends her rock samples to a reputable radio-isotope laboratory. She will usually tell them an approximate time period to expect, based on the ages published in the geologic chart that applies to that area. More samples mean more radiodates, and these often conflict, producing discordant dates. She must then decide which numbers to include in her publication, and then explain away the dates that she rejected, including dates from prior studies.

Discordant radiodates are very common. Many have been published in scientific literature, but many more are never reported. One researcher admitted, "In the majority of cases the ages are clearly off and the data disappear in a lab datafile."[3] Another study summarized 30 radioisotope "ages" that were all older than the relevant geologic chart said was possible.[4] Another study filled ten pages with reported discordant dates.[5] These show that radiodated samples do not lead the way—they follow the assigned timeframe. Researchers then find excuses for discordant radioisotope or other discordant age-informing techniques.

Secular scientists provide fancy terms for these excuses, like open system behavior, mixing, assimilation, or metasomatic alteration. The high volume of discordant radioisotope and other ages does not faze most researchers' confidence in evolutionary time—but it should. One geologist admitted, "There is no reliable objective way to assess the validity of given whole-rock (or mineral) isochron [radioisotope age plot] using the regressed data alone, or in combination with element concentration data." In other words, there is no objective way to calibrate or verify radiodates. He wrote that instead, one must assess the age assignment of a given rock layer or fossil "in the light of all available field, petrographic, geological, geochemical, and other geochronological evidence."[6] And the script that all that evidence must follow is the dogmatic teaching of evolutionary time. After all, it's written in black and white right there on the chart.

Two true stories illustrate how secular scientists age-date fossils by ensuring that "ages" conform to dogma.

Example 1: Age-Dating and a Human-Like Fossil

First is the story of changing date assignments for a layer of volcanic ash in Africa called the KBS tuff. The date of this ash layer needed to correlate with the evolutionary ages of extinct ape fossils and human tools that were found nearby and thought to indicate the beginnings of mankind. In 1970, researchers F. J. Fitch and J. A. Miller obtained an age for the tuff of 212 to 230 million years using the potassium-argon radioisotope system.[7] But this wildly conflicted with the presumed evolutionary age of the nearby ape and certain extinct pig fossils. So they rejected the date, excusing it as having resulted from contamination.

They then sent different samples of the tuff to a radioisotope lab and this time obtained 2.61 million years. Since this age agreed with the evolutionary story for the area, they accepted the 2.61 million, as did other researchers who confirmed that age for the KBS tuff layer by using a different technique called fission track dating. But more changes were soon to come.

The famous paleontologist Richard Leakey found a human-looking fossil skull *below* the KBS tuff. *National Geographic* readers in 1973 were therefore told that the newly discovered human ancestor was at least 2.7 million years old—supposedly the oldest human fossil yet found.[8] But because secular scientists already "knew" that humans had not yet evolved from ape-like ancestors—an event that supposedly occurred 2.4 million years ago—something had to change.

G. H. Curtis, a University of California at Berkeley expert in potassium-argon radioisotope dating, led a team that dated the KBS tuff again. This time, they obtained an age of 1.82 million years.[9] Because this agreed with the evolutionary age of the skull, and because the skull fossil represented a high-profile part in the story of evolution, they reached a new consensus that revised the once-well-accepted age assignment of 2.61 million years to this new, younger age. Additional fission track dates "confirmed" the 1.8 million-year assignment.

Radioisotope ages for this volcanic layer in Africa played second fiddle to the evolutionary scheme. This example is not isolated, but characterizes the assumption-first procedure that underlies fossil age-dating.

Creation scientists recognize that the KBS tuff formed during the post-Flood Ice Age, when many catastrophes occurred as the earth settled from the turmoil of the great Flood. Different peoples had recently migrated to Africa from Babel, as their stone tools testify. They also lived among ape-like creatures—totally unrelated to humans—that have since gone extinct, much like wooly mammoths or any number of Ice Age animals.

Circular Reasoning

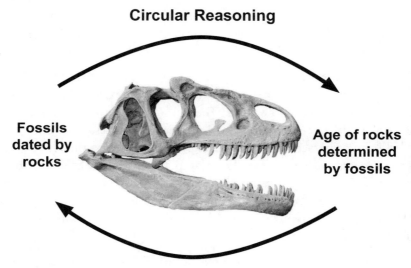

Fossils dated by rocks

Age of rocks determined by fossils

Example 2: Age-Dating a Dinosaur Rock Layer

Some of the world's most exquisite dinosaur fossils and the sedimentary rock formation in which they lie provide a second example of how secular researchers age-date fossils by rigorously filtering data through a naturalistic narrative. Nearly whole dinosaurs—many of them naturally mummified, some with skin, ligament, and bone, and some with still-flexible original proteins, arteries, bone and blood cells—are contained in Montana's Hell Creek Formation.[10]

Based on differences in pollen fossils, early researchers assigned the lower majority of the Hell Creek Formation to the Cretaceous system and its upper portion to the Paleogene system. The Paleogene supposedly began 66 or so million years ago, and includes Paleocene, Eocene, and Oligocene layers. Some marker should delineate the older Cretaceous portion from the later-forming Paleogene layers—perhaps an erosion event that deposited a different type of sediment, or an impact or volcanic event that deposited a recognizable signature. Many outcrops of the Hell Creek Formation contain a thin clay layer that paleontologists attribute to an impact event that somehow killed all the dinosaurs before the Paleogene supposedly began. (Strangely, it did not kill the more environmentally sensitive frogs, salamanders, mammals, fish, or turtles fossilized alongside the dinosaurs as well as above them, the descendants of which live today.)

Secular attempts to age-date these fossils would be simpler if all the dinosaurs in Hell Creek were below the thin clay layer or the change in pollen fossils that supposedly marks dinosaur extinction—but that is not the case.

Geologists reported "Dinosaurs from the Paleocene Part of the Hell Creek Formation" in 1987.[10] Having supposedly gone extinct before Paleocene "time," dinosaurs should be there. The authors presented a number of good reasons why Paleogene dinosaur fossils from six dig sites could not have been eroded from a Cretaceous deposit, then re-deposited into the Hell Creek Formation a few million years later. For example, the vertebrate fossils had unbroken fine and delicate features. Plus, there was little to no abrasion on the bone surfaces, as would have resulted from tumbling in fast-flowing water during re-deposition. A dinosaur younger than 65 million years is unacceptable, so something had to change.

Evolutionists invoke at least three "solutions" to this dinosaur-dating dilemma. The first is to ignore the Paleogene dinosaur fossils. As an example, CNN interviewed a geology student named Luke Padgett at a Hell Creek dinosaur excavation in 2007. He was a student of the famous paleontologist Jack Horner. Luke said, "We know by that [thin clay layer] there was an impact at the end of the Cretaceous. At that layer we can see really easily out here with no trees. And there's an interesting pattern. There's dinosaurs below it and no dinosaurs above it."[12] Maybe Jack did not tell Luke about the 1987 report of dinosaurs above it.

A second "solution" is to counter-assert that the fossils were reworked from older sediments after all. Right on cue, in 1990 scientists listed criteria that any Paleogene dinosaur fossil claims should meet, then conveniently found that prior dinosaur claims did not meet their criteria.[13] However, the authors did not adequately address the evidence showing that Paleocene Hell Creek dinosaur remains were buried only once.

Another "solution" raises the upper border of that which is designated "Cretaceous" so that it includes the dinosaur fossils. After all, as one researcher summarized for *Discover Magazine*, "A great achievement of 19th-century science was learning to use fossils as distinctive time indicators."[14] It was really only an "achievement" in evolutionary circular reasoning, not science.

Evolutionary age assignments for Hell Creek Formation layers and their dinosaur, bird, plant, mammal, amphibian, and marine fossils are still in contention, despite confident-sounding assertions of their vast age. One intensive 2002 Geological Society of America study summarized that "the age and duration of the Hell Creek Formation are long-standing and still partially unanswered questions." Its upper boundary is in constant dispute, and "estimates of the age of the lower contact of the Hell Creek Formation are few and poorly delimited."[15] The authors had no explanation for why one report based on assumed sediment accumulation rates said that the formation formed over a span of 1.3 million years, but another report that was based on designated ages for its ammonite fossils indicated that it formed over a 4.6 million-year time span. It can't be both. Perhaps all these age assignments are entirely wrong.

Flood geologists interpret the entire Hell Creek Formation as having been deposited in no more than months by the waters that were retreating, or abating, off of the then newly formed North American continent.

The last step in dating a fossil is to publish the results. Secular science journals do not accept young ages for fossils, even if the data are there— ICR scientists know this because we have submitted careful research to secular journals only to have our papers summarily rejected. If scientists want to obtain funding from secular institutions for research and thereby maintain their livelihood, they must conform their results to the consensus perspective. Thus, several checkpoints throughout the process ensure that age assignments given to rocks and fossils match the expectation of evolutionary time. It is bad science.

Notes

1. Kemp, T. S. 1985. A Fresh Look at the Fossil Record. *New Scientist*. 108: 66-67.

2. Confusingly, geologists sometimes assign multiple periods to a single layer or rock unit, and certainly assign multiple rock layers to a single period.

3. Jagoutz, E. 1994. Isotopic systematics of metamorphic rocks. *Abstracts of the eighth International Conference on Geochronology, Cosmochronology, and Isotope Geology*. M. A. Lanphere, G. B. Dalrymple, and B. D. Turrin, eds. *US Geological Survey Circular 1107*. (157): 156.

4. Brooks, C., D. E. James, and S. R. Hart. 1976. Ancient Lithosphere: Its Role in Young Continental Volcanism. *Science*. 193: 1086-1094.

5. Woodmorappe, J. 1979. Radiometric Geochronology Reappraised. *Creation Research Society Quarterly*. 16

(2): 102-129.

6. Whitehouse, M. J. et al. 1996. Conflicting mineral and whole-rock isochron ages from the Late-Archaean Lewisian Complex of northwestern Scotland. *Geochemica et Cosmica Acta*. 60 (16): 3085-3102.

7. Fitch, F. J. and J. A. Miller. 1970. New Hominid Remains and Early Artefacts from Northern Kenya: Radioisotopic Age Determinations of Lake Rudolf Artefact Site. *Nature*. 226 (5242): 226–228.

8. Leakey, R. E. F. 1973. Skull 1470. *National Geographic*. 143: 819-829.

9. Curtis, G. H. et al. 1975. Age of KBS Tuff in Koobi Fora Formation, East Rudolf, Kenya. *Nature*. 258: 395-398.

10. As an aside, known protein decay rates set a maximum age limit on these remains, and secular researchers ignore this protein data when they cling to evolutionary ages. I discuss tissue fossils in Chapter 40. They also have to ignore dozens of carbon-14 results for comparable samples that indicate ages of only thousands of years. But the millions-of-years age assignment of some of these dinosaur fossils and their rocks has suffered enough torture even ignoring the protein and radiocarbon age implications.

11. Rigby, J. K. et al. 1987. Dinosaurs from the Paleocene Part of the Hell Creek Formation, McCone County, Montana. *Palaios*. 2 (3): 296-302.

12. Mielich, P. It's real life CSI for dinosaur detectives. CNN. Posted on edition.cnn.com March 8, 2007.

13. Lofgren, D. L., C. L. Hotton, and A. C. Runkel. Reworking of Cretaceous dinosaurs into Paleocene channel, deposits, upper Hell Creek Formation, Montana. *Geology*. 18 (9): 874-877.

14. Sasso, A. Geologists Create First New Period in 113 Years. *Discover Magazine*, January 2005.

15. Johnson, K. R., D. J. Nichols, and J. H. Hartman. 2002. Hell Creek Formation: A 2001 Synthesis. *Geological Society of America*. Special Paper 361: 503-510.

43

DINOSAURS AND DRAGON LEGENDS

Brian Thomas, M.S.

Christians are often curious about how dinosaurs fit into the biblical narrative. Dinosaurs certainly existed. Their fossil remains are found on every continent, and ancient historical records, including the Bible, chronicle human encounters with large reptiles whose descriptions best match dinosaurs. Dinosaurs that lived up to the time of the Flood were drowned in the Flood (except those on board the Ark), as were all land-dwelling creatures with nostrils, according to Genesis 7:22. Some of those outside the Ark were buried in fast-moving mud that quickly dried, turning their remains into fossils faster than their carcasses could decay. Most, if not all, dinosaur fossil layers also have fossil water creatures like fish and clams, and this is consistent with the Flood explanation.

Although there are hundreds of named dinosaur species, all of them belong to only about 50 or 60 different basic dinosaur kinds. That means that Noah and his sons only had to manage perhaps 120 individual dinosaurs on the Ark. Could they have fit on board a vessel with the dimensions given in Genesis 6? No matter how large some dinosaurs grew, the largest dinosaur egg was not much bigger than a football. Even the *Argentinosaurus*, which could grow into a 120-foot-long monster, could have fit on the Ark if it was represented by much-smaller young ones. In addition, many dinosaurs were small even when fully grown. For example, the *Sinosauropteryx*, which is of the same kind as *Compsognathus* (except the former was found in China and the latter in Europe), was about the size of a turkey. The average size of a dinosaur was about that of a medium dog. One hundred-twenty "dogs" would require barely a corner of one of the Ark's three decks.

We can infer from the reliable Genesis record that the descendants of the dinosaurs on the Ark travelled from the Middle East to places around the globe. This really only makes sense, however, when considering that the post-Flood climate was very different from today's. During the Ice Age, the Middle East was tropical and was constantly watered by heavy rains. This would have set up suitable conditions for dinosaurs to have been fruitful and filled many Earth environments. There are various clues, such as dinosaur fossils buried alongside tropical plant fossils, that indicate dinosaurs lived in swampy habitats.

This dinosaur migration happened only thousands of years ago. Archbishop James Ussher calculated a date for the Flood at 2348 B.C. This is probably a bit off, but it most likely falls within a few centuries of the real Flood date. How long did dinosaurs live after that, and why are they not still alive?

Immediately after the Flood, creatures like dinosaurs dispersed across Earth's surface. The first few generations of post-Flood people, however, were determined to rebel against God's command to fill the earth. Instead of filling the earth, they built a tower in Babel and remained in its growing city. In response, God supernaturally compelled them to disperse across Earth by confounding their languages. When families eventually migrated into far-flung places, they encountered the dinosaurs that had already been there for a few hundred years. Those encounters have been memorialized in writings, depictions, and legends from people groups across the globe. As humans filled the post-Flood Earth, dinosaur numbers would have dwindled due to hunting and loss of habitat. The changing climate itself may have ultimately rendered the earth inhospitable to these creatures, eventually leading to their extinction in many areas. Even so, dinosaurs must have been living at least within the last hundreds of years, judging by the tales of humans who saw them.

The sheer number of names given to dragons, or dinosaurs, worldwide builds a strong argument that dragon legends hearken back to encounters with real creatures. Most languages, either in written or oral tradition, have their own unique words for dragon. By "dragon," we do not refer to popular images of a bulky, fire-breathing reptile that somehow flies with tiny wings. Rather, we take "dragon" to mean one of the many kinds of post-Flood dinosaurs, or even flying reptiles. Other languages still use words like those shown in this table. The online encyclopedia Wikipedia lists many more dragon names.[1]

Name	Description	Location or Language
Aziwugum	Giant reptile	Innuit
Bax'an	Terrible water monster	Dakota Sioux
Behemoth	Giant swamp reptile	Hebrew (Job)
Drakon	Dragon	Greece
Grendel	Swamp monster	Denmark
Knucker	Swamp dragon	Wales
Long	Dragon	China
P'ih mw	Giant reptile	Egyptian hieroglyphs
Ro-qua-ho	Giant reptile	Iroquois
Smok	Dragon	Poland
Uk'tena	Horned water monster	Cherokee[2]
Worm (voorm)	Dragon	Germany

Ancient historians described dragons as real, living creatures, right alongside their descriptions of other creatures more familiar to today's readers. For example, in his book *Natural History* written in approximately 78 A.D., Pliny the Elder wrote that "it is India which produces the largest [elephants] as well as the dragon…and [the dragon] is itself of such enormous size as to envelop the elephants with its folds."

During that same era, Flavius Philostratus wrote:

> The whole of India is girt with dragons of enormous size; for not only the marshes are full of them, but the mountains as well, and there is not a single ridge without one. Now the marsh kind are sluggish in their habits and are thirty cubits long, and they have no crest standing up on their heads.[3]

History is littered with such accounts. Alexander the Great wrote of a dragon that his army encountered during his short time on Earth. The famous explorer Marco Polo described a dragon in his logbooks. Bill Cooper's book *After the Flood* describes many similar accounts from Europe. Cooper relayed a report written in 1484 by England's first printer, William Caxton, of a singular creature:

> About the marches [marshes] of Italy, within a meadow, was sometime a serpent of wonderful and right marvelous greatness, right hideous and fearful. For first he had a head greater than the head of a calf. Secondly, he had a neck greater than the length of an ass, and his body made after the likeness of a dog. And his tail was wonderfully great, thick and long, without comparison to

any other.[4]

The creature thus described matches Job's behemoth, which had a "tail like a cedar," lived in a marsh where it ate reeds, and as "the first of the ways of God" was obviously very large.[5]

People groups that did not maintain written records nevertheless retain oral traditions of dragon encounters. They describe the dragon's habitat and habits, and provide specific names for the dragons and the long-dead heroes who vanquished them. Towns, hillsides, and ponds across Europe still have their old dragon names—such as Drachenfels Castle and the town of Worms in Germany, Grindelwald in Switzerland, Dragon-hoard (near Garsington) in England, and many others.

But even more evidence shows that early peoples encountered dinosaurs. Dinosaur depictions occur in carvings, sculptures, bas reliefs, paintings, mosaics, tapestries, sculptures, pictographs, and petroglyphs from all over the world. Some of the telling features that help identify these images as dinosaurian are horns, spiky skin flaps along the spine called dermal frills, long tails, long necks, large teeth, and, perhaps most importantly, legs that went straight down from the body. Those walking reptiles with which we are most familiar today have legs that aim away from the sides of the body, then angle down to the ground at the elbows or knees. Dinosaur reptiles' legs were situated beneath their bodies (like a dog's are), just as shown on dozens of genuine, ancient depictions.

Evolutionists object that dinosaur-looking artifacts are fakes. However, this objection does not stem from rigorous analysis of the data. Instead, it stems from an argument that goes like this: "This ancient man-made artifact looks like a dinosaur. But dinosaurs died millions of years before man evolved, making it impossible for ancient men to know what dinosaurs looked like. Therefore this artifact is a fraud." This kind of argument takes as true the very evolutionary history that the artifacts challenge. Ignoring evidence leads to wrong conclusions.

The vast number of dragon descriptions and the similarities of those descriptions across geographic space and historical time are best explained by genuine dinosaur encounters. The late popular cosmologist Carl Sagan considered the historical evidence for dragons such a serious threat to the evolutionary paradigm that he tackled the subject in his 1977 book *The Dragons of Eden*. In it, he speculated that unknown human ancestor primates may have encountered dinosaurs millions of years ago. The memories of those interactions were so traumatic that they were indelibly stamped onto the primate genes so that ancient humans inherited and drew their dinosaur pictures based on those memories. Because there is no scientific evidence that memories can be inherited, many scientists shunned Sagan's unscientific speculation. But to assert that myriad dragon legends are all fraudulent without even investigating their historical evidence is equally unscientific.

If the Bible is correct that representatives of all land-dwelling, air-breathing creatures were on the Ark, and if it is correct in describing an Ice Age dinosaur in the book of Job, then it makes sense to infer that people encountered (and rid themselves of) the threatening and fearsome reptiles during the centuries after the Flood, leaving for us dragon legends—written, spoken, painted, and carved—from perhaps every ancient culture.

Notes

1. List of dragons in mythology and folklore. Wikipedia. Accessed August 1, 2012.

2. Thomas, B. 2010. Oblivious to the obvious: dragons lived with American Indians. A review of *Fossil Legends of the First Americans* by Adrienne Mayor. *Journal of Creation*. 24 (1): 32-34.

3. Flavius Philostratus (c170-c247 A.D.). 1912. *The Life of Apollonius of Tyana*, volume I, book III. F. C. Conybeare, trans. New York: Macmillan Co., 243-247.

4. Caxton, W. M. 1484. *Aesop*. Folio 138. Cited in Cooper, W. 1995. *After the Flood*. Chichester, UK: New Wine Press.

5. Job 40:15-24.

ASTRONOMY

CREATED COSMOS OR
THE BIG BANG?

44

A BIG BANG—REALLY?

Jason Lisle, Ph.D.

How did the universe begin? Many people say, "Well, it sort of 'exploded' into existence from nothing, billions of years ago. It all began with a Big Bang!"

It may sound like a joke, yet this is precisely what most secularists believe about the origin of all things. Of course, we shouldn't dismiss an idea just because it sounds silly. There are things that are counterintuitive (such as quantum physics) that are apparently true and good science. And it is certainly the case that most scientists believe in the Big Bang. For these reasons, many people think that they too should believe in the Big Bang, despite its apparent absurdity. But is there really good evidence for the Big Bang? Is it supported by science?

Normally, scientific theories are established by the *scientific method*. A hypothesis is proposed that makes specific testable predictions about the future outcome of an experiment or class of experiments. Then, various experiments are performed and repeated under a variety of conditions. If the experiments verify the predictions of the hypothesis, then it is eventually elevated to the level of a *theory*. The theory isn't necessarily proved, but there is good reason to think it truthfully represents some aspect of the universe. However, if even one experiment generates an outcome contrary to the hypothesis, then the hypothesis is considered refuted.

The Big Bang model cannot be considered a theory in this sense of the word. After all, Big Bang proponents conjecture that a universe can spring into existence from a "quantum mechanical fluctuation," or even out of nothing.[1] This has never been observed or confirmed by any experiment. Really, we can't even think of any way to test that claim. In general, historical claims can never be demonstrated by the scientific method.[2] This is because we cannot construct experiments in the past. The past cannot be observed or repeated— it is gone. At best, we can ask what kinds of things we might expect to find in the current world based on a *model* about what might have happened in the past. Such models can be very useful.

A good scientific model will make many correct specific predictions about what we should observe in the future. An example is Newton's law of gravity. This, along with the laws of motion, allows us to predict with very high accuracy the future positions of the planets. These predictions are (1) very specific, and (2) very numerous. We could make a million predictions about the position of Venus over the course of the next year and we would find that observations confirm every one. Now *that* is good science! But does the Big Bang model do this?

The Big Bang does not make (1) very specific or (2) very numerous predictions about future observations. To be honest, I'm not familiar with even one *specific* prediction made by the Big Bang model. Supporters might claim that the Big Bang predicted the Cosmic Microwave Background (CMB), a faint source of microwave radiation coming apparently from all directions in space. These microwaves "glow" with a characteristic temperature of 2.7 degrees above absolute zero (kelvins). Did the Big Bang predict this?

In a way, it did. However, it is not a *specific* prediction and hence not nearly as impressive as Big Bang supporters might want you to suppose.[3] Some Big Bang advocates did predict a background temperature of around 3 Kelvins, but other supporters thought it would be closer to 1 K, and still others thought it would be much higher. So, there was quite a wide range in predictions—no real consensus among these secular scientists. Also, the Big Bang model predicted that the CMB would have large variations in its temperature, with "hot spots" in some places and "cold spots" in others. But observations show the opposite—the CMB is very uniform, with only slight temperature fluctuations. So, the prediction was rather vague, and the observations don't really match the type of CMB that was predicted. It really should not be counted as a successful prediction. Instead, current Big Bang models have been adjusted to match the observed CMB.

You might be wondering "What about all the other successful predictions of the Big Bang?" Really, there are none! The Big Bang does not predict any of the observed properties or actions of the universe, such as the relative abundances of the elements, the expansion of the universe, or distribution of galaxies.[4] These things are known (at least approximately), but the Big Bang model did not *predict* them. Instead, it has largely been retrofitted to accommodate them. So the Big Bang is not so much a scientific theory as a philosophical interpretive framework. People use their belief in the Big Bang to explain the evidence as it is discovered. But it would be wrong to say that the Big Bang is supported by evidence. It just isn't. Often, evidence is discovered that is contrary to the Big Bang model (such as the uniform nature of the CMB), and then the Big Bang is adjusted to accommodate such evidence. But this isn't good science.

Let's consider some of the evidence that is contrary to the expectations of the Big Bang model.

1. The Flatness Problem

Observations of the redshifts of galaxies indicate that the universe is apparently expanding.[5] This effect would tend to make the universe bigger, constantly moving the galaxies farther away from each other. On the other hand, galaxies also have gravity, which (if it weren't for expansion) would cause the galaxies to move closer to each other, making the universe smaller. So these two effects oppose each other. It happens that the two effects (expansion and gravity) are very finely balanced—they match almost perfectly. Yet, according to the Big Bang, this perfect balance was somehow achieved by an accidental, uncaused explosion.[6] This explanation strains credulity to the breaking point.

2. The Horizon Problem

According to the Big Bang model, the universe started out very small, with large temperature fluctuations from place to place. That is, the universe had "hot spots" and "cold spots." Today, the universe is quite large, and the hot spots and cold spots are far away from each other. But the problem is this—the spots aren't hot or cold anymore. The distant universe seems to have the same temperature everywhere, with only minor fluctuations. By itself, this may not seem like a problem. After all, if you put an ice cube (a "cold spot") in hot coffee (a "hot spot"), you will eventually end up with lukewarm coffee. Energy naturally moves from hot areas to cold areas.[7] The issue is this: Even moving at the speed of light, there has not been enough time (even if we accept the Big Bang's timescale of 13.7 billion years) for the energy to travel from the hot spots to the cold spots to "even out" all the temperatures. This is a serious difficulty for the Big Bang model.

3. The Monopole Problem

Most people are familiar with magnets. Magnets always have two "poles"—a north pole and a south pole. Like poles repel each other, and opposite poles attract. A magnetic monopole is a hypothetical particle that has only one magnetic pole—a north pole with no south pole, or the reverse. According to our current understanding of physics, these particles should be produced at extremely high temperatures, the kinds of temperatures that would have occurred during the Big Bang. Yet not a single monopole has ever been discovered. This strongly suggests that the Big Bang never happened.

Inflation

We need to briefly discuss "cosmic inflation." When the above three problems were discovered, the Big Bang model was retrofitted somewhat to accommodate these unexpected observations. This new version of the Big Bang is called inflation because it suggests that the universe briefly underwent a period of accelerated expansion (the inflation phase) shortly after the very moment of the Big Bang. Then, the inflation turned off and the universe went back to its normal expansion rate—at least for our region of the universe. This inflation add-on is designed to reduce or eliminate the flatness, horizon, and monopole problems simultaneously. But, unfortunately for Big Bang supporters, inflation amounts to nothing more than additional assumptions, and inflation has problems of its own. These difficulties include the following: What would cause the inflation? What would stop it? How could it be stopped everywhere in the universe at the same time—the "graceful exit problem"? In addition, there are problems with the Big Bang model that would not be solved, even if inflation were true. We will now look at these issues.

4. The Baryon Number Problem

This problem has to do with the fact that the universe contains very little antimatter. Antimatter is identical to ordinary matter, except the charges of the particles are reversed. So antiprotons have a negative charge. The Big Bang model states that the early universe was made up only of energy; it was too hot for matter to exist. As the universe expanded and cooled, some of the energy transformed into the ordinary matter we have today. This includes particles like protons and neutrons, which are classified as *baryons*. We know that it is possible to make matter from energy, because this can be repeated in particle accelerators. However, every time we make matter from energy, we get a precisely equal amount of antimatter (e.g., antibaryons). There are absolutely no exceptions! So if the Big Bang were true and all the matter in the universe came from energy, there should be an exactly equal amount of antimatter. But there seems to be very little antimatter in the universe. Why do baryons out-number antibaryons? This is contrary to the Big Bang model.

5. Distant Mature Galaxies

As we build increasingly powerful telescopes and peer into distant regions of the universe, we continue to find galaxies of magnificent beauty and com-plexity. This is perfectly consistent with biblical creation. But it's a problem for the Big Bang. Such mature galaxies were not expected to exist at such distances because these distances are supposed to represent times in the early universe before galaxies would have had a chance to form.[8] But there they are! Many other problems could be listed. But hopefully you get the point: The Big Bang is not a good scientific model.

Why Do People Believe It?

With all these problems, and essentially no successful predictions, why do many people continue to believe in the Big Bang with religious fervor? Perhaps the primary reason is found in Romans 1:18-20. These verses tell us that God has revealed Himself to all mankind. God has hardwired us in such a way that when we look at the natural world, we instantly know that it was created by God—not by a fortuitous "Big Bang." According to Romans 1:20, creation is so obvious that the unbeliever literally has "no excuse" for his unbelief in God. The problem, therefore, is not that people can't see evidence for creation. The problem (according to Romans 1:18) is that they "suppress the truth in unrighteousness." In other words, they willfully deny what they know in their heart-of-hearts to be true.

Many unbelievers embrace the Big Bang model because they do not want to accept the existence of God—at least not the *biblical* God.[9] Many Chris-tians fail to realize that this is the real driving force behind belief in the Big Bang. And they get intimidated, drawn into this mindset, and decide they need to accept the Big Bang, since that's what most scientists believe. But what they probably do not realize is this—no one believes in the Big Bang for *scientific* reasons!

Notes

1. See chapters 49 and 46 on the multiverse and the claim that the laws of physics could have created the universe from nothing.

2. See the chapters on forensic science.

3. The CMB is an indication that the universe has an average temperature. But wouldn't almost any model of origins expect that? Indeed, virtually any model of the universe (regardless of how the universe began) would have a CMB. So the Big Bang's prediction is not unique. Historically, the main competitor to the Big Bang at the time the CMB was discovered (the steady state model) had not yet made the prediction of the CMB. So the discovery of the CMB was taken as evidence in favor of the Big Bang by default over the steady state model.

4. The expansion of the universe as deduced by the redshifts of galaxies was discovered in the late 1920s. The Big Bang was proposed by George Lematre in 1931 as a naturalistic explanation for that expansion.

5. There are actually several different phenomena that can cause light to be "redshifted" (to have its frequency reduced). However, universal expansion is currently the only known cause of redshift that will naturally explain the Hubble Law, the fact that distances of galaxies tend to be correlated with redshift. It should be noted that we do not actually observe expansion of the universe. It is a reasonable, though not definitive, inference from the Hubble Law.

6. This is not an "explosion" in the conventional sense of particles moving through space away from a common source. The entirety of space itself is allegedly contained in the singularity, which rapidly expands, carrying energy and space along with it.

7. This is a result of the second law of thermodynamics.

8. Richard, J. et al. First galaxies were born much earlier than expected. *Hubble News.* Posted on spacetelescope. org April 12, 2011.

9. People prefer a god that they make up—one who allows them the freedom to be their own ultimate standard in matters of truth. This is a form of idolatry.

45

THE AGE OF THE COSMOS—
WHAT YOU HAVE NOT BEEN TOLD

Jason Lisle, Ph.D.

Most people have been taught that the world is very ancient. We are told that the earth is 4.6 billion years old, that the universe is 13.7 billion years old, and that science has established both of these things as fact. We are also told that the biblical timescale of around 6,000 years is impossible given the scientific evidence.

However, we are usually *not* told that the billions-of-years age estimates are not based primarily on science, but on naturalistic assumptions (see chapter 33 on radioisotope dating). And we are usually *not* told that there is much evidence indicating our universe is *much younger* than billions of years. In this chapter, we explore some of these lines of evidence that confirm that the universe is much younger than what secular astronomers would want us to believe.

Unfortunately, the methods of science do not allow us to actually *measure* age as we would with something like mass or composition. Age is not a substance that can be detected in a laboratory. Rather, age is the concept of the total timespan of an object's existence throughout history. At best, we can make an educated guess about when a particular process began by knowing (1) its initial state, and (2) its rate of change. Unfortunately, the only thing we can actually measure in the present is the rate of change *today*. The rate of change of any process may have been different in the past. Furthermore, we can never really know the initial state because we weren't there when the process began.

Despite these difficulties, we can still make an estimation of the *maximum* age of a system (even if the initial condition is unknown) because, in many cases, the initial condition cannot realistically be outside of a certain range.

For example, we may not know the initial amount of salt in the ocean. But we can know for certain that it can't be less than zero percent—you can't have less salt than no salt!

Furthermore, most secularists assume the present rates of processes are indicative of past rates. While we may disagree, we can temporarily assume that it is true for argument's sake to show that it leads to an inconsistency. In other words, we hypothetically assume the worldview of a secular astronomer, and then show that based on present rates, some process cannot be as old as the secular timescale because it would exceed the maximum or minimum possible value for the initial conditions.

When we apply this type of reasoning, we find that the universe simply cannot be as old as secularists believe. But the evidence is consistent with a "young" 6,000-year-old universe.

1. Planetary Magnetic Fields

The earth has a magnetic field caused by electrical current in the core. The current constantly encounters resistance, and so the magnetic field naturally decays with time. We can measure the present strength of the magnetic field and the rate at which the energy is dropping. We don't know what its initial strength was, but we know it could not have been too strong or it would have been able to rip the iron out of your blood—making life impossible. The present rate of decay indicates that the magnetic field cannot be billions of years old; in fact, it can't even be millions of years old. Earth's decaying magnetic field is consistent with an age of a few thousand years.

And it's not just the earth. Jupiter, Saturn, Uranus, and Neptune all have strong magnetic fields. And yet, based on the expected rate of decay, these fields are far too strong for these planets to be billions of years old. Dr. Russell Humphreys is a creation physicist who has developed a particular model that infers the initial strength of the magnetic fields of the planets at the time of their creation.[1] It is noteworthy that Dr. Humphreys' model successfully computes the magnetic field of all the planets in the solar system, given an age of about 6,000 years. The model also successfully predicted the decay of Mercury's magnetic field.[2]

2. Comets

Comets are masses of ice and dirt that orbit the sun in elliptical paths.

Their orbits take them far away from the sun, where they move slowly and remain frozen icebergs a few miles across. Then they circle back and briefly pass much closer to the sun, where solar heat vaporizes some of the icy surface of the comet. The material is launched into space and pushed away from the sun by solar wind and solar radiation pressure. This is what forms a comet's long tail—it is a thin trail of material being blasted away from the comet's surface. Every time you see a comet, it is getting smaller—rapidly losing mass. But comets only have a finite amount of material. Eventually, the sun vaporizes away all of the source material and the comet is gone. We have witnessed instances of this happening in real time—a comet passes very near the sun and is completely obliterated. The point is this: Comets simply cannot last billions of years.

They can't even last one million years.[3] Our calculations show that a typical comet could last for about 100,000 years at most.[4] That's a long time, of course, but it is far less than the 4.6 billion years that most secular astronomers assume for the age of the solar system. And since the 100,000-year estimate is an upper limit, not the true age of any given comet, it is fair to say that comets are perfectly consistent with the biblical timescale, but they are in no way consistent with millions of years.

Secular astronomers are well aware of this difficulty, but they are unwilling to give up their belief in billions of years because they believe the entire system of naturalistic evolutionary processes requires vast amounts of time. Therefore, secular astronomers have proposed that there must be a ready source of new comets (a "comet-generator") that replenishes the solar system as old comets are constantly being destroyed. They have suggested that there is a vast reservoir of "potential" comets orbiting in the distant solar system where they cannot be detected. The small (and hypothetical) icy objects in this "Oort cloud" are supposedly occasionally "disturbed" from their orbit and thrown into the inner solar system to become brand new comets.[5,6] So as old comets disintegrate, new ones replace them. Pretty clever, isn't it? But such an Oort cloud has never been detected. As far as we can tell, it is just a speculative conjecture designed to protect the old-universe worldview from evidence to the contrary.

3. Internal Heat of the Giant Planets

Jupiter gives off about twice the amount of energy that it receives from the sun. It is losing enormous amounts of energy—in the form of heat—to space. But Jupiter only has a finite amount of energy, so it cannot do this forever. Just like taking a hot potato out of the oven, the potato radiates heat to space and eventually becomes cold again. And it doesn't take a long time. Since Jupiter is much bigger than a potato, it will take a lot longer to cool to the point where it no longer loses energy to space. But even for Jupiter, this process cannot last 4.6 billion years. The internal heat of Jupiter is an indication that the planet is simply not billions of years old.[7]

The problem is even more challenging for Neptune, which emits 2.7 times the amount of energy it receives from the sun. Neptune is large enough that it can do this for thousands of years—but certainly not billions. The internal heat of Neptune is an indication of its "youth." It is noteworthy that Uranus (which is essentially the same size, mass, and composition as Neptune) does not have this excess internal heat. This is very perplexing from a secular point of view, since these planets allegedly formed at the same time under nearly identical circumstances. However, it is certainly consistent with our Creator's love of variety.

4. Spiral Galaxy Wind-up

Spiral galaxies are comprised of hundreds of billions of stars organized into "arms" that are twisted around the disk. Spiral galaxies rotate differentially—the inner regions rotate faster than the outer regions. And so, the spiral structure must necessarily get slightly "tighter" every year. The rotation rate is slow enough that the spiral structure could persist for as long as 100 million years. But once we get to a billion years, the spiral arms would be twisted beyond recognition and the disk would be a uniform blend of stars. This "twist rate" places an upper limit on the age of spiral galaxies. One billion years is a long time, until we consider that secular astronomers believe that spiral galaxies are 10 billion years old. Spiral galaxies are consistent with the biblical timescale (since the one-billion-years estimate is an *upper* limit), but they are quite inconsistent with the secular timeframe.

Secular astronomers have proposed that there must be a process within spiral galaxies that creates new spiral arms as the old ones are twisted together. A "spiral density wave" is supposed to trigger star formation, creating new stars in a spiral pattern. It is very doubtful that such a wave could genuinely cause stars to form from interstellar gas. And it has other problems as well, such as what would cause such a density wave in the first place.

One problem in particular concerns galactic magnetic fields: The large-scale magnetic fields in spiral galaxies have been measured, and are locally parallel to the spiral arms. In other words, if you were located in a spiral arm (and yet not close to an individual star), your compass would line up parallel to the spiral arm. It is well-known in physics that plasma (ionized gas) cannot cross a field line. In other words, plasma can only move parallel to the direction of the magnetic field. Therefore, spiral arms (which contain a great deal of plasma) and their magnetic fields must rotate together (differentially). So when a new spiral arm is supposedly created, it would not align with the original (now highly twisted) magnetic field.[8] But that is contrary to our observations, so how could any of these spiral arms be relatively new?

Many other lines of evidence could be listed, and have been published in other literature.[9] Why is it that we do not often hear about these? Secularists often like to present their ideas on origins as if they were facts with no contrary evidence. But that just isn't the case. The secular timescale does not fit well with the data. And while it is always possible to construct auxiliary conjectures to explain apparently contrary evidence (e.g., the Oort cloud, spiral density waves), it is clear that the belief in billions of years is a faith position. It's not a position that a person is driven to by neutral or objective rational analysis of the observations. Instead, it is a philosophical framework or worldview in light of which evidence is interpreted.

The Bible—as the Word of the all-knowing God—gives us a much better worldview. Unlike the secular worldview, the Bible is rational and can make sense of the scientific evidence, as well as all of human experience. It is therefore no surprise that Bible tells us in Romans 1:20 that those who deny that God created the universe are without excuse.

Notes

1. Humphreys, D. R. 1984. The Creation of Planetary Magnetic Fields. *Creation Research Society Quarterly.* 21 (3).

2. Thomas, B. Mercury's Fading Magnetic Field Fits Creation Model. *Creation Science Update.* Posted on icr.org October 26, 2011.

3. Steidl, P. F. 1983. *Planets, comets, and asteroids, Design and Origins in Astronomy.* Terre Haute, IN: Creation Research Society Books, 73-106.

4. Humphreys, D. R. 2005. Evidence for a Young World. *Acts & Facts.* 34 (6).

5. The Oort cloud is named after its inventor, Jan Oort.

6. To be precise, the Oort cloud is invoked to explain the existence of long-period comets—those with an orbital period greater than 200 years. The Kuiper belt is supposed to replenish short-period comets. However, any objects so far detected in the region of the Kuiper belt are much too large to be progenitors for comets.

7. The earth also has substantial internal heat. However, it is thought that radioactive decay of the heavier ele-

ments might be sufficient to account for this heat. This will not work for the giant planets, because they are comprised primarily of the lighter elements, which are not radioactive.

8. Basically, this means that the magnetic fields should be highly twisted (and eventually destroyed by reconnection) if the galaxies were really billions of years old, since density waves cannot restore the magnetic fields. But this is not what we observe.

9. For more details, see Lisle, J. 2006. *Taking Back Astronomy.* Green Forest, AR: Master Books.

46

COULD THE LAWS OF PHYSICS HAVE CREATED THE UNIVERSE?

Jake Hebert, Ph.D.

Explaining the origin of the universe is an enormous challenge for those seeking to explain our existence apart from a creator. How could a universe come from nothing?

The challenge is so great that some have argued that the universe simply did not have a beginning, but has somehow existed eternally. However, because most professing atheists have accepted the Big Bang model, they have accepted the premise that our universe did indeed have a beginning.[1] Hence, they need to explain that beginning. Physicist Lawrence Krauss recently claimed, along with others, that the laws of physics could have created the universe from nothing.[2]

Before discussing this claim in detail, it is important to note that the law of conservation of energy (COE) is one of the most fundamental rules in physics. This law states that energy is neither created nor destroyed, although it can be transformed from one kind to another. Thus, evolutionists would prefer that their theories for the origin of the universe not violate this basic rule.

Another important rule in physics is the Heisenberg Uncertainty Principle (HUP), one version of which says that a rapidly changing quantum mechanical system cannot have a well-defined energy.[3] Theoretical physicists often interpret this version of the HUP to mean that COE is not truly absolute, but may be violated over very short time spans.

Evolutionary physicists claim that our universe could have resulted from a *quantum fluctuation*, the spontaneous appearance and disappearance of "virtual particles" from a vacuum. Virtual particles are thought to be responsible for a number of phenomena, including a very subtle effect on the spectrum of the hydrogen atom called the Lamb shift. Virtual particles have extremely short lifetimes, too short to be directly observed, and—in accordance with the HUP—the greater the energy of the particles, the shorter their lifetimes must be.

Although it is frequently said that the HUP allows short-term violations of COE, this claim is not universally accepted. One respected quantum mechanics textbook says that such an understanding of the HUP is simply wrong.[4] Even evolutionary theorists have acknowledged that the energy for quantum fluctuations could be coming from the vacuum itself, in which case COE is *not* violated, since the energy for the fluctuation was already present in the vacuum.[5] A respected creation physicist has made a similar argument.[6]

If the energy for the quantum fluctuation that supposedly created our universe came from the vacuum itself, then it is obvious that this evolutionary scenario does not *really* involve creation out of nothing—their "nothing" was actually a "something"—since the energy for the fluctuation was already present within the vacuum. At best, this would involve a transformation of pre-existing energy into other forms. As such, it is essentially a disguised version of the claim that the cosmos is eternal.

However, even granting the claim that energy *can* genuinely "pop" into existence, there are serious difficulties with the idea that the universe resulted from a quantum fluctuation. This idea is not new; it was suggested by Edward Tryon in 1973.[7] One would expect the energy content of the entire universe to be enormous. Even if one were to argue that the universe *did* pop into existence via a quantum fluctuation, the energy content of the universe would be so large that the HUP would require the corresponding time to be incredibly small, and the newly born universe would then immediately vanish.[8] How, then, could our universe have resulted from such a fluctuation?

Tryon argued that if the total energy of the universe were zero, it could have resulted from such a fluctuation and yet persist indefinitely without violating the HUP. Others have more recently argued that a quantum fluctuation did not need to persist indefinitely, but only long enough to initiate a process that rapidly "blew up" a volume of space that ultimately became our universe.

A component of the Big Bang model called *inflation theory* claims that our universe could have resulted from this process, without the need for any additional creation of energy. In such a scenario, the total energy of the universe would be exactly zero. As noted earlier, this is important, since the creation of a universe with zero total energy would not involve a large-scale violation of COE. Evolutionists admit that the initial quantum fluctuation in their models could involve a *tiny* violation of COE, but they do not see this as a problem, since they believe such a violation would be too small to be measured.[9]

Although secular cosmologists now seem to favor the second scenario, either scenario would require the energy of the universe to be exactly zero. This could be the case if the universe's negative gravitational potential energy were exactly balanced by the positive energy of particles within the universe. But *is* the total energy of the entire universe exactly zero?

Evolutionary theorists assert that it is, but in order to *confirm* this claim, one would have to account for *all* the forms of energy in the universe (gravitational potential energy, the energies of all particles, etc.), add them together, and then verify that the sum truly *is* exactly zero.[10] This is absolutely beyond the capability of any human being.

The claim of a "zero energy" universe is based not on *direct* measurements, but upon an *interpretation* of the data through the filter of the Big Bang model and inflation theory. But inflation was from the beginning an *ad hoc* idea that was attached to the original Big Bang model in order to solve a number of serious—and even fatal—difficulties.[11] Proponents are making the claim of a zero-energy universe simply because it is expected in inflation theory.[12, 13] For someone without a prior commitment to inflation theory, it would seem *extremely* unlikely that the universe's total energy would be exactly zero.

Likewise, when virtual particles momentarily appear within a vacuum, they are appearing in a space that *already exists*. Because space is part of our universe, the spontaneous creation of a universe requires space *itself* to somehow pop into existence.

Proponents have acknowledged this difficulty, but speculate that *quantum gravity* (a theory which merges quantum mechanics and general relativity) could allow for this.[14] An obvious problem with this argument is that a workable theory of quantum gravity does not yet exist!

Moreover, their argument suffers from serious *logical* difficulties. Our understanding of the laws of physics is based on *observations* from thousands of experiments. No one has *ever* observed a universe "popping" into existence. This means that any such laws of physics that would allow, even in principle, a universe to pop into existence are completely outside our experience. The laws of physics, as we know them, simply are not applicable here. Rather, the spontaneous creation of a universe would require higher "meta" or "hyper" laws of physics that might or might not be anything like the laws of physics that we know.

But this raises another problem. Since such hypothetical meta or hyper laws of physics are completely outside our experience, why do atheistic physicists naively assume that rules like the HUP and COE would even conventionally apply when describing the universe's creation? They freely speculate about other unobservable universes in an alleged "multiverse" that can have physical constants and even laws of physics that are different from our own. Since these laws are known to be valid only *within* our existing universe, it is not at all clear why they would necessarily apply at the universe's creation. Perhaps COE and the HUP are indeed part of these hyper laws of physics, but perhaps they are not. One can engage in all kinds of speculation here, but speculation is clearly not *science*.

This is why it is illogical for an evolutionist to argue that COE forbids a supernatural creation. Yes, such a supernatural creation of the universe *would* involve the creation of energy out of nothing. But again, the laws of physics (including COE) are known to apply only *within* our physical universe. The atheist can argue that COE forbids supernatural creation only if he *knows* that the laws of physics were operating before and at the universe's creation. Of course, he has no way of knowing this, since he wasn't present at the creation (Job 38:4). Of course, God is not bound by such laws, since He Himself established them![15]

This reasoning leads to still another difficulty for evolutionists' claim: In order for the laws of physics to create the universe, they must exist *apart* from the universe. But this presents a dilemma for the atheist who says that the cosmos is all that exists. Before his death, Carl Sagan acknowledged in correspondence with ICR scientist Larry Vardiman that he recognized this problem for his worldview: His view of origins required the laws of physics to *create* the cosmos, but because he did not acknowledge his Creator, he could not explain the origin of the laws *themselves*.[16] The existence of physical laws external to the universe itself was an obvious violation of his well-known axiom "the Cosmos is all that is or ever was or ever will be."[17]

Despite the impressive academic credentials of those promoting the claim that the laws of physics could have created the universe from nothing, it is utterly unreasonable, and no Bible-believing Christian should be intimidated by it.

Notes

1. Some evolutionists are now claiming that our universe is only one of infinitely many universes in a great *multiverse*, and that it is only *our* universe that began 13.7 billion years ago. See chapter 49 for details.

2. Krauss, L. 2012. *A Universe From Nothing*. New York: Free Press.

3. Griffiths, D. J. 2005. *Introduction to Quantum Mechanics*, 2nd ed. Upper Saddle River, NJ: Pearson Educational, Inc., 114-116.

4. Ibid, 118.

5. Pasachoff, J. M. and A. Filippenko. 2007. *The Cosmos: Astronomy in the New Millenium*, 3rd ed. Belmont, CA: Thomson Brooks/Cole, 474-475.

6. Humphreys, D. R., personal communication, May 23, 2012.

7. Tryon, E. P. 1973. Is the Universe a Vacuum Fluctuation? *Nature*. 246 (5422): 396-397.

8. Ross, H. 2001. *The Creator and the Cosmos*. Colorado Springs, CO: NavPress, 170. Cited in reference 11, 120. But beware Dr. Ross' promotion of the unbiblical Big Bang theory.

9. Pasachoff and Filippenko, *The Cosmos: Astronomy in the New Millenium*, 474.

10. Hawking, S. 1996. *A Brief History of Time*. New York: Bantam Books, 133.

11. Williams, A. and J. Hartnett. 2005. *Dismantling the Big Bang*. Green Forest, AR: Master Books, 121-125.

12. Krauss, *A Universe From Nothing*, 98-104.

13. Lemley, B. Guth's Grand Guess. *Discover Magazine*. Posted on discovermagazine.com April 1, 2002.

14. Krauss, *A Universe From Nothing*, 163-164.

15. This does not rule out the possibility that God may have used natural physical processes during the course of the six-day creation week, but He was certainly free to modify or suspend those rules as He pleased, and He is free to do so today if He pleases, as in the case of miracles.

16. Vardiman, L. 2012. Did the "God Particle" Create Matter? *Acts & Facts*. 41 (3): 12-14.

17. Sagan, C. 1985. *Cosmos*. New York: Ballantine books, 1.

47

DISTANT STARLIGHT IN A YOUNG UNIVERSE

Jason Lisle, Ph.D.

With modern technology, astronomers are able to detect individual stars at distances of 50 million light-years or more. (A light-year is a distance of about six trillion miles.) Beyond this distance—with the exception of an occasional supernova—only the combined light of all the stars in a given galaxy can be detected. Galaxies have been detected at distances of several billion light-years. Since a light-year is the distance that light travels in a time span of one year, it would seem that the light from these distant galaxies must have been produced billions of years ago in order to reach Earth today. But this is contrary to the biblical timescale, as well as other scientific data that indicate a universe that is about 6,000 years old.

This paradox has caused many Christians to stumble in their faith. Some Christians have tried to read the Bible in an unnatural and forced way to accommodate the billions of years. But we must concede that the author of Genesis certainly did not intend to suggest that the timescale of creation was anything but six ordinary days—six 24-hour days. Such compromises as "day-age" and the "gap theory" are simply not faithful to the clear narrative text.[1] Some people have rejected Genesis outright due to the distant starlight issue. They feel so confident that starlight establishes an old universe that they reject Scripture on this basis alone. It's really a shame, because a proper understanding of physics will show that distant starlight is perfectly compatible with a "young" (~6,000 years) universe. Even if it did not, it would be far more reasonable to conclude that our understanding of physics needs improvement than to conclude that Almighty God was mistaken, or even unclear.

It must be noted, however, that many of the proposed answers to the starlight paradox are simply not realistic. These include the following: the claim that the stars and galaxies are actually much closer than thought—all within 6,000 light-years; the claim that God made the light "in progress"; and the claim that the speed of light was much greater in the past or in the distant universe. In this brief chapter, we cannot cover in detail the problems with these positions. However, suffice it to say that they all have fatal logical or scientific problems (published in other literature) that render them untenable.[2] Other proposed solutions invoke relativistic time-dilation—the fact that clocks "tick" at different rates under different circumstances.[3] This effect, which was discovered by Albert Einstein, is very real. And attempts to solve distant starlight this way are intriguing.[4] However, so far no such solution using standard physics has been rigorously demonstrated to actually reconcile distant starlight with the biblical timescale.[5]

But there is a solution that is based on standard physics that shows that starlight can indeed reach Earth from the farthest galaxies in virtually no time at all. In order for this solution to make sense, it is instructive to review the basics of Einstein's theory of relativity. This theory has been verified in countless experiments, and has been very successful in accounting for what we observe in the universe.[6]

Einstein concluded that velocity affects the passage of time and the measurement of distances. Specifically, clocks tick slower when they are moving (relative to an observer) than when they are stationary, and lengths contract in the direction of motion when the object is moving. These effects seem very strange to us because they are so tiny at the velocities we normally travel that we cannot even detect them. And so, we tend to assume that motion has no effect on time or space, since we don't notice it. But the effects are there, and they become very substantial at velocities close to the speed of light.

The One-Way Speed of Light

Another well-established (though not commonly known) implication of relativity is that the speed of light in vacuum can be objectively measured *only* on a round trip. The speed of light in vacuum on a one-way trip cannot be measured without first assuming this speed—which is circular. Let's illustrate this with a thought experiment. Suppose we had access to a very long hallway—186,282.397 miles long!—and we placed a mirror at one end and a clock and flashlight at the other. We could measure the speed of light by turning on the flashlight exactly when the clock strikes noon, and then recording the time when the beam returns back to the clock. We would find it takes exactly two seconds for the beam to travel to the end of the hallway, reflect off of the mirror, and return to its source. Dividing the total distance (twice the length of the hallway) by the total time (two seconds) gives us the speed of light: 186,282.397 miles per second (which is 670,616,629 mph).

But this is a time-averaged speed. There is no guarantee that the light travelled this speed the entire trip. People tend to assume that the light took one second to reach the mirror and one second to return, but that need not be so. Perhaps the light took only a half-second to reach the mirror, and 1.5 seconds to return. We would get the same result. Or, perhaps the light took two seconds to reach the mirror and travelled back instantaneously. We would get the same result. Our experiment only gives us the two-way (round-trip) average speed of light. If we wanted to know the speed of light on a one-way path (from the flashlight to the mirror), how could we measure this?

To measure the speed of light on a one-way path, we will need a clock at both ends of the hallway, one to measure when the beam of light starts and the other to record when the beam reaches the other side of the hallway. When clock 1 strikes noon, the flashlight turns on, sending a beam streaming down the long hallway. Clock 2 records the time when it detects the light. Perhaps it detects that the light arrived at one second past noon. Then we would know that the light took one second to traverse the distance. And since we know the distance, we can compute the one-way speed of light, right? Well, no, we still don't know. Consider this: Perhaps clock 2 is one second slow ("behind" clock 1), in which case the light really took two seconds to traverse the distance. Or perhaps clock 2 is one second fast, in which case the light took no time at all to traverse the distance. So we can see that, in order for us to actually know the one-way speed of light, the two clocks must be precisely synchronized—they must *read* exactly the same time *at* the same time. But this seemingly simple task turns out to be remarkably difficult to achieve.

Synchronizing Distant Clocks

Suppose we synchronize the clocks by radio transmission. At exactly noon, we send a radio pulse from clock 1 to clock 2. When clock 2 receives this pulse, it is set to noon. But there is a problem. The radio pulse took a small amount of time to travel from clock 1 to clock 2. We could subtract this time and adjust clock 2 if we knew how long it took the radio pulse to arrive. But radio pulses travel at the speed of light—and the one-way speed of light is the very thing we do not yet know! In other words, to synchronize two clocks separated by a distance in order to measure the one-way speed of light, we would have to *already know* the one-way speed of light! So, such a method can never succeed.

Perhaps we could bring clock 1 and clock 2 together and synchronize them at the same location. This would indeed eliminate any ambiguity. We then move clock 1 and clock 2 to the two respective ends of the hallway. Now we have our synchronized clocks separated by a distance, right? No, again there is a problem. Remember from our previous discussion, Einstein discovered that motion affects the passage of time. The very act of moving the two clocks to their respective locations has caused them to become desynchronized. There is an equation that tells us by how much they have become desynchronized; so, we could compute how much they are off and then make the needed adjustment. But unfortunately, this equation contains the one-way speed of light!

It seems that no matter what we do, we would have to first know the one-way speed of light in order to synchronize clocks so we could then measure the one-way speed of light. But we cannot know the one-way speed of light unless we first measure it. We are stuck in a Catch-22. Einstein realized this dilemma and came to a very ingenious work-around. Einstein concluded that the one-way speed of light is not actually a property of nature per se, but a convention that is stipulated by human beings.[7] A convention is something that we get to decide, and then we use it to measure other things, such as twelve inches in a foot. There is no property of the universe that forces there to be twelve inches in a foot. We collectively made that decision. Likewise, Einstein decided for simplicity to make the one-way speed of light the same in all directions. But he agreed that other choices were equally valid.[8,9]

What if we chose the one-way speed of light to be instantaneous when travelling directly toward an observer? This is called an "anisotropic synchrony convention," or ASC. (Anisotropic means "not the same in all directions.") In such a case, the speed of light when moving directly away would be ½c, and the speed at right angles would be c. The round-trip speed would continue to be c (186,282.397 miles per second) as always. This choice would eliminate the distant starlight problem, because light from distant galaxies is moving toward the observers on Earth and hence requires no time to traverse the distance. It's a bit like travelling west across time zones on an airplane; you can arrive at essentially the same time you left.

Some might argue that it seems "strange" for light to have different speeds depending on its direction relative to an observer. But the speed of light is strange anyway! That the speed of light does not depend on the speed of the observer or the light source is also strange. The strangeness of relativistic physics appears whether we take the ASC or the standard isotropic convention. Either way, we must concede that the universe does not always behave as we would expect or prefer.

Some people may be tempted to ask, "But is ASC the correct convention?" But this is not a legitimate question because a convention is neither "correct" nor "incorrect." It is simply "useful" or "not useful." Driving on the right side of the road is a useful convention, but some countries choose the reverse and this is equally valid. So it is with ASC.

The real question is: Does the Bible use ASC or some other convention? I suggest that the Bible does use ASC, or at least the functional equivalent of it, because the Bible implies that starlight takes virtually no time to arrive on Earth. Consider Genesis 1:14-15. This indicates that the lights in the sky (which include the stars—see verse 16) were made "to give light on the earth." And the text also states, "and it was so"—affirming that the stars did indeed give light upon the earth instantly, or at least that day. Moreover, ancient cultures did not subtract light-travel times from celestial events. They were effectively using the ASC system, even if they didn't consciously think of it that way.

Since the Bible appears to use ASC, and since we can still use ASC today, it takes no time at all for light from the farthest galaxies to reach Earth. If, indeed, the Bible uses the ASC convention, then there really is no distant starlight problem. And there never has been. The notion that the Bible uses the equivalent of ASC when marking time is called the "ASC model." Like all scientific models, it could be wrong, of course, but it does seem to have scientific support.[10] So, we have a very plausible solution to distant starlight that is based on well-established physics.

Some might ask, "What if the ASC model is someday discovered to be wrong?" First, there are other theories of distant starlight, or perhaps there exists an as-yet-undiscovered solution. Second, and more importantly, to those who truly understand that the Bible is God's Word, such an event would not really be a big deal. God is not obligated to explain to us how He has done what He has done. The rational Christian has confidence that God really did create the entire universe in six days, even if he or she doesn't understand every nuance of how God did this. "Let God be true but every man a liar" (Romans 3:4).

Notes

1. See chapters 2 and 3 for more information on these ideas.

2. Lisle, J. 2005. *Distant Starlight: Not a Problem for a Young Universe*. DVD. Answers in Genesis.

3. Dr. Russell Humphreys was the first physicist to attempt to solve the distant starlight problem using gravitational time dilation. Although his original model does not appear to solve the problem, the concept of applying relativistic physics was a huge and innovative leap forward in creationist cosmology.

4. Humphreys, D. R. 1996. *Starlight and Time: Solving the Puzzle of Distant Starlight in a Young Universe*. Green Forest, AR: Master Books.

5. Some solutions using non-standard physics are very interesting. Dr. John Hartnett's model is one example.

6. Some people are upset by the name, as if relativity were somehow proposing that everything is relative (which would be a self-refuting claim). But the theory of relativity asserts nothing of the kind, and it is noteworthy that Einstein did not coin the term. He probably would have preferred the name "invariance." In fact, in relativity, it is the measured two-way speed of light that is absolute. But the current name has caught on, so we will use it as well. In any case, the science of relativity is very well-established.

7. Einstein, A. 1961. *Relativity: The Special and General Theory*. R. W. Lawson, trans. New York: Crown Publishers Inc., 23.

8. Ibid, 22-23.

9. Sarkar, S. and J. Stachel. 1999. Did Malament prove the non-conventionality of simultaneity in the Special Theory of Relativity? *Philosophy of Science*. 66 (2): 208-220.

10. Lisle, J. 2010. Anisotropic Synchrony Convention—A Solution to the Distant Starlight Problem. *Answers Research Journal*. 3 (2010): 191-207.

48

DO UFOS EXIST?

Jason Lisle, Ph.D.

The term UFO stands for "unidentified flying object." So, any flying object that you cannot identify is technically, to you, a UFO. Of course, to someone else, it may very well be an IFO (an identified flying object). UFOs need not be exotic, "alien," or miraculous. They can be perfectly ordinary flying objects—planes, birds, stars, planets, satellites, meteors, aurorae, lightning, and so on—that some people simply cannot identify.

People sometimes report UFOs to the local media or to a nearby observatory. The most commonly reported UFO, by far, is the planet Venus. Venus often appears in the western sky just after sunset or in the morning sky just before sunrise. The planet is extremely bright—brighter than any other planet or nighttime star. And this brightness sometimes surprises people who are not familiar with backyard astronomy.

Sometimes people think that Venus' image cannot be that of a planet because it seems to move in an unpredictable way. In reality, any apparent sudden movement of Venus is purely psychological. The mind is not good at perceiving motion when there is no good point of reference, as is often the case when Venus is high in the sky and other stars are not yet visible because twilight is still too bright. However, Venus can indeed appear to shimmer, twinkle, or rapidly change color when it is very low in the sky. This is due to turbulence in Earth's atmosphere, which causes minor deviations in the path of the incoming light. It may seem strange to those people who see it for the first time, but it's all perfectly natural.

Satellites are also sometimes reported as UFOs. Many people don't realize that it is indeed possible to see manmade satellites—at least, those satellites in low Earth orbit. Satellites appear as faint moving "stars." They are easy to see on dark summer nights, because the angle of the sun relative to the earth is optimal that time of year. You can easily see a dozen or more satellites on a summer evening if you are willing to stay up for a few watchful hours.

Most satellites maintain a fairly constant brightness—they are illuminated by sunlight. This may seem surprising since we see them at night, but at the altitude of the satellite, it is still "daytime"—the sun is still visible from the satellite's point of view. Satellites sometimes move into Earth's shadow and gradually fade out. Occasionally, a satellite will seem to "pulse" either regularly or erratically. A regular pulse is due to a rotating satellite (usually a spent rocket casing) that is catching the sunlight as it rotates. A satellite may appear to pulsate erratically by rotating in a more complex fashion or it may be oddly shaped (or both) such that an observer on Earth sees enhanced sunlight reflections at irregular intervals.

One of the most fascinating and startling appearances of a satellite (and one that is readily reported as a UFO) is called an *iridium flare*. These are produced by Iridium (the name of the company) communication satellites that have large door-size antennas that occasionally catch the sunlight at the right angle. When this happens, the satellites become extremely bright for several seconds, even outshining Venus! Such events are predictable, and there are even websites that can compute when an iridium flare will happen for a given location.[1]

A meteor (a "shooting star," or "falling star") can also be a UFO to those who are unfamiliar with them. A meteor is the bright, very brief trail produced by a piece of dust or a pebble that enters Earth's atmosphere from space. Since the intruder is moving at thousands of miles per hour, it is heated by air resistance and is quickly vaporized. Sometimes, meteors can be very bright, even brighter than the full moon, in which case they are called *fireballs*. They can have vivid color, depending on the composition of the source. Sometimes, meteors leave a fainter glowing trail, usually light blue in color, that lasts for a few seconds and is called a *train*. On rare occasions, the faint train can last for several minutes, in which case it is called a *persistent train*.

There are rare natural phenomena that can also be reported as a UFO. One example of this is called *ball lightening*. This seldom-seen and somewhat controversial phenomenon seems to manifest as a spherical, persistent ball of electrical activity associated with storms. Since it is so rare and strange, it is easy to see why it would count as an unidentified flying object to most people.

What UFOs Are Not

Due to the strong influence of science fiction and evolutionary influence in our nation, many people associate that term UFO with "aliens." A significant fraction of our population believes aliens from distant worlds have visited our planet and that many reports of UFOs are actually fleeting glimpses of these alien spacecraft. But as we have already discussed, virtually all reported UFOs are readily explained by natural or man-made items. Even the idea of interstellar travel is far less feasible than the simple "warp drive" that science fiction would lead people to believe. There are fundamental difficulties that advances in technology cannot simply circumvent.

Most importantly, Christians should evaluate the idea of extraterrestrial life in light of Scripture. Does the Bible make sense of such a concept? The motivation for believing in aliens is largely an evolutionary one. Evolutionists expect that since life supposedly evolved on Earth where the conditions just happened to be right, then life probably evolved elsewhere too. After all, it's a big universe. So, if the conditions were right on Earth for chemical evolution, then surely it has happened elsewhere, probably multiple times. But the consistent Christian knows better. The conditions on Earth were never favorable for chemical evolution. Life always and only comes from previous life. The original animals (and people) were created by God and did not evolve from microbes.

Some Christians might argue, "Yes, but God may have created other intelligent beings on other worlds." While there is no doubt God has the power to do that, we must ask if the Bible indicates that God has done this. There is no explicit mention in Scripture of any type of life beyond Earth.[2] Of course, there are undoubtedly many things that God has done of which He has not told us anything. But Scripture seems to strongly imply that Earth is unique among the worlds of creation. Consider that Earth was made on Day One of the creation week, but all the celestial lights (stars and planets) were made on Day Four (Genesis 1:16-19).

Most conspicuously, we find that the Bible states the earth was specifically designed for life. This is clear in Genesis 1 and is summarized in Isaiah 45:18. God formed the earth to be inhabited. The implicit inference is that the universe beyond Earth was not formed for such a purpose. The heavens certainly reflect God's glory (Psalm 19:1), and they mark the passage of time (Genesis 1:14), but they are not designed to house life.

Even more damaging to the notion of extraterrestrial intelligence are the soteriological considerations—those issues that deal with redemption. The Bible teaches that because of Adam's sin, the entire universe is cursed and awaits deliverance from its bondage of corruption (Romans 8:20-23; Genesis 3:17-19). Note that it wasn't extraterrestrial beings that caused the universe to be cursed. It was the sin of, specifically, a human being right here on Earth.

Science-fiction programming often depicts intelligent life in space, from Martians to Vulcans and Klingons. But consider the theological implications. Martians could not be saved from sin. Nor could Vulcans or Klingons. The reason is this: Not being human, they are not biologically related to Jesus. Jesus, the second person of the Trinity, is an actual descendant of Adam, just as we are. This means He is literally our blood-relative. That is why His shed blood on the cross counts as ours. We are of "one blood" (Acts 17:26). Jesus is God, and took on human nature to pay for our sins. He became one of us so that He could substitute for us. He died our death, and we inherit His righteousness.

But "Commander Worf" is out of luck! Klingons, Vulcans, and any other hypothetical extraterrestrials cannot be saved from sin. "Maybe Jesus went to their worlds to die for them too," some might say. But the Bible indicates that Jesus died only once, and will never again (Romans 6:10; Hebrews 7:27). "Maybe the extraterrestrials never sinned," some might say. But then they would be suffering the effects of sin, since all creation does (Romans 8:22). Clearly, the notion of intelligent alien life presents some real theological conundrums, but these alien scenarios are all speculative. It makes the most sense to recognize that the real universe is the one described by the Bible, not the one described by science-fiction programming.

Abductions?

Occasionally, we hear a report of someone who claims to have been actually abducted by aliens. What are we to make of this? In light of the previous discussion, we can pretty well eliminate this as a real event. There is no doubt that the person is either deliberately lying or severely mistaken. Eager to give people the benefit of the doubt, it is tempting for us to presume the latter. Perhaps some people genuinely do think that they have had some kind of inexplicable experience. But then again, some people sincerely believe that they have seen Elvis, years after his documented death.

Address: 2444 VISTA WAY
                            OCEANSIDE
                            CA 92054
Location: CLDKK
Device ID: -BTC01
Employee: 2623520

FedEx Express Package(s) - Dropped Off
790000819935   14.0 lbs. (S)

Total Pieces: 1

Subject to additional charges. See FedEx Service Guide
at fedex.com for details. All merchandise sales final.

Visit us at: **fedex.com**
Or call 1.800.GoFedEx
1.800.463.3339

May 17, 2016 10:03:28 AM

More saving.
More doing.℠

3838 VISTA WAY
OCEANSIDE CA 92056
(760)941-5990

0679 00058 33900   05/27/16 03:35 PM

CASHIER SELF CHECK OUT - SCOT58

```
029274354978 METAL POLE S <A>        2.48
     METAL WHITE CLOSET POLE SOCKETS
091111020025 EMT 0.75 10' <A>        3.40
     3/4" EMT CONDUIT X 10'
188670000015 FILL VALVE <A>         10.48
     HYDROCLEAN WATER SAVE FILL VALVE


                    SUBTOTAL         16.36
                    SALES TAX         1.31
                    TOTAL          $17.67
XXXXXXXXXXXXX2463 DEBIT             17.67
AUTH CODE 970409
```

0679 58 33900 05/27/2016 3827

RETURN POLICY DEFINITIONS
POLICY ID   DAYS   POLICY EXPIRES ON
  A   1   90   08/25/2016
THE HOME DEPOT RESERVES THE RIGHT TO
LIMIT / DENY RETURNS. PLEASE SEE THE
RETURN POLICY SIGN IN STORES FOR
DETAILS.

****

ENTER FOR A CHANCE TO WIN A $5,000 HOME DEPOT GIFT CARD!

Tell us about your store visit!
Complete our short survey and
enter for a chance to win at:

www.homedepot.com/survey

PARTICIPE EN UNA OPORTUNIDAD DE GANAR UNA TARJETA DE REGALO DE THD DE $5,000!

Comparta Su Opinion! Complete la breve
encuesta sobre su visita a la tienda y
tenga la oportunidad de ganar en:

www.homedepot.com/survey

User ID:
2PX2 68768 68147

Password:
16277 68089

Entries must be completed within 14 days
of purchase. Entrants must be 18 or
older to enter. See complete rules on
website. No purchase necessary.

DOWNLOAD THE HOME DEPOT MOBILE APP
View item location, inventory & reviews
Download from App store or text RECEIPT
to 65624. Message & Data rates may apply

The fact is that our senses are not always perfectly reliable. We sometimes do not actually see what we think we see. Magicians rely upon this fact. And there are conditions that can exacerbate our misperceptions of the world. Clearly, alcohol and other substance abuse can cause people to have all sorts of unreal experiences. But there are also medical conditions that, through no fault of the person, can cause severe hallucinations, panic attacks, and so on.

Some Christians have suggested demonic activity as the source for alleged alien experiences. We would do well to remember that demons are spirits. They do not have physical flesh and cannot manifest physically; God alone has the power to create flesh (John 1:3). Jesus pointed out that spirits do not have a physical body; they do not have flesh and bone (Luke 24:39). Since fallen angels are a type of spirit, it follows logically from Christ's words that they cannot have flesh and bone.

"But haven't angels appeared physically?" some might ask. On some occasions, God provided temporary bodies for his angels so that they could physically interact with people. But this was by God's power, not the angel's. They cannot create. But it doesn't make sense that God would provide a body for a fallen angel—and certainly not for the purpose of tricking people into believing in aliens.

The Bible doesn't tell us much about what angels (godly or fallen) can do in terms of the physical creation. But we do know that Satan can tempt. So he has at least a limited ability to influence our thinking. It is feasible that people who have opened themselves up to anti-Christian spiritualism have had demonic experiences in their mind, though not physically. But Christians have nothing to fear since we enjoy the protection of Almighty God. It is the Satanic powers of the world that fear and flee from us as we submit to God (James 4:7).

Conclusion

By understanding more about astronomy, virtually all UFOs become IFOs. Even very ordinary objects like satellites and meteors can be called a UFO to those who simply do not know what they are. A little education can make a big difference. We can enjoy the wonders of the universe more deeply when we understand what they truly are.

Notes

1. For instance, Heavens Above, located at www.heavens-above.com.

2. Unless you count angels as life. However, these are spiritual beings, not biological beings. So they are neither of the earth, nor of the physical universe.

49

DO OTHER UNIVERSES EXIST?

Jake Hebert, Ph.D.

Some evolutionary physicists argue that our universe is only one of infinitely many universes in a *multiverse*. Why do they say this, and is there any evidence to support their claim?

The idea of a multiverse has gained popularity in recent years primarily because it appears to be a logical consequence of modern *inflation theory*. Earlier versions of the Big Bang suffered from a number of serious difficulties, including the horizon problem, the flatness problem, and the magnetic monopole problem (see chapter 44). In an attempt to solve these problems, Big Bang advocates invoked inflation, an extremely large, but short-lived, increase in the expansion rate of the universe.

Although inflation seemed to solve these problems for the Big Bang, it is important to realize that it is an *ad hoc* explanation—inflation is *not* a successful prediction of the Big Bang, but rather something that has been "tacked onto" the original Big Bang model in order to "prop it up." The main arguments for inflation are essentially circular—the fact that the Big Bang doesn't work without inflation is taken as "evidence" that inflation must have happened! Although Big Bang theorists are hoping to someday find "smoking gun" evidence for inflation, such evidence does not currently exist.[1,2,3]

Inflationary theorists believe a hypothetical field called the *inflaton* drove inflation in the early universe.[4] Although early inflation theories viewed inflation as occurring shortly *after* the Big Bang, modern inflation theories (discussed below) see inflation as being the *cause* of the Big Bang.[5] An editorial by popular author and theoretical physicist Michio Kaku was published the day after the announcement of the likely discovery of the Higgs boson on July 4, 2012.[6] Because the editorial was titled "The Spark That Caused the Big Bang," it likely gave many the mistaken impression that the field associated with the

Higgs boson (the Higgs field) was actually the *cause* of the Big Bang. This is inaccurate, as Big Bang theorists generally believe that the inflaton *cannot* be the Higgs field and that the cause of the alleged Big Bang is still unknown.[7,8,9]

As noted earlier, inflation was originally proposed to be a *brief* accelerated expansion of the universe. However, theorists are now claiming that inflation, once started, would never completely stop! It is thought that quantum mechanical effects would cause different regions of space to stop inflating at different times. This would produce "islands" of non-inflating space that are surrounded by enormous regions of space that are still inflating. Each island of non-inflating space would contain matter and radiation, and would, in effect, be a universe unto itself. This process would continue without end, with inflation always occurring in some regions of space.[10]

Because this inflation process would never end, it would result in a multiverse filled with *infinitely* many universes. This would mean that, according to the Big Bang model, it was only *our* universe that had a beginning 13.8 billion years ago, *not* the multiverse itself.

So, is there any evidence for a multiverse, and what are the implications for Christianity and the creation/evolution controversy?

First, despite what you may see in science-fiction television shows and movies, there is *no evidence whatsoever* for the existence of universes other than our own.

Second, inflation theory, which is the basis for the claim of a multiverse, has become increasingly bizarre and is being criticized by a growing number of secular scientists.[11] Massachusetts Institute of Technology cosmologist Max Tegmark said, "Inflation has destroyed itself. It logically self-destructed."[12] Even Paul Steinhardt of Princeton University, one of the world's leading inflationary theorists, has become critical of inflation theory.[13]

Third, one can make a case that the idea of a multiverse is genuinely unscientific. Because of the enormous gulfs separating these supposed "island" universes, it is difficult to see how the existence of universes other than our own could ever be confirmed or denied, even in principle. Hence, because the idea of a multiverse cannot be falsified, it fails the test of a scientific hypothesis. Inflation theorists would likely counter that, although the idea of a multiverse per se falls outside the domain of science, it should not be classified as unscientific, since it is a consequence of inflation theory, which may potentially be falsified.

However, even if one grants this point, a critical issue must not be overlooked—the idea of a multiverse gives *no help whatsoever* to the person who is trying to explain our existence without God. Secularists are claiming that the multiverse somehow explains our seemingly improbable existence, arguing that these different universes could each have their own physical constants, or perhaps even their own laws of physics. They argue that it does seem wildly improbable for life to have spontaneously evolved, but that we just happen to live in one universe (out of infinitely many) having conditions which permit the existence of life. Therefore, we do not need a Creator to explain our existence.[14]

However, there are flaws in this argument, one of which is the following: In order for the idea of a multiverse to truly remove the need for a Creator, it is not sufficient for conditions in our universe to merely *permit* life to exist. Obviously, they do permit life to exist, or none of us would be here! Rather, these conditions (the laws of physics and chemistry, as well as the values of the physical constants) must also permit *evolution*. Specifically, they must allow for *abiogenesis*—they must allow life to come from non-life.

This, then, raises an obvious question: Do the laws of physics and chemistry in our universe permit abiogenesis?

Apparently not. For decades, creationists have been pointing out the *immense* difficulties with "chemical evolution" scenarios.[15,16] Even some evolutionists are occasionally candid enough to acknowledge the seriousness of these problems.[17] Details of some of these problems are discussed in other chapters in this book.

These difficulties don't simply vanish because someone claims that other (unobservable) universes might exist. In *this* universe, the one in which we actually live, spontaneous generation has never been observed.[18] Furthermore, everything we know about chemistry and physics is telling us that life simply cannot come from non-life.

Even if one were to argue that the chemistry and physics of *every single one* of these other supposed but unobservable universes did allow for life to spontaneously appear, this would not help one bit—how can the laws of physics and chemistry in *another* universe explain the existence of life in *this* universe? This is such an obvious point that one would think that it should have occurred to those making the argument, but the argument demonstrates "futile thoughts" and "foolish, darkened hearts" (Romans 1:21).

So, although the idea of a multiverse superficially may *seem* to make the evolutionary "goo-to-you" scenario more believable, a little careful reasoning shows that it gains the professing atheist *nothing* in his attempt to explain his existence without his Creator.

Notes

1. Faulkner, D. Have cosmologists discovered evidence of inflation? Creation Ministries International. Posted on creation.com March 29, 2006.

2. Appell, D. Planck Satellite Mission Set to Explore Cosmic Secrets. *Scientific American.* Posted on scientificamerican.com November 18, 2008.

3. As creation astronomer Danny Faulkner has noted (see reference 1), there is a great deal of circular reasoning in the interpretation of cosmological data, so even a claim that inflation has been "proven" should not be uncritically accepted.

4. A field assigns a value to each point in space. For instance, a field that describes how temperature varies from point to point within a room would be an example of a *scalar field*, while the familiar example of an electrical field surrounding a charged object would be an example of a *vector field*. The hypothetical *inflaton field* would be an example of a scalar field.

5. Guth, A. The Inflationary Universe: Alan Guth. *Edge: Conversations.* Posted on edge.org November 19, 2002.

6. Kaku, M. The Spark That Caused the Big Bang. *The Wall Street Journal.* Posted on wsj.com on July 5, 2012.

7. Steinhardt, P. J. The Inflation Debate. *Scientific American.* April 2011: 36-43.

8. Krauss, L. What is the Higgs boson and why does it matter? *New Scientist.* Posted on newscientist.com December 13, 2011.

9. Falk, D. Canadian physicist Robert Orr on the Big Bang breakthrough. *The Globe and Mail.* Posted on theglobeandmail.com July 6, 2011.

10. Steinhardt, The Inflation Debate, 41-42.

11. A number of physicists now claim that an argument for a multiverse can also be made from string theory, a highly speculative research program. However, one of the main criticisms of string theory is that it currently is not capable of being tested.

12. Gefter, A. What kind of bang was the big bang? *New Scientist.* Posted on newscientist.com on July 2, 2012.

13. Ibid.

14. Guth, A. Eternal inflation and its implications. Text of talk presented at the 2nd Int. Conf. on Quantum Theories and Renormalization Group in Gravity and Cosmology. Barcelona, Spain. Text posted on arxiv.org June 11-15, 2012.

15. McCombs, C. 2004. Evolution Hopes You Don't Know Chemistry: The Problem of Control. *Acts & Facts.* 33 (8).

16. McCombs, C. 2009. Chemistry by Chance: A Formula for Non-Life. *Acts & Facts.* 38 (2): 30.

17. Williams, A. 2007. Great minds on the origin of life. *Journal of Creation.* 21 (1): 38-42.

18. According to the Bible, some people *did* witness supernatural transformations of non-life into life (Exodus 7:8-13; 8:16-19), not to mention the raising of the dead in Luke 24! But skeptics reject this eyewitness testimony, since acknowledging these events would require them to acknowledge the supernatural in general, and God's existence in particular.

CONCLUSION

One of the reasons that many of us at the Institute for Creation Research began to study science is because it so powerfully reveals the wonder and majesty of the Lord. It is exciting to see how science lines up with the Bible. And there are few greater thrills than sharing these wonders with others and watching them grow in their love and knowledge of God as a result. It is our desire to reach as many people as possible with the message that science confirms that the Bible is true! We pray that the information in this book will be used by many readers to open a door in conversations with unbelieving friends and family. People are often very open to talking about science, whereas they would not be so open to a conversation that starts with "religion."

We pray that this book begins a journey—the first step into the exciting world of creation science and the defense of the Christian faith. Then what is the next step? This may depend very much on the individual reader.

For those readers who are not Christians, who doubted the veracity of the Bible, the next step may very well be repentance. The objection that "the Bible is wrong in matters of science and history and therefore cannot be trusted in other matters" is simply not tenable. The Bible has demonstrated itself to be trustworthy generation after generation. Therefore, there is no logical reason to reject the Bible's gracious call to repentance and salvation. The Bible teaches that all have sinned (Romans 3:23). Like Adam, we have rebelled against God and deserve death (Romans 6:23) and eternal separation from God in hell (Revelation 20:12-15). But the God-man Jesus took our place on the cross, paying our penalty, and then rose again, that whoever believes this and calls upon Him as Lord will be saved (Romans 10:9-10, 13). "In this the love of God was manifested toward us, that God has sent His only begotten Son into the world, that we might live through Him." (1 John 4:9).

For those readers who are Christians, there are many possible avenues for further study. Perhaps a particular topic or chapter in this overview-style book provoked a special interest. Then a great next step is to get a book or video on that topic that goes into greater detail. Many such resources are available at the Institute for Creation Research at www.icr.org. The website itself is a rich source of information and has a built-in search engine.

Certainly a great next step is to share this information with others. It really is exciting to see the "light bulb come on" as people begin to understand how science confirms Genesis. Sometimes this will lead to follow-up questions, prompting the need for further study on a specific topic. Learning about God through His Word and appreciating Him through creation is not a "once-and-you're-done" event. It is a lifelong process of joyful discovery and spiritual growth. We pray that the ministry of ICR and the resources we produce will continue to equip Christians to defend the faith, and to be one link in the chain by which God draws people unto Himself.

Jason Lisle, Ph.D.
Director of Research

APPENDIX

THE SCIENTIFIC CASE AGAINST EVOLUTION

Henry M. Morris, Ph.D.

Belief in evolution is a remarkable phenomenon. It is a belief passionately defended by the scientific establishment, despite the lack of any observable scientific evidence for macroevolution (evolution from one distinct kind of organism into another). This odd situation is briefly documented here by citing statements from leading evolutionists admitting their lack of proof. These statements inadvertently show that evolution on any significant scale does not occur at present, and never happened in the past, and could never happen at all.

Evolution Is Not Happening Now

First of all, the lack of a case for evolution is clear from the fact that no one has ever seen it happen. If it were a real process, evolution should still be occurring, and there should be many transitional forms that we could observe. What we see instead, of course, is an array of distinct kinds of plants and animals with many varieties *within* each kind, but with very clear and unbridgeable gaps between the kinds. For example, there are many varieties of dogs and many varieties of cats, but no "dats" or "cogs." Such variation is often called microevolution, and these minor horizontal (or downward) changes occur fairly often, but such changes are not true vertical evolution.

Evolutionary geneticists have often experimented on fruit flies and other rapidly reproducing species to induce mutational changes hoping they would lead to new and better species, but these have all failed to accomplish their goal. No truly new species has ever been produced, let alone a new basic kind.

Evolutionist Jeffrey Schwartz, professor of anthropology at the University of Pittsburgh, acknowledged:

It was and still is the case that, with the exception of Dobzhansky's claim about a new species of fruit fly, the formation of a new species, by any mechanism, has never been observed.[1]

The scientific method traditionally has required experimental observation and replication. The fact that macroevolution (as distinct from microevolution) has never been observed would seem to exclude it from the domain of true science. Even evolutionist Ernst Mayr, longtime professor of biology at Harvard, who alleged that evolution was a "simple fact," nevertheless agreed that it was a "historical science" for which "laws and experiments are inappropriate techniques"[2] by which to explain it. One can never actually *see* evolution in action.

Evolution Never Happened in the Past

Evolutionists commonly answer the above criticism by claiming that evolution goes too slowly for us to see it happening today. They used to claim that the real evidence for evolution was in the fossil record of the past, but the fact is that the billions of known fossils do not include a single unequivocal transitional form with transitional structures in the process of evolving.

> Given that evolution, according to Darwin, was in a continual state of motion…it followed logically that the fossil record should be rife with examples of transitional forms leading from the less to the more evolved.[1]

Even those who believe in rapid evolution recognize that a considerable number of generations would be required for one distinct kind to evolve into another more complex kind. There ought, therefore, to be a considerable number of true transitional structures preserved in the fossils—after all, there are billions of *non-transitional* structures there! But (with the exception of a few very doubtful creatures such as the controversial feathered dinosaurs and the alleged walking whales), they are *not* there.

> Instead of filling in the gaps in the fossil record with so-called missing links, most paleontologists found themselves facing a situation in which there were only gaps in the fossil record, with no evidence of transformational intermediates between documented fossil species.[1]

The entire history of evolution from the evolution of life from non-life to the evolution of vertebrates from invertebrates to the evolution of man from the ape is strikingly devoid of intermediates—the links are all missing in the fossil record, just as they are in the present world.

With respect to the origin of life, researcher Leslie Orgel, after noting that neither proteins nor nucleic acids could have arisen without the other, concluded:

> And so, at first glance, one might have to conclude that life could never, in fact, have originated by chemical means.[3]

Being committed to total evolution as he was, Orgel could not accept any such conclusion as that. Therefore, he speculated that RNA may have come first, but then he still had to admit that:

> The precise events giving rise to the RNA world remain unclear.... investigators have proposed many hypotheses, but evidence in favor of each of them is fragmentary at best.[3]

Translation: "There is no known way by which life could have arisen naturalistically." Unfortunately, two generations of students have been taught that Stanley Miller's famous experiment on a gaseous mixture practically proved the naturalistic origin of life. But not so!

Neither is there any clue as to how the one-cell organisms of the primordial world could have evolved into the vast array of complex multi-cell invertebrates of the Cambrian period. Even dogmatic evolutionist Stephen Gould admitted:

> The Cambrian explosion was the most remarkable and puzzling event in the history of life.[4]

Equally puzzling, however, is how some invertebrate creature in the ancient ocean, with all its hard parts on the outside, managed to evolve into the first vertebrate—that is, the first fish—with its hard parts all on the inside.

> Yet the transition from spineless invertebrates to the first backboned fishes is still shrouded in mystery, and many theories abound.[5]

Other gaps are abundant, with no real transitional series anywhere. A very bitter opponent of creation science, paleontologist Niles Eldredge, acknowledged that there is little, if any, evidence of evolutionary transitions in the fossil record. Instead, things remain the same!

> It is a simple ineluctable truth that virtually all members of a biota

remain basically stable, with minor fluctuations, throughout their durations....[6]

So how do evolutionists arrive at their evolutionary trees from fossils of organisms that didn't change during their durations?

Fossil discoveries can muddle over attempts to construct simple evolutionary trees—fossils from key periods are often not intermediates, but rather hodge podges of defining features of many different groups....Generally, it seems that major groups are not assembled in a simple linear or progressive manner—new features are often "cut and pasted" on different groups at different times.[7]

As far as ape/human intermediates are concerned, the same is true, although anthropologists have been eagerly searching for them for many years. Many have been proposed, but each has been rejected in turn.

All that paleoanthropologists have to show for more than 100 years of digging are remains from fewer than 2000 of our ancestors. They have used this assortment of jawbones, teeth and fossilized scraps, together with molecular evidence from living species, to piece together a line of human descent going back 5 to 8 million years to the time when humans and chimpanzees diverged from a common ancestor.[8]

Anthropologists supplemented their extremely fragmentary fossil evidence with DNA and other types of molecular genetic evidence from living animals to try to work out an evolutionary scenario that will fit. But this genetic evidence really doesn't help much either because it contradicts fossil evidence. Anthropologist Roger Lewin notes:

The overall effect is that molecular phylogenetics is by no means as straightforward as its pioneers believed....The Byzantine dynamics of genome change has many other consequences for molecular phylogenetics, including the fact that different genes tell different stories.[9]

Summarizing the genetic data from humans, another author concludes, rather pessimistically:

Even with DNA sequence data, we have no direct access to the processes of evolution, so objective reconstruction of the vanished past can be achieved only by creative imagination.[10]

Appendix

Since there is no real scientific evidence that evolution is occurring at present or ever occurred in the past, it is reasonable to conclude that evolution is not a fact of science, as many claim. In fact, it is not even science at all, but an arbitrary system built upon faith in universal naturalism.

These negative evidences against evolution are, at the same time, strong positive evidences for special creation. They are, in fact, specific predictions based on the creation model of origins.

Creationists would obviously predict ubiquitous gaps between created kinds, though with many varieties capable of arising within each kind, in order to enable each basic kind to cope with changing environments without becoming extinct. Creationists also would anticipate that any vertical changes in organized complexity would be downward, since the Creator (by definition) would create things correctly to begin with. Thus, arguments and evidences against evolution are, at the same time, positive evidences for creation.

Notes

1. Schwartz, J. 1999. *Sudden Origins.* New York: John Wiley and Sons, Inc., 300.
2. Mayr, E. 2000. Darwin's Influence on Modern Thought. *Scientific American.* 283 (1): 83.
3. Orgel, L. 1994. The Origin of Life on the Earth. *Scientific American.* 271 (4): 78.
4. Gould, S. 1999. The Evolution of Life. *Evolution: Facts and Fallacies,* ed., J. Schopf. San Diego, CA: Academic Press, 9.
5. Long, J. 1995. *The Rise of Fishes.* Baltimore, MD: John Hopkins University Press, 30.
6. Eldredge, N. 1998. *The Pattern of Evolution.* New York: W. H. Freeman and Co., 157.
7. Shubin, N. 1998. Evolutionary Cut and Paste. *Nature.* 349: 12.
8. Tudge, C. 1995. Human Origins Revisited. *New Scientist.* 146: 24.
9. Lewin, R. 1998. Family Feud. *New Scientist.* 157: 39.
10. Takahata, N. 1995. Genetic Perspective on the Origin and History of Humans. *Annual Review of Ecology and Systematics.* 26: 343.

Dr. Henry M. Morris (1918-2006) was Founder of the Institute for Creation Research.

CONTRIBUTORS

HENRY M. MORRIS III, D. MIN.
CHIEF EXECUTIVE OFFICER

Dr. Henry Morris III holds four earned degrees, including a D.Min. from Luther Rice Seminary and the Presidents and Key Executives MBA from Pepperdine University. A former college professor, administrator, business executive, and senior pastor, he is the eldest son of the Institute for Creation Research's founder. Dr. Morris has served for many years in conference and writing ministry.

JOHN D. MORRIS, PH.D.
PRESIDENT

Dr. John Morris, perhaps best known for leading expeditions to Mt. Ararat in search of Noah's Ark, received his doctorate in geological engineering at the University of Oklahoma in 1980. He served on the University of Oklahoma faculty before joining the Institute for Creation Research in 1984. Dr. Morris held the position of professor of geology before being appointed president in 1996.

JASON LISLE, PH.D.
DIRECTOR OF RESEARCH

Dr. Jason Lisle graduated summa cum laude from Ohio Wesleyan University, where he double-majored in physics and astronomy and minored in mathematics. He earned a master's degree and a Ph.D. in astrophysics at the University of Colorado. Dr. Lisle specialized in solar astrophysics and has made a number of scientific discoveries regarding the solar photosphere and has contributed to the field of general relativity.

JAMES J. S. JOHNSON, J.D., TH.D.
CHIEF ACADEMIC OFFICER

Dr. James Johnson received his J.D. in 1984 from the University of North Carolina, which included studies at Duke University Law School, and in 1996 obtained his Th.D. His educational background includes earned degrees in religion and the natural sciences. For his scholarship in biblical languages and their cognates, Dr. Johnson was awarded the American Bible Society Award in 1982. He currently serves as Chief Academic Officer of ICR's School of Biblical Apologetics.

NATHANIEL JEANSON, PH.D.
DEPUTY DIRECTOR FOR LIFE SCIENCES

Dr. Nathaniel Jeanson received his Ph.D. in cell and developmental biology from Harvard Medical School in 2009. While at Harvard, he assisted in adult stem cell research, specifically on the role of Vitamin D in regulating blood stem cells. Dr. Jeanson has a B.S. in molecular biology and bioinformatics from the University of Wisconsin-Parkside.

RANDY GULIUZZA, P.E., M.D.
NATIONAL REPRESENTATIVE

Dr. Randy Guliuzza has a B.S. in engineering from the South Dakota School of Mines and Technology, a B.A. in theology from Moody Bible Institute, an M.D. from the University of Minnesota, and a Master's in Public Health from Harvard University. Dr. Guliuzza served nine years in the Navy Civil Engineer Corps and is a registered professional engineer. In 2008, he retired as Lt. Col. from the U.S. Air Force, where he served as Flight Surgeon and Chief of Aerospace Medicine.

JEFFREY TOMKINS, PH.D.
RESEARCH ASSOCIATE

Dr. Jeffrey Tomkins earned a master's degree in plant science in 1990 from the University of Idaho, where he performed research in plant hormones. He received his Ph.D. in genetics from Clemson University in 1996. While at Clemson, he worked as a research technician in a plant breeding/genetics program, with a research focus in the area of quantitative and physiological genetics in soybean.

LEO (JAKE) HEBERT III, PH.D.
RESEARCH ASSOCIATE

Dr. Jake Hebert earned a master's degree in physics in 1999 from Texas A&M University, where he studied optics and was a Dean's Graduate Fellow 1995-1996. He received his Ph.D. in 2011 from the University of Texas at Dallas, where his research involved a study of the possible connection between fair-weather atmospheric electricity and climate.

Frank Sherwin, M.A.
Research Associate, Senior Lecturer, and Science Writer

Frank Sherwin received his bachelor's degree in biology from Western State College, Gunnison, Colorado, in 1978. He attended graduate school at the University of Northern Colorado, where he studied under the late Gerald D. Schmidt, one of the foremost parasitologists in America. During his time in graduate school, Mr. Sherwin discovered a new species of parasite, the study of which was published in a peer-reviewed secular journal. In 1985, Mr. Sherwin obtained a masters degree in zoology.

Brian Thomas, M.S.
Science Writer

Brian Thomas received his bachelor's degree in biology from Stephen F. Austin State University, Nacogdoches, Texas, in 1993. After beginning graduate studies at the Institute for Creation Research Graduate School, he returned to Stephen F. Austin, where he earned a master's degree in biotechnology in 1999. He taught biology and chemistry at high school and undergraduate levels.

CREDITS

Certain chapters were adapted, at least in part, from the following resources.

Morris III, H. 2012. Genesis and the Character of God. *Acts & Facts*. 41 (5): 4-6.

Johnson, J. J. S. 2012. The Gap Theory. *Acts & Facts*. 41 (10): 8-10.

Johnson, J. J. S. 2011. Genesis Is History, Not Poetry. *Acts & Facts*. 40 (6): 8-9.

Johnson, J. J. S. 2008. How Young Is the Earth? Applying Simple Math to Data in Genesis. *Acts & Facts*. 37 (10): 4.

Johnson, J. J. S. 2008. The Evidence of Nothing. *Acts & Facts*. 37 (4): 4.

Johnson, J. J. S. 2012. Genesis Critics Flunk Forensic Science 101. *Acts & Facts*. 41 (3): 8-9.

Johnson, J. J. S. 2011. DNA and RNA: Providential Coding to "Revere" God. *Acts & Facts*. 40 (3): 8-9.

Johnson, J. J. S. 2012. Of Grackles and Gratitude. *Acts & Facts*. 41 (7): 8-10.

Guliuzza, R. 2010. All-or-Nothing Unity. *Acts & Facts*. 39 (9): 10-11.

Guliuzza, R. 2009. Made in His Image: Human Reproduction. *Acts & Facts*. 38 (1): 14.

Guliuzza, R. J. 2009. Made in His Image: Human Gestation *Acts & Facts*. 38 (2): 10.

Thomas, B. and F. Sherwin. 2009. Darwin's Withering Tree of Life. *Acts & Facts*. 38 (5): 16.

Tomkins, J. 2011. New Human-Chimp Chromosome 2 Data Challenge Common Ancestry Claims. *Acts & Facts*. 40 (5): 6.

Morris, J. 2012. *The Global Flood: Unlocking Earth's Geologic History*. Dallas, TX: Institute for Creation Research.

Morris, J. and J. J. S. Johnson. 2012. The Draining Floodwaters: Geologic Evidence Reflects the Genesis Text. *Acts & Facts*. 41 (1): 12-13.

Morris, J. 2010. The Real Nature of the Fossil Record. *Acts & Facts*. 39 (2): 12-14.

Morris, H. 2000. The Scientific Case Against Evolution: A Summary Part 1. *Acts & Facts*. 29 (12).

INDEX

NEW FROM ICR

FOR MORE INFORMATION

Sign up for ICR's FREE publications!

Our monthly *Acts & Facts* magazine offers fascinating articles and current information on creation, evolution, and more. Our quarterly *Days of Praise* booklet provides daily devotionals—real biblical "meat"—to strengthen and encourage the Christian witness.

To subscribe, call 800.337.0375 or mail your address information to the address below. Or sign up online at www.icr.org.

Visit ICR online

ICR.org offers a wealth of resources and information on scientific creationism and biblical worldview issues.

- ✓ Read our news postings on today's hottest science topics
- ✓ Explore the evidence for creation
- ✓ Investigate our graduate and professional education programs
- ✓ Dive into our archive of 40 years of scientific articles
- ✓ Listen to current and past radio programs
- ✓ Watch our *That's a Fact* video show
- ✓ Order creation science materials online
- ✓ And more!

Visit our online store at www.icr.org/store for more great resources.

INSTITUTE FOR
CREATION
RESEARCH

P. O. Box 59029
Dallas, TX 75229
800.337.0375